Second Edition

ALGEBRA
for Math R3

Stephen Majewicz

Custom Publishing

New York   Boston   San Francisco
London   Toronto   Sydney   Tokyo   Singapore   Madrid
Mexico City   Munich   Paris   Cape Town   Hong Kong   Montreal

Cover Art: *Excavation Series*, by Brian Stevens

Printed in the United States of America

33 2021

2008360547

KC

**Pearson
Custom Publishing**
is a division of

www.pearsonhighered.com

ISBN 10: 0-536-89123-0
ISBN 13: 978-0-536-89123-5

A Note to the Instructor

Mat R3 is an introductory course in Algebra. It is designed to prepare the students who wish to eventually take a full course in College Algebra, which is our Mat 9 course. This book contains the material which the students are required to know in order to proceed onto Mat 9. There are two fundamental resources of any mathematics course which students need to take advantage of in order to succeed, a good instructor and a good textbook. It is your job to be a good instructor. By providing the students with a clear lecture and thorough notes, you are supplying them with the necessary background that they need in order to succeed. The job of the textbook is to provide the student with clear explanations of worked examples, plenty of exercises for the students to work on and comfortable reading material which the student can understand.

Algebra for Mat R3 provides the student with clear explanations of worked examples, plenty of exercises and material which supplements the notes given by the instructor. Each chapter is divided into sections. Whenever a new topic is discussed, it is accompanied by an exhaustive number of worked examples, along with in-depth detailed explanations. At the end of each section (or chapter), there is a set of examples (called 'Try These') for the student to try out. The solutions to these examples are given at the end of the text. Each chapter (or section) concludes with numerous exercise problems, as well as a multiple choice quiz on the material from the chapter. The exercise problems very in their level of difficulty and the solutions to the odd numbered problems are given in detail at the end of the text. The quizzes will prepare the student for taking a multiple choice exam, hence prepare them for taking the Mat R3 final exam.

This textbook is a supplement to your lessons. It has numerous exercise problems, which make excellent homework problems. The quizzes and 'Try These' problems should be assigned to the students as well. It will provide you with the adequate teaching material for Mat R3. It is important that your students get enough practice in order to succeed in Mat R3. By providing them with homework problems and reading material, they will be guided in the right direction.

Professor Stephen Majewicz

A Note to the Student

Algebra may seem very difficult and confusing when you begin learning it because there are fancy symbols and weird looking expressions with letters in them. In fact, it can be discouraging when you encounter a topic which makes no sense to you whatsoever. At this point, you may want to give up and forget all about it. These emotions that you feel are very common and I've seen them expressed by many students in the past. In order to succeed, you must have confidence and patience. You cannot accomplish your goals (such as passing a math class) without being confident that you can succeed. When things become tough, it is very easy to just back off and quit. Patience is the key; you need to assess the problem or topic which you are stuck on and try again. Without patience, you may be too quick to give up. Don't! You will succeed in this course if you have the proper attitude and approach to learning the topics.

The two resources at your disposal which will aid you in doing well in this course are the lectures and the textbook. It is important to attend class regularly and take notes. The instructor will be able to explain something to you that you do not understand. Ask questions when an explanation is not clear to you. Don't be afraid and don't ever think that your question is stupid. Every question is a good one. Remember that the instructor is there to help you. The textbook contains all of the material that you will need to learn in the course. It has plenty of worked out examples for you to read. After looking over the examples, you should do the 'Try These' examples to convince yourself that you understand the material. Make sure that you do all of the homework assignments. Homework can be time consuming, but it is given to you for a reason. Nobody can become good in Algebra only by attending class; don't think that you are such a person. By doing homework, you are strengthening your mathematics skills, as well as becoming a disciplined student. Such skills and discipline are key necessities for success in your college career, as well as in your life. After completing each chapter of the text, you should try the 'Try These' examples once more and the 'End of Chapter Quiz'. The quiz is designed to prepare you for the final exam known as the 'exit exam'. If you read over your notes, read the book and do your homework regularly, you will do well in the class.

I wish you the best of luck in Mat R3. Remember to have confidence and patience. You will succeed!

Professor Stephen Majewicz

Acknowledgements

I would like to thank Professor Rina Yarmish, Chair of the Department of Mathematics and Computer Science at Kingsborough Community College for her support. I would also like to thank Ms. Judith Khan and Mrs. Heung Mui Lew for pointing out several errors that were found in the first edition of the text.

TABLE OF CONTENTS

Chapter 1: The Real Numbers and an Introduction to Algebra

In order to understand Algebra, you must be familiar with the set of real numbers and the properties of real numbers. As you are learning about different types of algebraic expressions and methods of solving equations, you will encounter situations in which the properties of real numbers help in solving such problems. After all, when we study algebra, we use letters (called **variables**) to represent real numbers. Hence, in order to understand Algebra, you must understand the properties of numbers.

In this chapter, we will study the real numbers and the properties which they satisfy. In Section 1.1, we will learn how to build the set of real numbers by taking the set of natural numbers and enlarging it by adding numbers to it. By doing so, the set of real numbers will emerge. We will also recall some basic arithmetic. Section 1.2 contains a review of arithmetic for the real numbers. We will recall the rules for the signs (without proving why these rules work the way they do) and how to work with fractions. In Section 1.3, we will briefly recall how to round off and truncate a decimal to a specified decimal place (this is called an **approximation** of a number). In Section 1.4, we will look at how to evaluate an arithmetic problem containing several operations in it. We will learn the order of operations, which basically tells us in what order we need to do the problem. Section 1.5 is devoted to a discussion of the properties which the real numbers satisfy. These properties are used throughout this book, so you should build a strong understanding of them. Sections 1.6 and 1.7 deal with graphing real numbers on a number line, comparing two numbers using the inequality symbol, and finding the distance between two numbers on the number line using absolute value. The chapter concludes with an introduction to Algebra and algebraic expressions (Section 1.8). We will practice evaluating algebraic expressions by utilizing the order of operations.

Section 1.1 The Classification of Numbers

Our goal in this section is to classify numbers. Let's begin with a definition of a **set** and how to write a set of elements symbolically.

Definition: A **set** is a collection of objects. The objects in a set are called the **members** or **elements** of the set.

The symbol that we'll use to write a set is the 'squiggly parentheses' (called **braces**) { }. For example, if we want to write the set of numbers 1, 2, and 3 symbolically, we'll simply write {1, 2, 3}. If we want to write the set of colors red, white, and blue, we'll write {red, white, blue}.

I) The Natural Numbers (or Counting Numbers)

The set of **natural numbers** is {1, 2, 3, ...}.

These are just the numbers which we use to count with. The three dots (called an **ellipsis**) after the comma indicates that this set of numbers continues without ever ending. Obviously, we couldn't continue to write down **all** of the numbers which follow 3 since there is a never ending list of them (we say that there are **infinitely** many). Notice that the pattern which occurs in the set is 'add 1 to get the next element'. Hence, the next three numbers in the set will be 4, 5, and 6. Whenever you see an ellipsis, look for a pattern for which the numbers in the set satisfy.

II) The Whole Numbers

The set of **whole numbers** is the set {0, 1, 2, 3, ...}.

Observe that the set of whole numbers is just the set of natural numbers together with the number 0.

1

III) **The Integers** or **The Signed Numbers**

The set of **integers** (or **signed numbers**) is the set $\{\ldots,\ -2,\ -1,\ 0,\ +1,\ +2,\ +3,\ \ldots\}$.

As you can see, an integer is formed by taking a whole number and putting a **sign** (either a **negative sign** '−' or a **positive sign** '+') in front of it. Notice that the number 0 has no sign. If an integer has a '−' sign, we call it a **negative integer**. If an integer has a '+' sign, we call it a **positive integer**. For example, $-2, -16$, and -9 are negative integers, whereas $+2, +13$, and $+9$ are positive integers. Whenever we have a positive integer, we may omit the '+' sign. For example, $+2 = 2$ and $13 = +13$.

Integers appear in many places in the real world. For example, when dealing with banking, an account with $+\$150$ means that you have \$150 in the bank, whereas an account with $-\$150$ means that you owe \$150 to the bank. Notice that \$0 means that you have no money in the bank and you owe no money to the bank. Another example of integers being used arises when discussing the weather. If you've taken a basic Chemistry course, you'll know that the freezing temperature of water (in celsius) is $0°C$. If you took at a thermometer, you'll notice that there are numbers above and below the number 0. If you took the temperature of a liquid and its measurement is below the value 0, say $10°C$ below the 0, you would say that the temperature is $10°C$ below zero and write this temperature as $-10°C$. On the other hand, if the temperature is above the value 0, say $35°C$ above the 0, you would say that the temperature is $35°C$ above zero and write this temperature as $35°C$. In conclusion, the positive and negative signs are used to compare the temperature of an object to the freezing temperature of water (in Celsius). These are just a couple of examples of where integers are used.

Notice that the set of integers contains all of the whole numbers.

IV) **The Rational Numbers**

To describe this set, I will use the letters (or **variables**) p and q to represent certain types of numbers.

The set of **rational numbers** is the set $\left\{\dfrac{p}{q}, \text{ where } p \text{ and } q \text{ are integers and } q \neq 0\right\}$. Hence, a rational number is a fraction whose numerator and denominator are integers, provided that the denominator is not zero. For example, the following are rational numbers:

$$\frac{1}{2}, \frac{3}{-7}, \frac{-6}{-12}, \frac{0}{9}, \frac{-10}{285}, \text{ and } \frac{11}{1}.$$

However, the expressions

$$\frac{1}{0}, \frac{8}{0}, \frac{0}{0}, \text{ and } \frac{-16}{0}$$

are undefined. Notice that every integer, n, can be written as a rational number by writing

$$n = \frac{n}{1}.$$

In fact, there are infinitely many ways to write an integer as a rational number. For example, we have

$$4 = \frac{4}{1} = \frac{8}{2} = \frac{12}{3} = \frac{16}{4} = \ldots.$$

We call such rational numbers **equivalent** because they all reduce to the same number, 4. Since every integer can be written as a rational number, we see that the set of rational numbers contains the set of integers.

Recall that every rational number can be written as a decimal by dividing the denominator into the numerator. For example, to express $\frac{1}{2}$ as a decimal, we divide $1 \div 2$ as follows:

$$
\begin{array}{r}
0.5 \\
2\overline{)\,1.0} \\
-10 \\
\hline
0
\end{array}
$$

2

Remember that you can keep on working out this division problem by adding infinitely many more 0's after the 1.0. However, if you do this, your answer will just be 0.5 with infinitely many more 0's following the 5:

$$
\begin{array}{r}
0.5000... \\
2)\overline{1.0000...} \\
-1\,0 \\
\hline
0
\end{array}
$$

Therefore, we simply write $\frac{1}{2} = 0.5$. Writing the answer as $0.500000...$ would not change the value, but just make it look different. A decimal which has infinitely many 0's after a certain decimal place is called a **terminating decimal**. Other examples of terminating decimals are 0.12, 0.7, 3.14, and -5.11193. Now let's express $\frac{25}{99}$ as a decimal. We divide $25 \div 99$ as follows:

$$
\begin{array}{r}
0.2525... \\
99)\overline{25.00000...} \\
-19\,8 \\
\hline
5\,20 \\
-\,4\,95 \\
\hline
250 \\
-\quad 198 \\
\hline
520 \\
-\quad 495 \\
\hline
25
\end{array}
$$

Notice that this division problem contains a repeating pattern. After we perform the first two subtraction steps, we get the number 25 (the same number we began with). In other words, if we keep adding more 0's after 25.00000, the answer will contain the same **block** of digits, namely 25. In other words, we will obtain $\frac{25}{99} = 0.252525252525....$ Since the '25' repeats itself forever, we call this a **non-terminating, repeating decimal**. It is non-terminating because you will never get 0's at the end of the decimal and it is repeating since the block of 25's always appears. Since the decimal is repeating, we write $0.252525252525... = 0.\overline{25}$ for short. The 'bar' symbol is put above the repeating block. For another example, if we write $\frac{1}{6}$ as a decimal, we will obtain $0.16666... = 0.1\overline{6}$. This time, only the 6 gets the bar since it is the repeating number and not the 1. Here's one for you to verify on your own:

$$
\frac{3}{7} = 0.428571428571... = 0.\overline{428571}
$$

So, why do we care about all of this? Well, it turns out that **every** rational number can be expressed as one of these two types of decimals.

> Every rational number can be expressed as either a
> **terminating decimal** or a **non-terminating, repeating decimal.**

Similarly, by using algebraic techniques, we can express a terminating or a non-terminating but repeating decimal as a fraction.

> Every decimal which is either a terminating or non-terminating,
> repeating can be expressed as a **rational number.**

We conclude from the above that a rational number can be represented in fractional form (with integers in the numerator and denominator and no zero in the denominator) or in decimal form as one of the types mentioned above. Now, there is one type of decimal which hasn't been mentioned yet a decimal which is **non-terminating and non-repeating**. Such a decimal **cannot** be expressed as a rational number. These decimals make up our next set.

V) The Irrational Numbers

The set of **irrational numbers** is the set {non-terminating, non-repeating decimals}.

Examples.

1) π is irrational. I will assume that you have seen this symbol (pronounced as 'pi') before. If not, the number represented by this symbol is the ratio of the circumference of a circle to its diameter. Most of the time, it is approximated to either 3.14 or $\frac{22}{7}$. However, the actual value of π could not be written down in full, nor with the repeating 'bar' symbol.

2) The number 9.62622622262222... is irrational. It is non-terminating because there will always be 6's and 2's in its decimal if you continued the pattern. It is also non-repeating because the pattern which arises is to increase the number of 2's by one once you go past a 6. There will never be a repeating block since there will always be one more 2 tossed in as you continue the pattern.

3) There is a number, n, for which $n \times n = 2$. The number n is irrational. For those of you who have learned about square roots before, we write this number as $n = \sqrt{2}$ and read it as 'the square root of 2'. We will learn about square roots in Chapter 5.

Later, we will learn that there are infinitely many irrational numbers which come from square roots. What I want you to understand for now is that an irrational number is a non-terminating, non-repeating decimal and that such decimals really do exist. When we put all of the rational numbers and all of the irrational numbers together in one set, we obtain the set of real numbers.

VI) The Real Numbers

The set of **real numbers** is the set {rational numbers and irrational numbers}. The set of real numbers contains every decimal that can be written down by using positive integers for its digits. These are the numbers which we will be concerned with.

Try These (Set 1):

1) Express each fraction as a decimal. State whether it is terminating or non-terminating, repeating.

a) $\frac{3}{4}$ b) $\frac{5}{8}$ c) $\frac{2}{9}$ d) $\frac{0}{19}$

2) Which of the following real numbers are integers?

a) 8   b) -5.102 c) $\sqrt{2}$ d) $17\frac{2}{3}$ e) $10.\overline{76}$

3) Which of the following real numbers are rational numbers?

a) $\frac{4}{11}$ b) -6.372 c) -9 d) π e) $+31$

4) Which of the following are irrational numbers?

a) 15   b) 2.838338333...   c) $\frac{23}{0}$ d) $\frac{-16}{-36}$ e) π

Section 1.2 Arithmetic of Real Numbers

In this section, we will review the rules for doing arithmetic with real numbers. We'll begin by recalling the different ways in which the operations of arithmetic can be written. To do this, we will use variables to represent real numbers. We will review how to do arithmetic of integers, followed by arithmetic of rationals. As we do these arithmetic problems, you will see the rules for arithmetic show up (for example, how to add two negative numbers). If you remember how these rules work, you may just want to skim through this section. I will not go into detail as to how to obtain the different rules, although they are interesting to learn. I will only demonstrate how they work. Later in this chapter, I will mention some of the properties which give us these rules.

Operations Used in Arithmetic

1. Addition

When doing an addition problem, the 'plus' symbol, $+$, is used. We can read the mathematical sentence '$x + y$' as 'x plus y', 'x added to y', or 'the sum of x and y'.

2. Subtraction

When doing a subtraction problem, the 'minus' symbol, $-$, is used. We can read the mathematical sentence '$x - y$' as 'x minus y', 'y subtracted from x', 'x take away y', 'the difference between x and y', or 'x less y'.

3. Multiplication

There are various ways to write a multiplication statement. If we want to multiply x and y, we can write it as

$$xy, \ (x)(y), \ x(y), \ (x)y, \ x \cdot y, \ (x) \cdot (y), \ x \cdot (y), \ \text{or} \ (x) \cdot y.$$

Notice that I didn't use the multiplication symbol, '$\times$', because it can easily be confused with the variable x. Of course, if my variables were called u and v instead, then I could have certainly written $u \times v$ for the product of u and v. We can read the mathematical sentence 'xy' as 'x times y', 'x multiplied by y', 'the product of x and y', or 'x by y'.

4. Division

If we want to divide x by y, we can write

$x \div y$ (recall that '$\div$' is called the **division** or **quotient symbol**), $(x) \div y$, $x \div (y)$, $(x) \div (y)$, $\dfrac{x}{y}$, or x/y.

We can read the mathematical sentence '$x \div y$' as 'the quotient of x and y' or 'x divided by y'.

5. Exponentiation

If you've never learned about exponents before, don't worry. I will only mention the definition at this point and present a couple of examples. Suppose we want to multiply a real number by itself several times. Rather than writing down a long product, we can express the product using an exponent.

Definition: Suppose that n is a natural number and a is any real number. Then

$$\underbrace{a \cdot a \cdots a}_{n \text{ of these}} = a^n.$$

5

We read the expression 'a^n' as 'a raised to the nth power' or 'a to the power n'. We call 'a' the *base* and 'n' the *exponent* of the expression. If the exponent is 1, then we write $a^1 = a$.

For example,

$$6^2 = 6 \times 6 = 36, \ 2^4 = 2 \times 2 \times 2 \times 2 = 16, \text{ and } 7^1 = 7.$$

Chapter 2 is devoted to the study of exponents and the properties they satisfy. For now, I want you to know what the 'little number upstairs' (the exponent) represents.

Now that we've reviewed the different symbols used in arithmetic and algebra, let's practice writing verbal sentences/expressions as mathematical sentences/expressions and vice-versa. We will use a letter (or **variable**) to represent a real number.

Examples. Write each verbal expression as a mathematical expression/sentence.

1) 'The sum of 8 and 13' is written as $8 + 13$.

2) '19 subtracted from 28' is written as $28 - 19$.

3) 'The product of 7 and 4' is written as $(7)(4)$. Note that we could've written the answer as $7(4)$, $(7)4$, $(7) \cdot (4)$, etc.

4) 'The quotient of 32 and 2' is written as $32 \div 2$ or $\dfrac{32}{2}$.

5) 'x added to 7' is written as $7 + x$.

6) '9 times t' is written as $9t$. As in Example 3, there are other ways to write this answer. We have $9 \cdot t$, $9(t)$, $(9)t$, etc.

7) '1 divided by y' is written as $1 \div y$ or $\dfrac{1}{y}$.

8) 'x minus 13 is 10' is written as $x - 13 = 10$. Notice how the word 'is' corresponds to the mathematical symbol '$=$', the **equals** symbol.

9) 'n added to 6 is 20' is written as $6 + n = 20$. We could also write this as $n + 6 = 12$.

10) 'The sum of 6 and the product of 2 and x is 19' is written as $6 + 2x = 19$. To get this, we have to break down the sentence by looking for key words which represent mathematical symbols:

$$\text{The } \underbrace{\text{sum of 6 and}}_{6+} \text{ the } \underbrace{\text{product of 2 and } x}_{2x} \underbrace{\text{ is 19}}_{=19}.$$

11) '17 minus 4 equals the quotient of y and 3' is written as $17 - 4 = y \div 3$. Observe:

$$\underbrace{17 \text{ minus } 4}_{17-4} \underbrace{\text{ equals}}_{=} \underbrace{\text{ the quotient of } y \text{ and } 3}_{y \div 3}.$$

6

Examples. Describe each mathematical expression as a verbal expression/sentence.

1) $x + 5$ is 'x plus 5'.

2) $7y$ is 'the product of 7 and y'.

3) $\dfrac{x}{3} = 9$ is 'the quotient of x and 3 is 9'.

4) $1 - 8n = 6$ is '1 minus the product of 8 and n equals 6'.

5) $7x + 2 = x - 12$ is 'the sum of 7 times x and 2 is x minus 12'.

6) $a - 7 = a \div 9$ is 'the difference between a and 7 is a divided by 9'.

Try These (Set 2):

I) Write each of the verbal expressions as a mathematical expression/sentence.

  1) 8 added to 12   2) the product of 5 and 2.

  3) 17 less 2   4) x divided by 4 is 3.

  5) The sum of y and 1 is 8 times 4.   6) 7 take away x equals the quotient of x and 11.

II) Describe each of the mathematical expressions as a verbal expression/sentence.

  1) $15 + 3$ 2) $7 - 4$ 3) $6\,(8)$

  4) $x + 7 = 19$ 5) $3a - 2 = a$ 6) $\dfrac{y}{4} = 9y + 1$

When we've converted from verbal espressions/sentences to mathematical expressions/sentences (and vice-versa), we saw that the **equal sign** '$=$' was used to represent that two mathematical expressions are equivalent to each other. In the English language, every sentence has a **verb**. The equal sign acts as a verb of a mathematical sentence. Such a sentence is called an **equation**. There are several properties which are important to know regarding the equality of mathematical expressions.

<u>**Properties of Equality**</u>

For the properties below, suppose that a, b, and c represent any three real numbers.

I) <u>**The Addition Property:**</u> If $a = b$, then $a + c = b + c$.

II) <u>**The Subtraction Property:**</u> If $a = b$, then $a - c = b - c$.

III) <u>**The Multiplication Property:**</u> If $a = b$, then $a \cdot c = b \cdot c$.

IV) <u>**The Division Property:**</u> If $a = b$ and $c \neq 0$ (that is, c is **not** equal to 0), then $\dfrac{a}{c} = \dfrac{b}{c}$.

Examples.

1) If $x = 4$, then $x + 6 = 4 + 6$ by the Addition Property.

2) If $y = 13$, then $y - 8 = 13 - 8$ by the Subtraction Property.

3) If $a = 5$, then $a\,(6) = 5\,(6)$ by the Multiplication Property.

4) If $b = 24$, then $\dfrac{b}{4} = \dfrac{24}{4}$ by the Division Property.

Arithmetic with Integers

We learned in grade school how to add whole numbers, so I won't waste time going over how to add $6 + 3$ or $93 + 125$. What I do want to go over is how to work with negative integers. Once again, I am assuming that you have learned this before. This is only meant to be a review.

Recall that if x is a positive number, then $-x$ represents the number x with a negative sign in front of it. For example, if $x = 7$, then $-x = -7$.

Definition: Suppose that a is any real number and b is a positive number. Then $a - b = a + (-b)$.

This definition states that if you want to subtract a positive number from any real number, you can think of it as an addition problem instead. In fact, we will soon see that b can represent **any** real number once we understand what $-b$ means when b is a **negative** number.

We can establish either rules for adding and subtracting real numbers (integers, in particular) by using this definition, along with either the real number line or the properties of real numbers. Let's remind ourselves of these rules by looking at some examples.

Examples. Add or subtract.

1) $(-2) + (-5) = -7$

When we **add two negative numbers**, we add them as if they were positive instead. When we get our answer, we put a negative sign in front of it. In other words, we figure out that $2 + 5 = 7$. After putting a negative in front, we'll get -7.

2) $(-6) + (+9) = +3 = 3$

When we **add two real numbers of different signs**, we make believe the numbers are both positive and subtract the smaller from the larger. The answer that we'll obtain will then take the same sign as that of the larger number. In other words, we take $9 - 6$, forgetting that the 6 is really -6. We'll obtain 3, which will be $+3$ because the sign of the larger number, $+9$, is positive.

3) $(-17) + 11 = -6$

The larger minus the smaller (without worrying about their signs) will be $17 - 11 = 6$. Since the larger number, 17, is really -17, the sign of the answer will also be negative. Hence, the answer is -6.

4) $-8 - 7 = -15$

By the definition above, we can write the problem as $-8 + (-7)$, which is the sum of two negatives. Now we add them just like in Example 1.

5) $9 + (-9) = 0$

6) $(+16) + (-33) = -17$

7) $4 - 12 = -8$ (since $4 - 12 = 4 + (-12)$ by definition)

Let's now recall how to multiply and divide integers. The rules for multiplication (and division) which we often memorize without questioning come from several properties. We will take them for granted here, although I will mention their origins later in this chapter. An important definition which allows us to relate division and multiplication is:

Definition: Suppose that a and b represent two real numbers and $b \neq 0$. Then $a \div b = \dfrac{a}{b} = a\left(\dfrac{1}{b}\right)$.

This definition says that you can always interpret a division problem as a multiplication problem and vice-versa. From this definition, as well as some properties that we will soon learn about, we have the following rules for multiplication and division:

$$(+)(+) = + \qquad\qquad (+) \div (+) = +$$
$$(+)(-) = - \qquad\qquad (+) \div (-) = -$$
$$(-)(+) = - \qquad\qquad (-) \div (+) = -$$
$$(-)(-) = + \qquad\qquad (-) \div (-) = +$$

The following property is important to know.

Property I: If a is any real number, then $-(-a) = a$.

For example, $-(-4) = 4$ and $-(-1) = 1$. As you can see, the negative signs cancel each other out. Notice that we can also write $-(-a) = -1(-a)$ since $1(-a) = -a$. In Section 1.5, we will see why this property holds. By the way, we now have that $a - b = a + (-b)$ makes sense for **any** real numbers, a and b. Let's see why.

Examples. Evaluate.

1) $\underbrace{2 - (-1) = 2 + [-(-1)]}_{\text{Let } a=2 \text{ and } b=-1 \text{ and use } a-b=a+(-b).} = 2 + 1 = 3$

A shortcut to doing this is to remember that the two negative signs cancel each other out and we obtain a positive sign. Hence,

$$\underbrace{2 - (-1) = 2 + 1}_{\text{The } -\text{'s cancel out.}} = 3.$$

In the proceding examples, try them by using the shortcut. I've done them the long way.

2) $\underbrace{8 - (-14) = 8 + [-(-14)]}_{\text{Let } a=8 \text{ and } b=-14 \text{ and use } a-b=a+(-b).} = 8 + 14 = 22$

3) $-7 - (-4) = -7 + [-(-4)] = -7 + 4 = -3$

4) $-10 - (-10) = -10 + [-(-10)] = -10 + 10 = 0$

5) $-3 - (-9) = -3 + [-(-9)] = -3 + 9 = 6$

Property II: If a and b are any integers and $b \neq 0$, then $\dfrac{-a}{b} = \dfrac{a}{-b} = -\dfrac{a}{b}$.

9

This says that if you have a negative sign in a fraction, you may put it in either the numerator, the denominator, or outside of the fraction. For example, the fractions $\frac{-4}{11}$, $\frac{4}{-11}$, and $-\frac{4}{11}$ are all equivalent (that is, they all have the same value). Let's do some examples with multiplication and division.

Examples. Multiply or divide.

1) $(2)(-5) = -10$ since a positive times a negative is a negative.

2) $(6)(-7) = -42$ since a negative times a positive is a negative.

3) $(-9)(-4) = 36$ since a negative times a negative is a positive.

4) $(+10)(+10) = 100$ (remember that the positive sign may be left out).

5) $-2(-3) = 6$ since $-2(-3) = -[2(-3)] = \underbrace{-[-6] = 6}_{\text{by Property I}}$.

6) $32 \div (-8) = -4$ since a positive divided by a negative is a negative.

7) $(-60) \div (-10) = 6$ since a negative divided by a negative is a positive.

8) $\frac{-56}{7} = -8$ since a negative divided by a positive is a negative.

9) $\frac{-27}{-9} = 3$ since a negative divided by a negative is a positive.

10) $-(-2) = 2$ by Property I.

Try These (Set 3): Evaluate.

1) $6 + (-1)$	2) $(-9) + (-13)$	3) $7 - 22$	4) $-1 - 5$
5) $0 - 14$	6) $-19 - (-3)$	7) $(6)(-6)$	8) $(-3)(-5)$
9) $-(-19)$	10) $(-24) \div 3$	11) $(-64) \div (-16)$	12) $\frac{32}{-2}$

Arithmetic with Rational Numbers

I) Adding and Subtracting

Recall that in order to add (or subtract) two fractions, you need to have common denominators. Once you have common denominators, you can combine the fractions by combining their numerators.

> If A, B, and C are any integers but $C \neq 0$, then $\frac{A}{C} + \frac{B}{C} = \frac{A+B}{C}$ and $\frac{A}{C} - \frac{B}{C} = \frac{A-B}{C}$.

Sometimes, as you know, you may have to change the denominators in a given problem to get what is called the **least common denominator** (or **LCD**). For example, to add $\frac{1}{6} + \frac{3}{8}$, you find the LCD of the denominators 6 and 8 first, which is 24 (since both 6 and 8 are **divisors** of 24). You rewrite your fractions into equivalent ones which have denominator 24, and then add the fractions together.

$$\frac{1}{6} + \frac{3}{8} = \frac{1(4)}{6(4)} + \frac{3(3)}{8(3)} = \frac{4}{24} + \frac{9}{24} = \frac{13}{24}$$

Let me mention that another name for the LCD of the denominators in the example $\frac{1}{6} + \frac{3}{8}$ is the **least common multiple** (abbreviated as **LCM**) of the numbers 6 and 8. I will assume that you know how to find the LCM of two natural numbers.

Examples. Add or subtract.

1) $\frac{1}{6} + \frac{5}{6} = \frac{1+5}{6} = \frac{6}{6} = 1$

2) $\frac{10}{11} - \frac{3}{11} = \frac{10-3}{11} = \frac{7}{11}$

3) $\underbrace{\frac{5}{8} + \frac{1}{10} = \frac{5\,(5)}{8\,(5)} + \frac{1\,(4)}{10\,(4)}}_{\text{The LCM of 8 and 10 is 40.}} = \frac{25}{40} + \frac{4}{40} = \frac{25+4}{40} = \frac{29}{40}$

4) $\underbrace{\frac{9}{22} - \frac{2}{11} = \frac{9}{22} - \frac{2\,(2)}{11\,(2)}}_{\text{The LCM of 22 and 11 is 22.}} = \frac{9}{22} - \frac{4}{22} = \frac{9-4}{22} = \frac{5}{22}$

5) $\frac{6}{7} - \left(-\frac{15}{7}\right) = \frac{6-(-15)}{7} = \frac{6+15}{7} = \frac{\overset{3}{\cancel{21}}}{\underset{1}{\cancel{7}}} = 3$

6) $-\frac{4}{9} - \left(-\frac{1}{9}\right) = \frac{-4-(-1)}{9} = \frac{-4+1}{9} = \frac{\overset{1}{\cancel{-3}}}{\underset{3}{\cancel{9}}} = -\frac{1}{3}$

7) $\underbrace{-\frac{1}{9} + \frac{2}{3} = \frac{-1}{9} + \frac{2(3)}{3(3)}}_{\text{The LCM of 9 and 3 is 9.}} = \frac{-1}{9} + \frac{6}{9} = \frac{-1+6}{9} = \frac{5}{9}$

8) $\underbrace{-\frac{3}{2} + \left(-\frac{1}{5}\right) = \frac{-3(5)}{2(5)} + \frac{-1(2)}{5(2)}}_{\text{The LCM of 2 and 5 is 10.}} = \frac{-15}{10} + \frac{-2}{10} = \frac{-15+(-2)}{10} = \frac{-17}{10} \text{ or } -\frac{17}{10}$

9) $\underbrace{\frac{1}{4} - \frac{5}{6} = \frac{1(3)}{4(3)} - \frac{5(2)}{6(2)}}_{\text{The LCM of 4 and 6 is 12.}} = \frac{3}{12} - \frac{10}{12} = \frac{3-10}{12} = \frac{-7}{12} \text{ or } -\frac{7}{12}$

10) $\underbrace{\frac{9}{-10} - \frac{5}{12} = \frac{-9(6)}{10(6)} - \frac{5(5)}{12(5)}}_{\text{The LCM of 10 and 12 is 60.}} = \frac{-54}{60} - \frac{25}{60} = \frac{-54-25}{60} = \frac{-79}{60} = -\frac{79}{60}$

11

11) $\dfrac{3}{17} + \left(-\dfrac{3}{17}\right) = \dfrac{3}{17} - \dfrac{3}{17} = 0$

12) $-\dfrac{16}{21} + \left(+\dfrac{16}{21}\right) = \dfrac{-16}{21} + \dfrac{16}{21} = \dfrac{-16+16}{21} = \dfrac{0}{21} = 0$

13) $\underbrace{\dfrac{1}{6} - \left(-\dfrac{5}{18}\right) = \dfrac{1(3)}{6(3)} - \left(-\dfrac{5}{18}\right)}_{\text{The LCM of 6 and 18 is 18.}} = \dfrac{3}{18} - \left(\dfrac{-5}{18}\right) = \dfrac{3-(-5)}{18} = \dfrac{3+5}{18} = \dfrac{\overset{4}{\cancel{8}}}{\underset{9}{\cancel{18}}} = \dfrac{4}{9}$

II) Multiplying and Dividing

To multiply or divide two rational numbers, we use the following properties:

> **Multiplication.** If A, B, C, and D are integers and both $B, D \neq 0$, then $\dfrac{A}{B} \cdot \dfrac{C}{D} = \dfrac{AC}{BD}$.

and

> **Division.** If A, B, C, and D are integers and $B, C, D \neq 0$, then $\dfrac{A}{B} \div \dfrac{C}{D} = \dfrac{A}{B} \cdot \dfrac{D}{C} = \dfrac{AD}{BC}$.

So, to multiply two rational numbers, you multiply numerators and then multiply denominators (recall that you may be able to simplify first, then multiply). To divide two rational numbers, you 'flip over' (or take the **reciprocal** of) the second fraction and change the division problem into a multiplication problem. Note that the division problem $\dfrac{A}{B} \div \dfrac{C}{D}$ can also be written as $\dfrac{\frac{A}{B}}{\frac{C}{D}}$. An expression of this form is called a **mixed quotient** or **complex fraction**. We will see that our examples are written with the division symbol '$\div$'. We will study mixed quotients in Chapter 4.

Examples. Multiply or divide.

1) $\left(-\dfrac{3}{4}\right)\left(\dfrac{1}{2}\right) = -\dfrac{3}{8}$

2) $\left(\dfrac{7}{6}\right)\left(-\dfrac{5}{6}\right) = -\dfrac{35}{36}$

3) $\left(-\dfrac{3}{10}\right)\left(-\dfrac{1}{4}\right) = \dfrac{3}{40}$

4) $\left(\dfrac{10}{11}\right)\left(-\dfrac{3}{20}\right) = \left(\dfrac{\overset{1}{\cancel{10}}}{11}\right)\left(-\dfrac{3}{\underset{2}{\cancel{20}}}\right) = -\dfrac{3}{22}$

5) $(5)\left(-\dfrac{13}{15}\right) = \left(\dfrac{\overset{1}{\cancel{5}}}{1}\right)\left(-\dfrac{13}{\underset{3}{\cancel{15}}}\right) = -\dfrac{13}{3}$

6) $\left(-\dfrac{9}{2}\right) \div \left(\dfrac{6}{7}\right) = \left(-\dfrac{\overset{3}{\cancel{9}}}{2}\right)\left(\dfrac{7}{\underset{2}{\cancel{6}}}\right) = -\dfrac{21}{4}$

7) $\left(-\dfrac{8}{15}\right) \div (-12) = \left(-\dfrac{8}{15}\right) \div \left(-\dfrac{12}{1}\right) = \left(-\dfrac{\overset{2}{\cancel{8}}}{15}\right)\left(-\dfrac{1}{\underset{3}{\cancel{12}}}\right) = \dfrac{2}{45}$

8) $1 \div \left(-\dfrac{1}{6}\right) = 1\left(-\dfrac{6}{1}\right) = -6$

12

Try These (Set 4): Evaluate.

1) $\dfrac{7}{12} + \dfrac{1}{12}$ 2) $\dfrac{15}{16} - \dfrac{7}{16}$ 3) $-\dfrac{1}{9} + \dfrac{8}{9}$ 4) $\dfrac{4}{7} - \dfrac{6}{7}$

5) $\dfrac{2}{5} - \left(-\dfrac{1}{10}\right)$ 6) $\dfrac{2}{5} + \left(-\dfrac{2}{3}\right)$ 7) $\dfrac{-1}{18} - \dfrac{1}{4}$ 8) $\left(\dfrac{3}{4}\right)\left(-\dfrac{5}{6}\right)$

9) $(-5)\left(-\dfrac{4}{7}\right)$ 10) $\left(-\dfrac{1}{4}\right) \div \left(-\dfrac{7}{20}\right)$ 11) $24 \div \left(-\dfrac{10}{11}\right)$ 12) $1 \div \dfrac{7}{3}$

To end this section, I would like to mention a few more useful properties.

Property III: If $a \neq 0$ is a real number, then $\dfrac{0}{a} = 0$.

For example, $\dfrac{0}{1} = 0$, $\dfrac{0}{-6} = 0$, and $\dfrac{0}{25} = 0$. Notice that $\dfrac{0}{0}$ is undefined.

Property IV: If a is any real number, then $\dfrac{a}{0}$ is undefined.

For example, $\dfrac{1}{0}$, $\dfrac{8}{0}$, and $\dfrac{-9}{0}$ are undefined.

Property V: If $a \neq 0$ is a real number, then $\dfrac{a}{a} = 1$.

For example, $\dfrac{2}{2} = 1$, $\dfrac{-16}{-16} = 1$, and $\dfrac{-3}{-3} = 1$.

Property VI: If a is any real number, then $a \cdot 0 = 0$.

For example, $8 \cdot 0 = 0$, $\dfrac{2}{7}(0) = 0$, and $0 \cdot 0 = 0$.

Property VII: If a and b are real numbers for which $ab = 0$, then either $a = 0$, or $b = 0$, or both.

Property VII is known as the **Zero Product Property**. Note that this can be 'reversed' to read:

$$\text{If either } a = 0, \text{ or } b = 0, \text{ or both, then } ab = 0.$$

For example, if $x \cdot 6 = 0$, then $x = 0$ (since $6 \neq 0$). If $8\,(t) = 0$, then $t = 0$ (since $8 \neq 0$). Observe that if $0y = 0$, then y may or may not equal 0.

13

Section 1.3   Approximation of a Decimal

A decimal which is non-terminating can never be written down entirely since the digits in the decimal go on forever. What we can do, however, is 'cut down' the number of digits in the decimal, using only part of it. This is known as **approximating** a decimal or **decimal approximation**. There are two ways a decimal can be approximated. One way is by **rounding off** to a specified decimal place. The other is by **truncation** to a specified decimal place. Let me discuss how these work.

When you want to round off a decimal to a certain decimal place (for example, to the nearest tenth or nearest thousandth), you first find the digit in the place which you want to round off to. If the next digit is less than 5, you delete everything after the digit which you are rounding off to. On the other hand, if the next digit is 5 or more, you increase the digit which you are rounding off to by 1 and then delete everything after it. For example, suppose you want to round off the decimal 6.249093 to the nearest tenth (or to one decimal place). Notice that, after the tenths place, a 4 appears. Since 4 is less than 5, you leave the digit in the tenths place (the 2) as it is and delete everything afterwards. By doing this, you'll get 6.2. Let's round off $\pi = 3.14159...$ to the nearest thousandth (or to three decimal places). In the third decimal place, there is a 1. We go to the next digit and observe that it is a 5. We now increase the previous digit (the 1) by 1 and delete everything after it. By doing this, we'll obtain the decimal 3.142.

When you want to truncate a decimal to a certain decimal place, all you need to do is delete everything that comes after the decimal place which you are truncating to. For example, to truncate the decimal 0.333333... to the nearest ten-thousandth (that is, to four decimal places), just throw away all the digits which come after the fourth decimal place. By doing so, we obtain 0.3333. Notice that this is the same thing that we would've obtained if we were rounding off to the nearest ten-thousandth. You may wonder whether or not truncating a decimal will always give the same answer as rounding off. Let's see an example where the two are different. Let's truncate the decimal 9.81223 to the nearest whole number (that is, to zero decimal places). If we delete everything after the whole number, we'll obtain 9. However, if we round off the decimal 9.81223 to the nearest whole number, we need to examine the digit following the whole number. This digit, 8, is more than 5 and, consequently, we must increase the 9 by 1. By doing this, we'll obtain 10 and so the truncation is different from the rounded off answer.

Examples. Round off each number to one decimal place and to two decimal places.

1) $2.71143 = 2.7$ to one decimal place and $2.71143 = 2.71$ to two decimal places.

2) $3.6745 = 3.7$ to one decimal place and $3.6745 = 3.67$ to two decimal places.

3) $10.1853 = 10.2$ to one decimal place and $10.1853 = 10.19$ to two decimal places.

4) $27.951 = 28.0$ to one decimal place and $27.951 = 27.95$ to two decimal places.

5) $0.0126 = 0.0$ to one decimal place and $0.0126 = 0.01$ to two decimal places.

Examples. Truncate each number to one decimal place and to two decimal places.

1) $3.1174 = 3.1$ to one decimal place and $3.1174 = 3.11$ to two decimal places.

2) $12.0558 = 12.0$ to one decimal place and $12.0558 = 12.05$ to two decimal places.

3) $9.00632 = 9.0$ to one decimal place and $9.00632 = 9.00$ to two decimal places.

4) $31.965 = 31.9$ to one decimal place and $31.965 = 31.96$ to two decimal places.

1) 3.24108   2) 8.90614   3) 43.60082

4) 12.332777   5) 60.101808   6) 0.1491625

Section 1.4   The Order of Operations

Whenever you have to do a computation with several arithmetic operations involved, there is a specific order that you need to follow in order to evaluate the expression. This order is known as the **order of operations**. In this section, we will discuss the order of operations.

The following rules for the order of operations must be obeyed when evaluating an arithmetic problem:

1. Start by working out what is in the **parenthesis**, beginning with the innermost and working outward.
2. Next, work out any **exponentiation**.
3. Perform any **multiplications** and **divisions**, going from left to right.
4. Perform any **additions** and **subtractions**, going from left to right.

To help you remember this ordering, it is useful to remember the initials **PEMDAS**, where **P** is **parenthesis**, **E** is **exponentiation**, **M** is **multiplication**, **D** is **division**, **A** is **addition**, and **S** is **subtraction**. A phrase that students sometimes remember with the same initials is:

$$\textbf{P}\text{lease } \textbf{E}\text{xcuse } \textbf{M}\text{y } \textbf{D}\text{ear } \textbf{A}\text{unt } \textbf{S}\text{ally}$$

Take a look at the next set of examples. I've worked out each one step by step following the PEMDAS order.

Examples. Evaluate.

1) $\underset{12}{\underbrace{3(4)}} + 9 = 12 + 9 = 21$

2) $3\underset{13}{\underbrace{(4 + 9)}} = 3(13) = 39$

3) $2 - \underset{18}{\underbrace{6 \times 3}} = 2 - 18 = -16$

4) $\underset{-4}{\underbrace{(2 - 6)}} \times 3 = (-4) \times 3 = -12$

5) $(-3) + \underset{4}{\underbrace{12 \div 3}} = (-3) + 4 = 1$

6) $\underset{9}{\underbrace{(-3 + 12)}} \div 3 = 9 \div 3 = 3$

7) $\underset{-2}{\underbrace{(8 - 10)}}^2 + 16 = \underset{4}{\underbrace{(-2)^2}} + 16 = 4 + 16 = 20$

8) $\underset{-27}{\underbrace{-23 - 4}} + 15 = -27 + 15 = -12$

9) $-23 - \underset{19}{\underbrace{(4 + 15)}} = -23 - 19 = -42$

10) $\underset{5}{\underbrace{45 \div 9}} \cdot 2 \div 10 \cdot 9 = \underset{10}{\underbrace{5 \cdot 2}} \div 10 \cdot 9 = \underset{1}{\underbrace{10 \div 10}} \cdot 9 = 1 \cdot 9 = 9$

11) $\underset{-4}{\underbrace{(-3 - 1)}}\underset{8}{\underbrace{(-4 + 12)}} - 7 \times 4 = \underset{-32}{\underbrace{(-4)(8)}} - 7 \times 4 = -32 - \underset{28}{\underbrace{7 \times 4}} = -32 - 28 = -60$

12) $\underset{25}{\underbrace{5^2}} - \underset{4}{\underbrace{(1 + 3)^2}} \times 2 + 11 = 25 - \underset{16}{\underbrace{4^2}} \times 2 + 11 = 25 - \underset{32}{\underbrace{16 \times 2}} + 11 = \underset{-7}{\underbrace{25 - 32}} + 11 = -7 + 11 = 4$

13) $3 + 5\{2 - 8(11 - 16)\} = 3 + 5\{2 - 8(-5)\} = 3 + 5\{2 + 40\} = 3 + 5\{42\} = 3 + 210 = 213$

14) $\dfrac{-2 + 5(3 + 7)}{15 - 3^2} = \dfrac{-2 + 5(10)}{15 - 9} = \dfrac{-2 + 50}{6} = \dfrac{48}{6} = 8$

In Example 14, notice that the numerator and denominator were worked out before dividing. Think of the numerator and denominator as being in parenthesis when you get such an example.

Try These (Set 6): Evaluate.

1) $6 - 2(4 + 1)$

2) $0 - 1 - 2 - 3$

3) $6 \cdot 8 \div (2 + 2)$

4) $4^2 - 7 + 2(3)$

5) $-1 - (2^3 - 5^2)$

6) $36 \div 2 + 20 \div 10$

7) $17 - 8(2 - 3)^2 + 3$

8) $(-3 - 2)^2 \cdot \{5 + 2(-4)\}$

9) $\dfrac{3 \times 8 - 12}{-2 \cdot 3}$

10) $-5 + 3[2 + 7(2 - 4)] - 10$

11) $(3 + 1)(2 - 6) \cdot (4 - 7)(0)$

12) $9 - 9 + 9 \cdot 9 - 9$

Section 1.5   Properties of the Real Numbers

In this section, we will learn about some properties that the real numbers satisfy. It is these properties which give us the rules for doing arithmetic with real numbers.

The Commutative Properties

Suppose that a and b are any real numbers. Then

$$a + b = b + a$$
and
$$ab = ba.$$

For example, $4 + 8 = 8 + 4$ and $3 \times 2 = 2 \times 3$. Notice that the Commutative Property only works for addition and multiplication. For example, observe that $7 - 1 \neq 1 - 7$ and $28 \div 4 \neq 4 \div 28$.

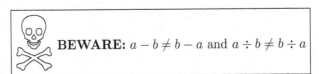 **BEWARE:** $a - b \neq b - a$ and $a \div b \neq b \div a$

The Associative Properties

Suppose that a, b, and c are any real numbers. Then

$$(a + b) + c = a + (b + c) = a + b + c$$
and
$$(ab)c = a(bc) = abc.$$

16

For example, $(1 + 3) + 10 = 4 + 10 = 14$ and $1 + (3 + 10) = 1 + 13 = 14$. As for multiplication, observe that $(4 \times 5) \times (-3) = 20 \times (-3) = -60$ and $4 \times (5 \times (-3)) = 4 \times (-15) = -60$. Note that the Associative Property only works for addition and multiplication. For example, you can check and see that $(1 - 3) - 7 \neq 1 - (3 - 7)$ and $(60 \div 4) \div 2 \neq 60 \div (4 \div 2)$ by using the order of operations.

 BEWARE: $(a - b) - c \neq a - (b - c)$ and $(a \div b) \div c \neq a \div (b \div c)$

The Distributive Property

Suppose that a, b, and c are any real numbers. Then
$$a(b + c) = ab + ac$$
and
$$(a + b)c = ac + bc.$$

For example, when we evaluate $6(4 + 5)$, we work out the sum in the parenthesis first:
$$6(4 + 5) = 6(9) = 54.$$

We can also compute this by using the Distributive Property as follows:
$$6(4 + 5) = 6(4) + 6(5) = 24 + 30 = 54$$

We get the same answer as before. Clearly, it is easier to do it using the order of operations rather than the Distributive Property. However, when we learn how to multiply algebraic expressions together, the Distributive Property will come in handy. For example, if we want to multiply $8(x + 7)$, we couldn't add x and 7 together into a single expression since we don't know what x equals. Nevertheless, we can multiply the two expressions together by using the Distributive Property as follows:
$$8(x + 7) = 8(x) + 8(7) = 8x + 56$$

Recall that Property I states that if a is any real number, then $-(-a) = a$. Let's see why this is true. Consider the expression $-1((-a) + a)$. Since $(-a) + a = -a + a = 0$, we have $-1((-a) + a) = -1(0) = 0$. On the other hand, the distributive property gives us
$$-1((-a) + a) = -1(-a) + (-1)(a) = -(-a) - a.$$

Therefore, we have
$$0 = -(-a) - a.$$

If we add a to both sides of the equation, we'll obtain
$$a = -(-a).$$

The Additive and Multiplicative Identities

The number 0 is called the **additive identity** and satisfies the following property:
If a is any real number, then $a + 0 = 0 + a = a$.

The number 1 is called the **multiplicative identity** and satisfies the following property:
If a is any real number, then $a \cdot 1 = 1 \cdot a = a$.

For example, $4 + 0 = 4$ and $\frac{3}{5} \cdot 1 = \frac{3}{5}$.

The Additive and Multiplicative Inverse Properties

Suppose that a is any real number. Then $-a$ is called the **additive inverse** of a and satisfies

$$a + (-a) = (-a) + a = 0.$$

The additive inverse of a real number is just the number itself with a different sign.

Suppose that $a \neq 0$ is a real number. Then $\frac{1}{a}$ is called the **multiplicative inverse** (or **reciprocal**) of a and satisfies

$$a\left(\frac{1}{a}\right) = \left(\frac{1}{a}\right)a = 1.$$

It turns out that the reciprocal of a number (written in fraction form) is obtained by 'flipping over' the fraction.

Examples. Find the additive inverse and reciprocal of each number.

1) 2 has additive inverse -2 and reciprocal $\frac{1}{2}$ $\left(\text{write } 2 = \frac{2}{1} \text{ and flip over } \frac{2}{1} \text{ to obtain the reciprocal } \frac{1}{2}\right)$.

2) -5 has additive inverse 5 and reciprocal $\frac{1}{-5} = -\frac{1}{5}$.

3) $-\frac{4}{13}$ has additive inverse $\frac{4}{13}$ and reciprocal $-\frac{13}{4}$.

4) $9\frac{3}{4} = \frac{39}{4}$ has additive inverse $-\frac{39}{4}$ and reciprocal $\frac{4}{39}$.

5) 0 has additive inverse 0 and no reciprocal since $\frac{1}{0}$ is undefined.

6) 1 has additive inverse -1 and reciprocal 1.

Try These (Set 7):

I) State the property being used.

1) $7 + 9 = 9 + 7$

2) $(1 + 2) + (-6) = 1 + (2 + (-6))$

3) $(13)(-5) = (-5)(13)$

4) $2(x - 7) = 2(x) + 2(-7)$

II) Find the additive inverse and reciprocal (multiplicative inverse) of 15 and $-\frac{2}{5}$.

III) True or False: $x \div y = y \div x$ for any real numbers x and y.

IV) Multiply.

1) $3(x + 5)$

2) $-6(a + 6)$

3) $a(b - 9)$

4) $-1(18 - x)$

Section 1.6 The Real Number Line and Inequalities

We've learned that the set of real numbers consists of the rational numbers (numbers which are expressible as either terminating or non-terminating, repeating decimals), together with the irrational numbers (the set of non-terminating, non-repeating decimals). What we will now do is to develop a picture, or geometrical representation, of the set of real numbers. To do this, we take a line (which we will draw horizontally) and label the integers on it as follows:

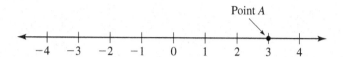

As you can see, each integer corresponds to a point on the line. We say that the integer is the **coordinate** of the point on the line which it corresponds to and we call the point the **graph** of the integer. For example, the point labelled A on the line above has coordinate 3 and point A is the graph of 3. Clearly, we can't label (or **graph**) all of the integers, so we use the 'arrows' to denote the fact that there are more integers on the number line (even though we haven't labelled them). Notice that the integers have been placed on the number line in increasing order from left to right (recall that a negative integer is always smaller than a positive integer). We call the number 0 the **origin**. Now, if we want to find the location of **any** real number on the number line, whether it is rational or irrational, we find the pair of integers which it lies in between and label the number accordingly. To do this, however, you will have to approximate its location. Several numbers have been located on the number line below.

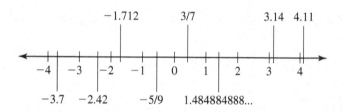

The number line is a graphical representation of the set of all real numbers. For this reason, we call it the **real number line**. No matter which real number you choose, it will have a home on the real number line.

Now, suppose that you are given two different real numbers, say a and b, and you are interested in knowing which is the larger (or smaller) of the two. Since the real number line is constructed in such a way that the numbers get larger from left to right, we can find the location of a and b on it and see which of the two is on the right-hand side of the other. The number on the right is always larger than the number on the left. When comparing two numbers, we use one of the **inequality symbols**, written as either $>$ or $<$. The sentence $a < b$ is read as "a is **less than** b" and the sentence $a > b$ is read as "a is **greater than** b". As usual, if the two numbers are equal to each other, we use the **equality symbol** $=$. The following law for comparing two numbers always holds:

The Law of Trichotomy

If a and b are any two real numbers, then exactly one of the following holds:

$$a > b, \ a < b, \text{ or } a = b.$$

Graphically, this means that if you pick two numbers, then one number will be on the right-hand side of the other, unless the two numbers are equal to each other. Let's now recall how to compare numbers. We will do this **without** using the real number line.

Examples. Compare the numbers.

1) $3 < 20$ is obvious.

2) $\dfrac{3}{8} > \dfrac{1}{3}$

To obtain this, you could either rewrite the fractions as equivalent ones with the same denominator and compare their numerators or write each fraction as a decimal and compare the decimals instead. For the first method, notice that the LCM of 8 and 3 is 24, so $\dfrac{3(3)}{8(3)} = \dfrac{9}{24} > \dfrac{8}{24} = \dfrac{1(8)}{3(8)}$. As for the second method, notice that $\dfrac{3}{8} = 0.375$ and $\dfrac{1}{3} = 0.333\ldots$. We have $0.375 > 0.333\ldots$ since the second digit of 0.375 is larger than the second digit of $0.3\overline{33}\ldots$.

3) $0.6565 < \dfrac{65}{99}$

Observe that $\dfrac{65}{99} = 0.\overline{65} = 0.656565\ldots$, which is a non-terminating, repeating decimal. When we compare $0.6565 = 0.6565000\ldots$ to $0.656565\ldots$, we see that the fifth digit of $0.656565\ldots$ is greater than the fifth digit of $0.6565000\ldots$. Therefore, $0.6565 < 0.\overline{65} = \dfrac{65}{99}$.

4) $0 < 5$ is obvious since zero is less than every positive number.

5) $0 > -9$ is also obvious since zero is greater than every negative number.

6) $-16 < -7$

One way of comparing two negative numbers is to first compare the numbers WITHOUT the negative signs. Then reverse the inequality. In this example, we have $16 > 7$. Therefore, $-16 < -7$. Another way of comparing them is to use the real number line and to notice that -7 is closer to zero than -16 is.

7) $-0.334 < -\dfrac{1}{3}$

To compare these, you should first compare 0.334 and $\dfrac{1}{3}$. Observe that $\dfrac{1}{3} = 0.\overline{3} = 0.3333\ldots$ and, consequently, $0.334 > \dfrac{1}{3}$ (by comparing the third digit of each decimal). Therefore, you'll reverse the inequality and obtain $-0.334 < -\dfrac{1}{3}$.

8) $-\pi > -4$

Recall that $\pi \approx 3.14 < 4$. Therefore, $-\pi > -4$.

9) $-\dfrac{1}{8} > -\dfrac{1}{4}$

First, compare $\dfrac{1}{8}$ and $\dfrac{1}{4}$. Observe that $\dfrac{1}{8} < \dfrac{2}{8} = \dfrac{1}{4}$. Hence, $-\dfrac{1}{8} > -\dfrac{1}{4}$.

10) $-3 < 5$

Comparing a positive number to a negative number is simple: the positive number is always greater than the negative number.

Try These (Set 8):

I) Locate the numbers on the real number line.

1) 3   2) −1   3) $\frac{2}{3}$ 4) −3.5   5) $2\frac{1}{2}$

6) −π   7) $-\frac{7}{5}$ 8) $-2.\overline{412}$ 9) 4.2   10) 0.39

II) Fill in the space with the inequality symbol < or >.

1) 4 _____ 9   2) −8 _____ − 11   3) $\frac{1}{7}$ _____ $\frac{1}{4}$ 4) −3.022 _____ − 3.0225

5) $-1.\overline{5}$ _____ $1.\overline{5}$ 6) π _____ 3.12   7) −1.56 _____ $-\frac{155}{99}$

Section 1.7   Absolute Value

In the last section, we saw that the real number line is a graphical representation of the set of all real numbers. By using an inequality (or equal) symbol, we can write down a mathematical sentence which compares two numbers. In this section, we will learn how to find the distance between two numbers on the real number line.

Definition: Let n represent any real number. The **absolute value** of n, written as $|n|$, is the distance between 0 and n on the real number line.

Examples. Find the absolute value each number.

1) $|5| = 5$

By using the real number line, you can see that the number 5 is 5 units from 0 (see the figure below).

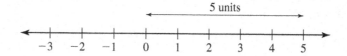

It turns out that $|n| = n$ for any positive number n (which is the same as saying that $n > 0$).

2) $|-4| = 4$

Once again, you can see that the number −4 is 4 units from 0 (see the figure below)

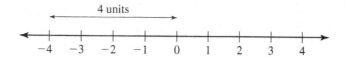

Notice that the answer is just the number -4, but without the negative sign. In fact, if n is any negative number (which is the same as saying that $n < 0$), then $|n|$ is just n, but without the negative sign.

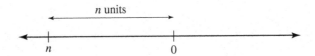

3) $|0| = 0$

This makes perfect sense. The distance between 0 and 0 on the real number line is just 0.

When we write the 'rules' mentioned above algebraically, we'll have

$$|n| = n \text{ if either } n > 0 \text{ or } n = 0 \qquad \text{and} \qquad |n| = -n \text{ if } n < 0.$$

By the way, instead of writing '$n > 0$ or $n = 0$', we can simply write $n \geq 0$. Don't worry too much about the algebraic interpretation mentioned above at the moment. Just make sure that you know that the absolute value of a positive number is the number itself and the absolute value of a negative number is the number, but **without** the negative sign. The absolute value of zero is zero. Let's continue with our examples.

4) $|8| = 8$

5) $|-3.92| = 3.92$

6) $\left|\dfrac{10}{13}\right| = \dfrac{10}{13}$

7) $\left|-\dfrac{6}{23}\right| = \dfrac{6}{23}$

8) $\left|-29\dfrac{1}{3}\right| = 29\dfrac{1}{3}$

9) $\left|5\dfrac{1}{2}\right| = 5\dfrac{1}{2}$

10) $|6.\overline{31}| = 6.\overline{31}$

11) $|-\pi| = \pi$

12) $|7 - 12| = |-5| = 5$

13) $|7| - |12| = 7 - 12 = -5$

14) $|-2| \cdot |15| = 2 \cdot 15 = 30$

15) $|(-2)(15)| = |-30| = 30$

By definition, the absolute value of a number tells us the distance between 0 and the number on the real number line. Suppose we want to find the distance between any two real numbers on the real number line. The following formula tells us how to do this.

The Distance Formula

If A and B are two points on a real number line with coordinates a and b, respectively, then the distance, d, between A and B is

$$d = |b - a|.$$

Examples. Find the distance between the points whose coordinates are given.

1) 8 and 25

It doesn't matter which number you label as a or b since the distance between a and b is the same as the distance between b and a. Let's choose $a = 8$ and $b = 25$. Then

$$d = |b - a| = |25 - 8| = |17| = 17.$$

Therefore, the distance is 17.

22

2) -3 and -8

Let $a = -3$ and $b = -8$. Then

$$d = |b - a| = |-8 - (-3)| = |-8 + 3| = |-5| = 5.$$

Therefore, the distance is 5.

3) $\dfrac{3}{4}$ and $-\dfrac{5}{6}$

Let $a = \dfrac{3}{4}$ and $b = -\dfrac{5}{6}$. Then

$$d = |b - a| = \left| -\frac{5}{6} - \frac{3}{4} \right| = \left| -\frac{5(2)}{6(2)} - \frac{3(3)}{4(3)} \right| = \left| -\frac{10}{12} - \frac{9}{12} \right| = \left| \frac{-19}{12} \right| = \frac{19}{12}.$$

Therefore, the distance is $\dfrac{19}{12}$.

Next we list some properties which absolute value satisfies.

Properties of Absolute Value

Suppose that a and b are any two real numbers. Then:

Property 1. $|a| \geq 0$ **Property 4.** $|-a| = |a|$

Property 2. $|a|^2 = a^2$ **Property 5.** $\left| \dfrac{a}{b} \right| = \dfrac{|a|}{|b|}, b \neq 0$

Property 3. $|a \cdot b| = |a| \cdot |b|$ **Property 6.** $|a + b| \leq |a| + |b|$

Property 6 is called the **Triangle Inequality**.

Observe that $|a^2| = \underbrace{|a \cdot a| = |a| \cdot |a|}_{\text{by Property 2}} = |a|^2$. Consequently, we have:

     Property 7. $|a^2| = a^2$

More generally, we have:

     Property 8. $|a^n| = a^n$ if n is even and $|a^n| = |a|^n$ if n is odd.

Examples. Simplify.

1) $|a|^2 = a^2$ by Property 2

2) $\underbrace{|7y| = |7| \cdot |y|}_{\text{by Property 3}} = 7|y|$

3) $\underbrace{|x^3| = |x^2 \cdot x| = |x^2| \cdot |x| = x^2|x|}_{\text{by Properties 3 and 7}}$

4) $\underbrace{\left| \dfrac{-2}{b} \right| = \dfrac{|-2|}{|b|} = \dfrac{2}{|b|}}_{\text{by Property 5}}$ (assuming that $b \neq 0$)

5) $\underbrace{\left| \dfrac{a^2}{8} \right| = \dfrac{|a^2|}{|8|} = \dfrac{a^2}{8}}_{\text{by Properties 5 and 7}}$

Try These (Set 9):

I) Evaluate.

1) $|3|$ 2) $|-1|$ 3) $|-20|$ 4) $|17|$

5) $\left|-\frac{2}{11}\right|$ 6) $|2.852\overline{3}|$ 7) $-|-19+4|$ 8) $-\left(7+|2-3^2|\right)$

II) Find the distance between the given numbers on the real number line.

1) 9 and -5 2) 18 and 2   3) -34 and -13 4) $\frac{3}{4}$ and $\frac{-5}{3}$

III) Simplify.

1) $|x|^2$ 2) $|-12y|$ 3) $|7ab^2|$

4) $\left|\frac{1}{x}\right|$, $x \neq 0$ 5) $\left|-\frac{t}{8}\right|$ 6) $\left|\frac{a^3b^2}{-10}\right|$

Section 1.8   Introduction to Algebra

As we have already seen, we can use letters (called **variables**) to write mathematical statements or sentences. For example, when we wrote down the distance formula for two numbers on the real number line, we actually used variables to write the formula

$$d = |b - a|.$$

In this formula, the letters a, b, and d are the variables and the equality symbol is used to tell us how these variables are related to one another. When we used this formula to figure out some distance problems, we plugged the given values for a and b into the formula and computed d. In Algebra, we are interested in working with formulas, expressions, and equations which contain variables. Throughout this text, you will encounter such algebraic objects and be required to know how to perform a computation involving the replacement of a variable by a specified value. As you will now see, this amounts to using the order of operations.

Examples. Evaluate each expression if $x = 3$, $y = -7$, and $z = 1$.

1) $x + y + 2z$

The first thing that you should do is to put parentheses around each of your variables. By doing so, you will avoid making mistakes with signs (I've seen such mistakes made numerous times in the past). After inserting parentheses, you'll replace each variable with the given value and use the order of operations to compute the answer. Here, we obtain

$$(x) + (y) + 2(z) = (3) + (-7) + 2(1) = -4 + 2 = -2.$$

2) $3x - 5y$

$$3(x) - 5(y) = 3(3) - 5(-7) = 9 + 35 = 44$$

3) $-2x + 2yz - z^2 + 7$

$$-2\,(x) + 2\,(y)\,(z) - (z)^2 + 7 = -2\,(3) + 2\,(-7)\,(1) - (1)^2 + 7$$
$$= -6 + (-14) - (1) + 7$$
$$= -6 - 14 - 1 + 7$$
$$= -14$$

4) $\dfrac{3z - 2x}{-9y - 10}$

$$\frac{3\,(z) - 2\,(x)}{-9\,(y) - 10} = \frac{3\,(1) - 2\,(3)}{-9\,(-7) - 10} = \frac{3 - 6}{63 - 10} = \frac{-3}{53} = -\frac{3}{53}$$

5) $x^2 + x - 7 + \dfrac{2}{x}$

$$(x)^2 + (x) - 7 + \frac{2}{(x)} = (3)^2 + (3) - 7 + \frac{2}{(3)}$$
$$= 9 + 3 - 7 + \frac{2}{3}$$
$$= 5\frac{2}{3}$$

6) $\left| 3y - 7x - z^2 \right|$

$$\left| 3\,(y) - 7\,(x) - (z)^2 \right| = \left| 3\,(-7) - 7\,(3) - (1)^2 \right|$$
$$= |-21 - 21 - 1|$$
$$= |-43| = 43$$

Sometimes you may be working with an algebraic expression which does not allow certain numbers to be plugged into it. For example, when we plug $x = 3$ into the expression $\dfrac{1}{x - 3}$, we'll obtain

$$\frac{1}{(x) - 3} = \frac{1}{(3) - 3} = \frac{1}{0}$$

which is undefined. We call the set of numbers that a variable can be replaced by the **domain of the variable**. For $\dfrac{1}{x - 3}$, the only 'bad' number is $x = 3$ (since this is the only number for which $x - 3 = 0$). We say that the domain of x is the set of all real numbers **except** 3. Let's see some examples on finding domains.

Examples. Find the domain of x in each expression.

1) $\dfrac{2}{x - 8}$ is undefined when the denominator equals 0. Well, let's find out which x-values do this (I'll assume that you know how to solve some basic equations).

$$\begin{array}{r} x - \cancel{8} = 0 \\ \underline{+\cancel{8} \quad +8} \\ x \qquad = 8 \end{array}$$

If $x = 8$, the expression is undefined. This means that the domain of x is the set of all real numbers except 8.

2) $\dfrac{-8}{x+5}$ is undefined when $x+5=0$. Let's find the value of x.

$$\begin{array}{rl} x+\cancel{5} &= 0 \\ -\cancel{5}\ \ -5 & \\ \hline x\ \ \ \ \ \ &= -5 \end{array}$$

This means that if $x=-5$, the expression is undefined. The domain of x is, therefore, the set of all real numbers except -5.

3) $\dfrac{5}{12-x}$ is undefined when $12-x=0$. Let's find the value of x.

$$\begin{array}{rl} 12-\cancel{x} &= 0 \\ +\cancel{x}\ \ +x & \\ \hline 12\ \ \ \ &= x \end{array}$$

$x=12$ makes the expression $\dfrac{5}{12-x}$ undefined. This means that the domain of x is the set of all real numbers except 12.

Try These (Set 10):

I) Evaluate each expression when $a=-6$, $b=2$, and $c=-3$.

1) $3a+b$ 2) $c(b-4a)$ 3) $\dfrac{a+c}{2a+5b}$

4) $1-b-c^2$ 5) $\dfrac{1}{a}-\dfrac{1}{c}$ 6) b^2-4ac

II) Find the domain of x in each expression.

1) $\dfrac{7}{x-1}$ 2) $\dfrac{10}{x+5}$ 3) $\dfrac{3}{-x+9}$

Exercise 1

In Exercises 1-12, place a check mark in the correct columns. Exercises 1 and 2 have been done for you.

	Number	Natural Number	Integer	Rational Number	Irrational Number
1.	4	✓	✓	✓	
2.	$-\dfrac{1}{6}$			✓	
3.	$+12$				
4.	-7				
5.	$-4.2\overline{36}$				
6.	$1.\overline{524}$				
7.	9.5523				
8.	$\dfrac{11}{39}$				
9.	$18.070770777\ldots$				
10.	π				
11.	16.0				
12.	14.29766				

26

In Exercises 13-42, express the fraction as either a terminating or non-terminating, repeating decimal.

13. $\dfrac{3}{4}$ 14. $\dfrac{2}{5}$ 15. $\dfrac{5}{2}$ 16. $\dfrac{1}{4}$ 17. $\dfrac{7}{8}$

18. $\dfrac{5}{8}$ 19. $-\dfrac{7}{10}$ 20. $-\dfrac{3}{10}$ 21. $\dfrac{17}{3}$ 22. $\dfrac{22}{3}$

23. $-\dfrac{2}{9}$ 24. $-\dfrac{4}{9}$ 25. $\dfrac{16}{5}$ 26. $\dfrac{13}{5}$ 27. $\dfrac{16}{99}$

28. $\dfrac{28}{99}$ 29. $\dfrac{100}{999}$ 30. $\dfrac{2}{999}$ 31. $\dfrac{209}{990}$ 32. $\dfrac{33}{990}$

33. $-\dfrac{12}{25}$ 34. $-\dfrac{6}{25}$ 35. $\dfrac{35}{6}$ 36. $\dfrac{41}{7}$ 37. $\dfrac{24}{6}$

38. $\dfrac{28}{4}$ 39. $\dfrac{0}{6}$ 40. $\dfrac{0}{-11}$ 41. $\dfrac{87}{87}$ 42. $\dfrac{-21}{-21}$

In Exercises 43-58, write each statement as a mathematical expression/sentence.

43. 3 added to 9 44. the sum of 16 and 3 45. 12 less 3

46. 14 subtracted from 26 47. the product of 9 and 5 48. 6 times 11

49. 18 divided by 3 50. 15 divided by 5 51. The sum of x and 10 is 12.

52. 17 added to y equals 28. 53. 25 minus 4 equals y. 54. 9 take away x equals 3.

55. n times 3 is 14 divided by 2. 56. n divided by 4 is the product of 6 and 7.

57. The sum of 11 and x is 28 subtracted from 2 times x. 58. The sum of 3 and y is 21 less y.

In Exercises 59-74, write each statement as a verbal expression/sentence.

59. $8 + 4 = 12$ 60. $9 + 2 = 11$ 61. $23 - 6 = 17$ 62. $5 - 5 = 0$

63. $2 \cdot 7 = 14$ 64. $8(10) = 80$ 65. $\dfrac{36}{9} = 4$ 66. $56 \div 7 = 8$

67. $x + 5 = 12$ 68. $y + 6 = 11$ 69. $14 - a = 2$ 70. $b - 8 = 3$

71. $5y + 6 = 12$ 72. $4x - 1 = 13$ 73. $72 \div 9 = n - 6$ 74. $\dfrac{m}{10} = 7(3)$

In Exercises 75-91, state the Property of Equality which is being used.

75. If $x = 3$, then $x + 5 = 3 + 5$. 76. If $x = 6$, then $x - 1 = 6 - 1$. 77. If $y = 10$, then $y - 8 = 10 - 8$.

78. If $y = 12$, then $y + 7 = 12 + 7$. 79. If $a = 8$, then $a(2) = 8(2)$. 80. If $b = 16$, then $b(9) = 16(9)$.

81. If $x = 36$, then $\dfrac{x}{9} = \dfrac{36}{9}$. 82. If $y = 22$, then $\dfrac{y}{2} = \dfrac{22}{2}$. 83. If $t = 7$, then $t \div 7 = 7 \div 7$.

84. If $s = 15$, then $s \div 5 = 15 \div 5$. 85. If $x = 4 + 3$, then $x + 8 = (4 + 3) + 8$.

86. If $x = 2 + 9$, then $x - 1 = (2 + 9) - 1$.

87. If $y = 10 + 4$, then $y - 3 = (10 + 4) - 3$.

88. If $n = 3 + 8$, then $m + 17 = (3 + 8) + 17$.

89. If $y = 21 - 4$, then $y \div 5 = (21 - 4) \div 5$.

90. If $b = 32 - 14$, then $\dfrac{b}{6} = \dfrac{32 - 14}{6}$.

91. If $a = 15 - 7$, then $a(6) = (15 - 7)(6)$.

In Exercises 92-115, add or subtract.

92. $8 + (+4)$

93. $11 + (+4)$

94. $(-4) + (-7)$

95. $(-7) + (-11)$

96. $(-24) + (+10)$

97. $(-22) + (+5)$

98. $(-8) + (+17)$

99. $(+15) + (-3)$

100. $29 + (-18)$

101. $26 + (-13)$

102. $-11 + 18$

103. $-30 + 9$

104. $-10 + 13$

105. $-7 + 13$

106. $-16 - 5$

107. $-17 - 1$

108. $-1 - 18$

109. $-19 - 5$

110. $8 - 15$

111. $10 - 12$

112. $17 + (-17)$

113. $31 + (-31)$

114. $-46 + 46$

115. $-13 + 13$

In Exercises 116-147, multiply or divide.

116. $(+9)(-3)$

117. $(-2)(+7)$

118. $(-6)(+7)$

119. $(+4)(-11)$

120. $(5)(-15)$

121. $(7)(-10)$

122. $(-8)(7)$

123. $(-2)(16)$

124. $(-6)(-3)$

125. $(-8)(-4)$

126. $(-1)(-10)$

127. $(-18)(-1)$

128. $(+45) \div (-9)$

129. $24 \div (-6)$

130. $(-60) \div 4$

131. $(-49) \div 7$

132. $20 \div (-5)$

133. $36 \div (-18)$

134. $(-40) \div (-5)$

135. $(-90) \div (-9)$

136. $(-12) \div (-3)$

137. $(-56) \div (-8)$

138. $\dfrac{-72}{+9}$

139. $\dfrac{-42}{+2}$

140. $\dfrac{-56}{+7}$

141. $\dfrac{-88}{+11}$

142. $\dfrac{-46}{2}$

143. $\dfrac{-52}{4}$

144. $\dfrac{-42}{-7}$

145. $\dfrac{-100}{-10}$

146. $\dfrac{-64}{-16}$

147. $\dfrac{-121}{-11}$

In Exercises 148-187, add or subtract.

148. $\dfrac{2}{7} + \dfrac{5}{7}$

149. $\dfrac{6}{11} + \dfrac{2}{11}$

150. $\dfrac{9}{17} - \dfrac{3}{17}$

151. $\dfrac{14}{5} - \dfrac{11}{5}$

152. $\dfrac{1}{9} + \dfrac{2}{9}$

153. $\dfrac{5}{16} + \dfrac{3}{16}$

154. $\dfrac{19}{10} - \dfrac{13}{10}$

155. $\dfrac{9}{15} - \dfrac{4}{15}$

156. $\dfrac{1}{8} + \dfrac{1}{4}$

157. $\dfrac{1}{5} + \dfrac{1}{10}$

158. $\dfrac{1}{3} + \dfrac{1}{6}$

159. $\dfrac{1}{21} + \dfrac{1}{7}$

160. $\dfrac{1}{3} - \dfrac{1}{12}$

161. $\dfrac{1}{6} - \dfrac{1}{18}$

162. $\dfrac{1}{8} - \dfrac{1}{16}$

163. $\dfrac{1}{7} - \dfrac{1}{14}$

164. $\dfrac{1}{7} + \dfrac{2}{3}$

165. $\dfrac{5}{7} + \dfrac{1}{3}$

166. $\dfrac{1}{6} + \dfrac{7}{8}$

167. $\dfrac{7}{10} + \dfrac{5}{8}$

168. $\dfrac{3}{4} - \dfrac{2}{5}$

169. $\dfrac{9}{13} - \dfrac{1}{2}$

170. $\dfrac{7}{10} - \dfrac{1}{4}$

171. $\dfrac{8}{9} - \dfrac{5}{6}$

172. $\left(-\dfrac{4}{5}\right)+\dfrac{1}{5}$ 173. $\left(-\dfrac{3}{7}\right)+\dfrac{2}{7}$ 174. $\dfrac{11}{13}+\left(-\dfrac{5}{13}\right)$ 175. $\dfrac{8}{15}+\left(-\dfrac{1}{15}\right)$

176. $\left(-\dfrac{7}{8}\right)+\left(-\dfrac{1}{8}\right)$ 177. $\left(-\dfrac{2}{9}\right)+\left(-\dfrac{7}{9}\right)$ 178. $\left(-\dfrac{3}{5}\right)+\left(-\dfrac{7}{10}\right)$

179. $\left(-\dfrac{1}{5}\right)+\left(-\dfrac{7}{20}\right)$ 180. $-\dfrac{1}{6}-\dfrac{1}{6}$ 181. $-\dfrac{1}{12}-\dfrac{1}{12}$

182. $-\dfrac{5}{21}-\dfrac{2}{14}$ 183. $-\dfrac{2}{3}-\dfrac{5}{24}$ 184. $-\dfrac{1}{18}-\dfrac{1}{6}$

185. $-\dfrac{7}{12}-\dfrac{5}{16}$ 186. $-\dfrac{8}{13}+\dfrac{8}{13}$ 187. $-\dfrac{9}{10}+\dfrac{9}{10}$

In Exercises 188-245, multiply or divide.

188. $\left(\dfrac{2}{3}\right)\left(\dfrac{1}{7}\right)$ 189. $\left(\dfrac{1}{5}\right)\left(\dfrac{3}{5}\right)$ 190. $\left(\dfrac{7}{9}\right)\left(\dfrac{2}{5}\right)$ 191. $\left(\dfrac{8}{9}\right)\left(\dfrac{4}{5}\right)$

192. $\left(\dfrac{2}{9}\right)\left(\dfrac{27}{4}\right)$ 193. $\left(\dfrac{6}{11}\right)\left(\dfrac{22}{3}\right)$ 194. $\left(\dfrac{7}{16}\right)\left(\dfrac{33}{21}\right)$ 195. $\left(\dfrac{7}{12}\right)\left(\dfrac{9}{14}\right)$

196. $\left(-\dfrac{1}{4}\right)\left(\dfrac{1}{9}\right)$ 197. $\left(-\dfrac{1}{2}\right)\left(\dfrac{1}{3}\right)$ 198. $\left(\dfrac{2}{5}\right)\left(-\dfrac{2}{3}\right)$ 199. $\left(\dfrac{6}{7}\right)\left(-\dfrac{8}{5}\right)$

200. $\left(-\dfrac{7}{10}\right)\left(\dfrac{25}{8}\right)$ 201. $\left(-\dfrac{13}{12}\right)\left(\dfrac{8}{5}\right)$ 202. $\left(\dfrac{12}{17}\right)\left(-\dfrac{7}{8}\right)$ 203. $\left(\dfrac{1}{16}\right)\left(-\dfrac{10}{11}\right)$

204. $(12)\left(\dfrac{4}{3}\right)$ 205. $(24)\left(\dfrac{7}{8}\right)$ 206. $(-15)\left(\dfrac{5}{18}\right)$ 207. $(-10)\left(\dfrac{7}{12}\right)$

208. $\left(-\dfrac{11}{12}\right)\left(-\dfrac{6}{11}\right)$ 209. $\left(-\dfrac{10}{21}\right)\left(-\dfrac{7}{10}\right)$ 210. $\left(-\dfrac{4}{6}\right)(-27)$ 211. $\left(-\dfrac{9}{16}\right)(-12)$

212. $\left(-\dfrac{5}{4}\right)\left(-\dfrac{14}{25}\right)$ 213. $\left(-\dfrac{13}{12}\right)\left(-\dfrac{27}{26}\right)$ 214. $\dfrac{3}{5}\div\dfrac{2}{5}$ 215. $\dfrac{2}{3}\div\dfrac{1}{3}$

216. $\dfrac{7}{8}\div\dfrac{14}{3}$ 217. $\dfrac{2}{7}\div\dfrac{4}{5}$ 218. $\dfrac{12}{5}\div\dfrac{4}{3}$ 219. $\dfrac{9}{10}\div\dfrac{3}{4}$

220. $\dfrac{1}{2}\div 7$ 221. $\dfrac{1}{4}\div 3$ 222. $8\div\dfrac{2}{5}$ 223. $6\div\dfrac{3}{7}$

224. $\left(-\dfrac{1}{8}\right)\div\dfrac{3}{4}$ 225. $\left(-\dfrac{1}{22}\right)\div\dfrac{4}{11}$ 226. $\left(-\dfrac{1}{9}\right)\div\dfrac{1}{9}$ 227. $\left(-\dfrac{1}{2}\right)\div\dfrac{1}{2}$

228. $\dfrac{5}{6}\div\left(-\dfrac{1}{12}\right)$ 229. $\dfrac{2}{5}\div\left(-\dfrac{10}{9}\right)$ 220. $\dfrac{3}{5}\div(-2)$ 231. $\dfrac{7}{10}\div(-5)$

232. $\left(-\dfrac{3}{10}\right)\div\left(-\dfrac{1}{10}\right)$ 233. $\left(-\dfrac{9}{20}\right)\div\left(-\dfrac{1}{20}\right)$ 234. $\left(-\dfrac{1}{6}\right)\div\left(-\dfrac{8}{9}\right)$ 235. $\left(-\dfrac{3}{8}\right)\div\left(-\dfrac{1}{12}\right)$

236. $(-6)\div\left(-\dfrac{1}{12}\right)$ 237. $(-2)\div\left(-\dfrac{1}{2}\right)$ 238. $\left(-\dfrac{9}{7}\right)\div(-9)$ 239. $\left(-\dfrac{5}{14}\right)\div(-3)$

240. $\left(-\dfrac{1}{3}\right)\div(-1)$ 241. $\left(-\dfrac{7}{16}\right)\div(-1)$ 242. $1\div\left(-\dfrac{10}{17}\right)$ 243. $1\div\left(-\dfrac{2}{5}\right)$

244. $0\div\left(-\dfrac{2}{21}\right)$ 245. $0\div\left(-\dfrac{5}{22}\right)$

In Exercises 246-309, evaluate.

246. $5(3) + 1$ 247. $7(3) + 11$ 248. $10(-3) + 15$ 249. $7(-5) + 26$

250. $3(-8) - 3$ 251. $4(-4) - 4$ 252. $9 - 5 \times 7$ 253. $5 - 6 \times 3$

254. $7(2 + 9)$ 255. $8(6 - 3)$ 256. $(6 - 14) \times 3$ 257. $(3 + 11) \times 2$

258. $(10 + 7) \times (-3)$ 259. $(5 - 11) \times (-5)$ 260. $(-4) + 32 \div 4$ 261. $(-9) + 11 \div 11$

262. $-12 - 8 \div 4$ 263. $-5 - 24 \div 6$ 264. $(-12 - 9) \div 7$ 265. $(-3 - 24) \div 3$

266. $7 - 12 - 3 + 4$ 267. $6 + 2 - 12 - 5$ 268. $28 \div 2 \times 14 \div 7$ 269. $12 \times 4 \div 2 \times 3$

270. $(7 - 12) - (3 + 4)$ 271. $(6 + 2) - (12 - 5)$ 272. $(12 \times 4) \div (2 \times 3)$ 273. $(28 \div 2) \times (14 \div 7)$

274. $4^2 + 5$ 275. $7^2 - 6$ 276. $(4 + 2)^2$ 277. $(5 - 8)^2$

278. $10 + 5 \times 3 - 7 \times 2$ 279. $14 - 18 \div 3 + 5 \times 2$ 280. $(8 + 2) \times (4 - 9) \div 5$

281. $(12 - 18) \div 3 + 6 \times 2$ 282. $(3 + 3)^2 (5 - 8)$ 283. $(13 - 7)^2 (4 - 5)$

284. $-12 - (-4)^2 \times 3$ 285. $6^2 \div (-18) - 9$ 286. $\dfrac{(6 - 14)^2}{2 - (5 - 7)}$

287. $\dfrac{1 + 2(4 - 15)}{2^2 + 3}$ 288. $-2 + 4\{3 - 8(9 - 7)\}$ 289. $9 - 4\{1 + 2(6 \div 3)\}$

290. $10 + (5 + 1)^2 \cdot (-2)$ 291. $4 \cdot 9 + 5(2)^2$ 292. $(-4)\left(\dfrac{1}{10}\right)\left(-\dfrac{7}{6}\right)$ 293. $(-12)\left(-\dfrac{3}{2}\right)\left(\dfrac{1}{4}\right)$

294. $-6 + 2\left(-\dfrac{1}{4}\right)$ 295. $5 + 3\left(-\dfrac{1}{12}\right)$ 296. $(-6 + 2)\left(-\dfrac{1}{4}\right)$ 297. $(5 + 3)\left(-\dfrac{1}{12}\right)$

298. $\left(\dfrac{5}{24} - \dfrac{1}{6}\right) - \dfrac{3}{4}$ 299. $\dfrac{4}{5} - \left(\dfrac{1}{30} - \dfrac{2}{3}\right)$ 300. $\dfrac{5}{24} - \left(\dfrac{1}{6} - \dfrac{3}{4}\right)$ 301. $\dfrac{4}{5} - \dfrac{1}{30} - \dfrac{2}{3}$

302. $\dfrac{1}{2} + 12 \div \dfrac{6}{7}$ 303. $\dfrac{1}{4} \times \left(4 - \dfrac{8}{9}\right)$ 304. $\left(\dfrac{1}{2} + 12\right) \div \dfrac{6}{7}$ 305. $\left(\dfrac{1}{4} \times 4\right) - \dfrac{8}{9}$

306. $\dfrac{7}{12} + \dfrac{1}{12} - \dfrac{1}{2} \times \dfrac{1}{2}$ 307. $\dfrac{2}{5} + \dfrac{2}{5} - \dfrac{2}{5} \times \dfrac{2}{5}$ 308. $\dfrac{7}{12} + \left(\dfrac{1}{12} - \dfrac{1}{2}\right) \times \dfrac{1}{2}$ 309. $\dfrac{2}{5} + \left(\dfrac{2}{5} - \dfrac{2}{5}\right) \times \dfrac{2}{5}$

In Exercises 310-325, round off and truncate to two decimals.

310. 0.281 311. 0.984 312. 6.2104 313. 8.9342

314. 12.5193 315. 10.4162 316. 321.75501 317. 78.98502

318. 5.19941 319. 68.79933 320. 0.0002 321. 0.0007

322. 39.9994 323. 29.9982 324. 100.60506 325. 96.3454

In Exercises 326-343, replace the question mark (?) with the appropriate answer and state the property being used.

326. $x + 4 = ? + x$ 327. $8 + y = y + ?$ 328. $3(7 + 1) = 3(7) + 3(?)$ 329. $2(x + 1) = 2(?) + 2(1)$

330. $3 \times (? \times 8) = (3 \times 5) \times 8$ 331. $9 + (3 + ?) = (9 + 3) + 7$ 332. $4[(-2)(?)] = [4(-2)](-7)$

333. $(?)[(-3)(0)] = [(4)(-3)](0)$ 334. $(? + 3)a = 2(a) + 3(a)$ 335. $(t - ?)(12) = t(12) - 1(12)$

336. $9 + ? = 0$ 337. $? + (-3) = 0$ 338. $(-5)(?) = 1$ 339. $(?)\left(\dfrac{7}{9}\right) = 1$

340. $a \cdot (?) = 1, a \neq 0$ 341. $a + ? = a$ 342. $\left(\dfrac{3}{4}\right)(-2) = (?)\left(\dfrac{3}{4}\right)$ 343. $(y)(?) = (18)(y)$

In Exercises 344-365, fill in the space with the inequality symbol $<$ or $>$.

344. 4 ____ 12 345. 14 ____ 3 346. $\dfrac{1}{6}$ ____ $\dfrac{1}{2}$ 347. $\dfrac{4}{5}$ ____ $\dfrac{1}{10}$

348. -7 ____ 16 349. -7 ____ 16 350. -5 ____ -14 351. -16 ____ -30

352. 0 ____ -11 353. -8 ____ -3 354. $\dfrac{2}{9}$ ____ 0.21 355. $\dfrac{1}{9}$ ____ 0.11

356. 0.334 ____ $\dfrac{1}{3}$ 357. 0.623 ____ $\dfrac{62}{99}$ 358. 0.18 ____ $\dfrac{17}{99}$ 359. 0.435 ____ $\dfrac{43}{99}$

360. -12.011 ____ -12.0111 361. -3.226 ____ -3.2262 362. $-\dfrac{5}{9}$ ____ -0.05

363. $-\dfrac{2}{9}$ ____ $-0.0\overline{2}$ 364. π ____ 3.16 365. $-\pi$ ____ -3.16

In Exercises 366-393, evaluate.

366. $|6|$ 367. $|12|$ 368. $|-8|$ 369. $|-23|$

370. $|+27|$ 371. $|-14|$ 372. $|-37|$ 373. $|+17|$

374. $\left|-\dfrac{4}{7}\right|$ 375. $\left|+\dfrac{10}{13}\right|$ 376. $|0.172|$ 377. $|-29.5893|$

378. $|18 - 12|$ 379. $|24 - 16|$ 380. $|7 - 22|$ 381. $|11 - 32|$

382. $|-7 - 7|$ 383. $|-22 - 4|$ 384. $|0 - 14 + 6|$ 385. $|0 + 5 - 27|$

386. $|13| - |-2|$ 387. $|-14| - |+6|$ 388. $|-12| + |-15|$ 389. $|+13| + |-19|$

390. $\left|-\dfrac{1}{6} - \dfrac{2}{5}\right|$ 391. $\left|\dfrac{1}{4} + \left(-\dfrac{3}{5}\right)\right|$ 392. $\left|-\dfrac{1}{6}\right| - \left|\dfrac{2}{5}\right|$ 393. $\left|\dfrac{1}{4}\right| + \left|-\dfrac{3}{5}\right|$

In Exercises 394-405, find the distance between the given numbers on the real number line.

394. 10 and 4 395. 12 and 3 396. -7 and 0 397. 0 and -7

398. -13 and 19 399. -3 and 20 400. $\dfrac{7}{10}$ and $-\dfrac{3}{4}$ 401. $-\dfrac{5}{6}$ and $\dfrac{3}{8}$

402. -17 and -26 403. -18 and -27 404. $-\dfrac{8}{27}$ and $-\dfrac{4}{9}$ 405. $-\dfrac{3}{16}$ and $-\dfrac{7}{6}$

In Exercises 406-417, simplify (assume that all variables are non-zero).

406. $|7x|$ 407. $|11y|$ 408. $|-18a|$ 409. $|-2b|$

410. $\left|3x^2\right|$ 411. $\left|5y^2\right|$ 412. $\left|-23x^2\right|$ 413. $\left|-8y^2\right|$

414. $\left|\dfrac{12}{x}\right|$ 415. $\left|\dfrac{27}{t}\right|$ 416. $\left|\dfrac{-13}{a^2}\right|$ 417. $\left|\dfrac{b^2}{-4}\right|$

In Exercises 418-435, find the value of the expression when $x = 4$, $y = -3$ and $z = 0$.

418. $2x + 3y - z$ 419. $4x - y + 5z$ 420. $2x^2 + 3y + z$

421. $-x + 3z^2 - 2y$ 422. $9y + 2z - 6xz$ 423. $-9x - y + 7yz$

424. $\dfrac{-3x + 2y}{-3y + 5z}$ 425. $\dfrac{x - 7y}{z + 3x}$ 426. $x^2 + 4x - 10$

427. $y^2 + 4y - 9$ 428. $z^2 + 3z + 14$ 429. $6 + 5z - 9z^2$

430. $\dfrac{1}{x + y}$ 431. $\dfrac{1}{x} + \dfrac{1}{y}$ 432. $|4x + 9y|$

433. $|-3x + 11z|$ 434. $|4x| + |9y|$ 435. $|-3x| + |11z|$

In Exercises 436-444, find the domain of the variable x.

436. $\dfrac{2}{x - 4}$ 437. $\dfrac{6}{x - 1}$ 438. $\dfrac{-5}{x + 6}$

439. $\dfrac{-10}{x + 8}$ 440. $\dfrac{4}{7 - x}$ 441. $\dfrac{10}{10 - x}$

442. $\dfrac{9}{2 + x}$ 443. $\dfrac{1}{9 + x}$ 444. $\dfrac{3}{x}$

In Exercises 445-450, find the required quantity using the given formulas.

445. The area, A, of a triangle (in square units) whose base is b and height is h is given by the formula $A = \frac{1}{2}bh$. Find the area of a triangle whose base is 6 inches and height is 4 inches.

446. The perimeter, P, of a rectangle whose length is l and width is w is given by the formula $P = 2l + 2w$. Find the perimeter of a rectangle whose length is 7 meters and width is 5 meters.

447. The volume, V, of a cube (in cubic units), each of whose edges measure s units, is given by the formula $V = s^3$. Find the volume of a cube whose edges are 7 feet each.

448. The area, A, of a trapezoid (in square units) whose bases are b_1 and b_2 and height is h is given by the formula $A = \dfrac{h}{2}(b_1 + b_2)$. Find the area of a trapezoid whose bases measure 2 yards and 6 yards and height is 10 yards.

449. The formula $C = \frac{5}{9}(F - 32)$ is used to convert degrees Fahrenheit, F, into degrees Celsius, C. Find the temperature, in Celsius, of the Fahrenheit temperature $212°F$.

450. The formula $F = \frac{9}{5}C + 32$ is used to convert degrees Celsius, C, into degrees Fahrenheit, F. Find the temperature, in Fahrenheit, of the Celsius temperature $-15°C$.

END OF CHAPTER 1   QUIZ

1. Which number is an integer?

    a) $\dfrac{1}{3}$ b) -4.91 c) 5 d) π e) $\dfrac{-9}{7}$

2. Which number is an irrational number?

    a) -7 b) $2.\overline{86}$ c) 0 d) π e) $\dfrac{13}{36}$

3. Which set contains only rational numbers?

    a) $\left\{5, -\dfrac{2}{5}, \pi\right\}$ b) $\{-12, 4.232332333\cdots\}$ c) $\{\sqrt{2}, 8\}$ d) $\left\{\dfrac{1}{9}, -\dfrac{2}{11}, \dfrac{5}{0}\right\}$ e) $\left\{\dfrac{-8}{-15}, -\dfrac{3}{10}, -1\right\}$

4. $-\dfrac{2}{3} + \dfrac{4}{9} =$

    a) $\dfrac{2}{9}$ b) $-\dfrac{2}{9}$ c) $-\dfrac{10}{3}$ d) $\dfrac{-10}{9}$ e) $\dfrac{10}{9}$

5. $-\dfrac{7}{8} - \dfrac{5}{6} =$

    a) $-\dfrac{6}{7}$ b) $\dfrac{35}{48}$ c) $\dfrac{41}{24}$ d) $-\dfrac{41}{24}$ e) $-\dfrac{41}{48}$

6. $12\left(-\dfrac{4}{3}\right) =$

    a) $\dfrac{8}{3}$ b) -16 c) 16 d) $\dfrac{-1}{9}$ e) $-\dfrac{32}{3}$

7. $\left(-\dfrac{1}{2}\right) \div \left(-\dfrac{9}{8}\right) =$

    a) $\dfrac{4}{9}$ b) $-\dfrac{4}{9}$ c) $\dfrac{9}{16}$ d) $\dfrac{9}{4}$ e) $\dfrac{8}{11}$

8. $7 - (8 - 12) =$
    a) -13 b) 11 c) -11 d) 3 e) -3

9. $-4 + 2\left(3^2 - 5\right) =$
    a) -2 b) -4 c) 4 d) -8 e) 0

10. Which property demonstrates a Commutative Property?

    a) $2(x + y) = 2x + 2y$ b) $5 + (-5) = 0$ c) $1 + (a + 4) = (1 + a) + 4$

    d) $4(3) = 3(4)$ e) $\left(-\dfrac{1}{5}\right)(1) = -\dfrac{1}{5}$

11. Which property demonstrates an Associative Property?

    a) $7\left(\dfrac{1}{7}\right) = 1$ b) $6(x + 4) = 6x + 24$ c) $a + (b + 5) = (a + b) + 5$
    d) $9 + 0 = 9$ e) $x + y = y + x$

12. The number 21.771683, rounded off to 3 decimal places, is:

   a) 21.772   b) 21.771   c) 21.7   d) 21.77   e) 21.7717

13. Which inequality is true?
   a) $1 > 7$ b) $-3 < 2$ c) $0 < -4$ d) $-19 > -2$ e) $6 < -6$

14. Which statement is false?
   a) $6.3 > 6.03$ b) $-7 < -6.8$ c) $\frac{1}{3} = 0.33$ d) $\frac{1}{5} = 0.2$ e) $\pi < 4$

15. $|-5| + |2| =$
   a) $|-3|$ b) -3 c) -7 d) 7 e) 3

16. The distance between $2\frac{3}{4}$ and $-1\frac{5}{6}$ on the real number line is:
   a) $4\frac{7}{12}$ b) $4\frac{5}{6}$ c) $\frac{11}{12}$ d) $-4\frac{7}{12}$ e) $3\frac{2}{3}$

17. The value of $a\left(b^2 - 3\right)$ when $a = -3$ and $b = 1$ is:
   a) -6 b) 6 c) 3 d) -4 e) 1

18. The value of $\dfrac{4x - 3y}{6x + y}$ when $x = 0$ and $y = -2$ is:

   a) 4 b) $\frac{5}{2}$ c) 3 d) -3 e) 0

19. Which of the numbers is **not** in the domain of x of the expression $\dfrac{x + 2}{x - 5}$?
   a) 2 b) -2 c) 0 d) 5 e) -5

20. Which equation describes the verbal statement 'the sum of x and 3 is 8 less than the product of 2 and x'?
   a) $x + 3 - 8 = 2x$ b) $x + 3 = 8 - 2x$ c) $x + 3 = 2x - 8$ d) $x + 3 = 8 - 2 + x$ e) $x - 3 = 2x - 8$

ANSWERS FOR QUIZ 1   1. c   2. d   3. e   4. b   5. d
                      6. b   7. a   8. b   9. c   10. d
                      11. c   12. a   13. b   14. c   15. d
                      16. a   17. b   18. d   19. d   20. c

Chapter 2: Integer Exponents

In this chapter, we will study integer exponents. Section 2.1 begins with the definition of an exponent which is a natural number. Numerous examples are provided which will give us a good grasp on computing expressions containing exponents. Afterwards, we will look at a couple of properties which natural valued exponents satisfy. From these two properties, other definitions and properties will emerge. For example, we will define the zero exponent and the negative exponent (hence, exhausting all possible integers which can be exponents). Once this is established, more properties which hold for exponents that are natural numbers will be shown to hold for all integer exponents.

Section 2.2 contains many examples pertaining to negative exponents. I will introduce the "flipping technique" which can be derived from the method involved in simplifying algebraic objects known as mixed quotients. We will study mixed quotients later in this book, at which time I will show why the "flipping technique" works. For now, we'll just take it for granted.

In the final section, Section 2.3, we will study scientific notation. Scientific notation appears in pretty much every field of science among other places. I will demonstrate how to convert back and forth between the scientific notation of a number and its actual value. We will also see how to use the properties mentioned in Sections 2.1 and 2.2 to simplify expressions which are in scientific notation.

Section 2.1 Definition and Properties of Integer Exponents

Definition: Suppose that n is a natural number larger than 1 and a is any real number. Then

$$\underbrace{a \cdot a \cdots a}_{n \text{ of these}} = a^n.$$

We read the expression 'a^n' as 'a raised to the nth power' or 'a to the power n'. We call 'a' the *base* and 'n' the *exponent* of the expression. By convention, we write $a^1 = a$.

Note: The expression 'a^2' is often read as 'a squared'. The expression 'a^3' is often read as 'a cubed'.

Exponents come in handy when writing a long multiplication problem of a number with itself. For example, instead of writing the expression $3 \times 3 \times 3 \times 3 \times 3$, one simply writes 3^5. Instead of writing $x \cdot x \cdot x \cdot x \cdot x \cdot x \cdot x$, one simply writes x^7. Some properties that we know for multiplication, such as the Associative and Commutative properties, will allow us to come up with properties for handling computations with exponents. We will study these properties as we go forward.

Examples. Write each product using exponents. State the exponent and base.

1) $2 \times 2 \times 2 = 2^3$. The exponent is 3 and the base is 2.

2) $(-5)(-5)(-5)(-5) = (-5)^4$. The exponent is 4 and the base is -5.

3) $\left(\dfrac{2}{7}\right) \cdot \left(\dfrac{2}{7}\right) = \left(\dfrac{2}{7}\right)^2$. The exponent is 2 and the base is $\dfrac{2}{7}$.

4) $9(9)(9)(9)(9) = 9^5$. The exponent is 5 and the base is 9.

5) $a \cdot a \cdot a \cdot a \cdot a \cdot a \cdot a \cdot a = a^8$. The exponent is 8 and the base is a.

6) $y(y)(y)(y) = y^4$. The exponent is 4 and the base is y.

7) $x = x^1$. The exponent is 1 and the base is x.

8) $(3x)(3x)(3x)(3x)(3x) = (3x)^5$. The exponent is 5 and the base is $3x$.

Examples. Evaluate.

1) $6^2 = 6 \times 6 = 36$

2) $2^3 = 2 \times 2 \times 2 = 8$

3) $\underbrace{(-8)^2 = (-8)(-8)}_{\text{Square the } -8.} = 64$

4) $\underbrace{-8^2 = -(8)(8)}_{\text{Only square the 8.}} = -64$

5) $\left(\dfrac{10}{7}\right)^1 = \dfrac{10}{7}$

6) $\left(\dfrac{2}{5}\right)^2 = \left(\dfrac{2}{5}\right)\left(\dfrac{2}{5}\right) = \dfrac{4}{25}$

7) $\left(-\dfrac{3}{2}\right)^4 = \left(-\dfrac{3}{2}\right)\left(-\dfrac{3}{2}\right)\left(-\dfrac{3}{2}\right)\left(-\dfrac{3}{2}\right) = \dfrac{81}{16}$

8) $\left(-\dfrac{3}{4}\right)^5 = \left(-\dfrac{3}{4}\right)\left(-\dfrac{3}{4}\right)\left(-\dfrac{3}{4}\right)\left(-\dfrac{3}{4}\right)\left(-\dfrac{3}{4}\right) = -\dfrac{243}{1,024}$

9) $(0.7)^3 = (0.7)(0.7)(0.7) = 0.343$

10) $(-18.3)^1 = -18.3$

11) $\underbrace{(-5)^3 = (-5)(-5)(-5)}_{\text{The exponent applies to} -5.} = -125$

12) $\underbrace{-5^3 = -(5)(5)(5)}_{\text{The exponent only applies to 5.}} = -125$

Notice that in Example 3, both the negative and the 8 get squared, whereas in Example 4, only the 8 gets squared. The reason for this is that the -8 is in parenthesis in Example 3 and not in Example 4. Examples 11 and 12 exhibit the same phenomenon. Remember the following rule:

> The exponent applies only to whatever is on the immediate left-hand side of it.

Another thing to remember is:

> $(-)^{\text{even number}} = +$ AND $(-)^{\text{odd number}} = -$

Try These (Set 1):

I) Write each product using exponents. State the exponent and base of each.

1) $3 \cdot 3$

2) $7 \times 7 \times 7 \times 7$

3) $(2.19)(2.19)(2.19)$

4) $(12)(12)(12)(12)$

5) $x \cdot x \cdot x \cdot x \cdot x$

6) $(-5y)(-5y)(-5y)$

II) Evaluate (**without** using a calculator).

1) 8^2

2) 3^3

3) $(-3)^2$

4) -3^2

5) $\left(\dfrac{2}{5}\right)^2$

6) $\left(-\dfrac{1}{5}\right)^4$

7) $-\left(\dfrac{1}{5}\right)^4$

8) $\left(-\dfrac{6}{7}\right)^3$

9) $-\left(\dfrac{6}{7}\right)^3$

10) $(122)^1$

11) $(0.39)^2$

12) $(-0.05)^3$

Let's know discuss two properties of exponents which are natural numbers. Remember that a natural number is any number in the set $\{1, 2, 3, \dots\}$.

> **PROPERTY I.** Let a be any real number and let m and n be any natural numbers. Then
> $$a^m \cdot a^n = a^{m+n}.$$

Let's look at a demonstration of why this property should work. Let's multiply $a^2 \cdot a^4$. According to the property, the answer should be $a^{2+4} = a^6$. Let's see why this happens. Well, observe that $a^2 \cdot a^4$ is the same as $\underbrace{(a \cdot a) \cdot (a \cdot a \cdot a \cdot a) = a \cdot a \cdot a \cdot a \cdot a \cdot a}_{\text{By the Associative Property, we can remove the parentheses.}} = a^6$, which is what we hoped for.

Notice how the base, a, remains the same when we use the property; only the exponents are added together. For example, $8^4 \cdot 8^5 = 8^{4+5} = 8^9$. A common mistake that I see students make is that they multiply the bases, which is incorrect.

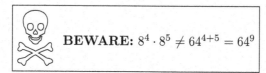 **BEWARE:** $8^4 \cdot 8^5 \neq 64^{4+5} = 64^9$

Examples. Multiply.

1) $x^3 \cdot x^8 = x^{3+8} = x^{11}$

2) $\left(a^2\right)\left(a^{10}\right) = a^{2+10} = a^{12}$

3) $\underbrace{y^3 \cdot (y^4 \cdot y) = y^3 \cdot y^4 \cdot y^1}_{\text{by the Associative Property}} = y^{3+4+1} = y^8$

4) $\left(x^7\right)\left(x^7\right)\left(x^7\right) = x^{7+7+7} = x^{21}$

5) $\underbrace{\left(3a^2\right)\left(4a^9\right) = 3 \cdot 4 \cdot a^2 \cdot a^9}_{\text{by the Associative and Commutative Properties}} = 12a^{2+9} = 12a^{11}$

6) $\left(-6x^8y^3\right)\left(9xy^2\right) = -54x^{8+1}y^{3+2} = -54x^9y^5$

7) $\left(2x^7y^3z\right)\left(8x^2z^9\right)\left(-4x^3y\right) = -64x^{7+2+3}y^{3+1}z^{1+9} = -64x^{12}y^4z^{10}$

> **PROPERTY II.** Let a be any non-zero real number and let m and n be any natural numbers. Suppose that $m > n$. Then
> $$\frac{a^m}{a^n} = a^m \div a^n = a^{m-n}.$$

Let's look at a demonstration of why this property should work. Let's divide $\dfrac{a^5}{a^3}$ (notice that the exponent in the numerator is larger than the exponent in the denominator). According to the property, the answer should be $a^{5-3} = a^2$. Let's see why this happens. Well, observe that $\dfrac{a^5}{a^3}$ is the same as $\dfrac{\overset{1}{\cancel{a}} \cdot \overset{1}{\cancel{a}} \cdot \overset{1}{\cancel{a}} \cdot a \cdot a}{\underset{1}{\cancel{a}} \cdot \underset{1}{\cancel{a}} \cdot \underset{1}{\cancel{a}}} = \dfrac{a \cdot a}{1} = \dfrac{a^2}{1} = a^2$ which is what we hoped for.

37

Notice how the base, a, remains the same when we use the property; only the exponents subtract from one another. For example, $\frac{9^{15}}{9^{13}} = 9^{15-13} = 9^2$. A common mistake that I see students make is that they cancel out the bases, which is incorrect.

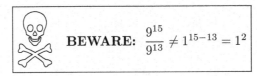

BEWARE: $\frac{9^{15}}{9^{13}} \neq 1^{15-13} = 1^2$

Examples. Divide. Assume that all variables represent non-zero real numbers.

1) $\frac{a^{13}}{a^5} = a^{13-5} = a^8$

2) $\frac{x^4}{x} = x^{4-1} = x^3$

3) $y^{21} \div y^{10} = y^{21-10} = y^{11}$

4) $\frac{27a^{15}b^5}{9a^7b^2} = \frac{27}{9} \cdot \frac{a^{15}}{a^7} \cdot \frac{b^5}{b^2} = 3a^{15-7}b^{5-2} = 3a^8b^3$

5) $\frac{-\overset{4}{\cancel{2}4}x^{10}y^{13}}{\underset{1}{\cancel{6}}x^7y^2} = -4x^{10-7}y^{13-2} = -4x^3y^{11}$

6) $\frac{\overset{10}{\cancel{40}}x^8y^{11}z^6}{\underset{3}{\cancel{12}}x^3z^2} = \frac{10}{3}x^{8-3}y^{11}z^{6-2} = \frac{10}{3}x^5y^{11}z^4$ or $\frac{10x^5y^{11}z^4}{3}$

Try These (Set 2):

I) Multiply and simplify.

1) $x^2 \cdot x^6$

2) $(y)\left(y^3\right)\left(y^{10}\right)$

3) $\left(-7a^5\right)\left(2a^9\right)$

4) $\left(-9x^5y^2\right)\left(-3y^2\right)$

5) $\left(3a^2b^7\right)\left(a^4b\right)\left(-3b^6\right)$

6) $\left(6x^5\right)^3$ (remember: $a^3 = a \cdot a \cdot a$)

II) Divide. Assume that all variables represent non-zero real numbers.

1) $\frac{x^{18}}{x^7}$

2) $\frac{a^5}{a^4}$

3) $\frac{42mn^{10}}{7mn^3}$

4) $\frac{14x^5y^{12}}{-2y^4}$

5) $\frac{-15a^{10}b^{17}c^{12}}{-9a^7c^6}$

6) $\frac{7^{40}}{7^{38}}$

Recall that Property II works whenever the exponent in the numerater is greater than the exponent in the denominator. We would like to allow this property to work for **any** exponents in the numerator and denominator, provided that they are natural numbers. First we will look at what happens when the exponents are equal. This will give us Property III. Afterwards, we will see what happens if the exponent in the denominator is larger than the exponent in the numerator. This will give us Property IV.

PROPERTY III. Let a be any non-zero real number. Then we define

$$a^0 = 1.$$

Let's look at a demonstration of why this definition is valid. Let's consider the expression $\frac{a^n}{a^n}$, where a is any non-zero real number and n is any natural number. We know that $\frac{a^n}{a^n} = 1$ since everything in the numerator will cancel out everything in the denominator. However, we would like Property II to work for this situation. By Property II, we obtain $\frac{a^n}{a^n} = a^{n-n} = a^0$. Since $\frac{a^n}{a^n}$ simplifies to both 1 and a^0, it makes sense to define $a^0 = 1$ whenever a is a non-zero real number. Notice that the expression 0^0 is **not** a well-defined expression since the fraction $\frac{0^n}{0^n}$ is **always** undefined.

Examples. Evaluate or simplify. Assume that all variables represent non-zero real numbers.

1) $2^0 = 1$ 2) $7^0 = 1$ 3) $(-8)^0 = 1$ 4) $-8^0 = -\underbrace{8^0}_{1} = -1$

5) $t^0 = 1$ 6) $(5a)^0 = 1$ 7) $5a^0 = 5(1) = 5$ (the exponent **only** applies to 'a')

8) $a^3 b^8 \left(a^8\right)^0 = a^3 b^8 (1) = a^3 b^8$

Try These (Set 3): Evaluate or simplify. Each of your answers should not contain any zero exponents.

1) 12^0 2) $10x^0$ 3) $(10x)^0$ 4) $\left(\dfrac{2}{5}\right)^0$

5) $\left(-7a^3 b\right)^0$ 6) $-7a^3 b^0$ 7) $(-2)^0$ 8) -2^0

PROPERTY IV. Let a be any non-zero real number and let n be any whole number. Then we define

$$a^{-n} = \frac{1}{a^n}.$$

Recall that a whole number is any number in the set $\{0, 1, 2, 3, \dots\}$. In Property IV, our exponent can be any such number.

Let's look at a demonstration of why this definition is valid. Consider the expression $\dfrac{a^0}{a^n}$, where a is any non-zero real number and n is any whole number. We know that $\dfrac{a^0}{a^n} = \dfrac{1}{a^n}$ since $a^0 = 1$ by Property III. However, we would like Property II to work for this situation as before. By Property II, we obtain $\dfrac{a^0}{a^n} = a^{0-n} = a^{-n}$. Since $\dfrac{a^0}{a^n}$ simplifies to both $\dfrac{1}{a^n}$ and a^{-n}, it makes sense to define $a^{-n} = \dfrac{1}{a^n}$ whenever a is a non-zero real number and n is a whole number. In fact, this property holds when n is *any* integer. We will study the case when n is a negative integer in the next section.

Examples. Evaluate or simplify. Assume that all variables represent non-zero real numbers.

1) $8^{-1} = \dfrac{1}{8^1} = \dfrac{1}{8}$ 2) $2^{-2} = \dfrac{1}{2^2} = \dfrac{1}{4}$

3) $4^{-3} = \dfrac{1}{4^3} = \dfrac{1}{64}$ 4) $(-9)^{-2} = \dfrac{1}{(-9)^2} = \dfrac{1}{81}$

5) $-9^{-2} = -(9^{-2}) = -\dfrac{1}{9^2} = -\dfrac{1}{81}$ 6) $(-6)^{-3} = \dfrac{1}{(-6)^3} = \dfrac{1}{-216} = -\dfrac{1}{216}$

7) $-6^{-3} = -(6^{-3}) = -\dfrac{1}{6^3} = -\dfrac{1}{216}$ 8) $y^{-1} = \dfrac{1}{y^1} = \dfrac{1}{y}$

9) $t^{-4} = \dfrac{1}{t^4}$ 10) $b^{-11} = \dfrac{1}{b^{11}}$

Notice how the exponent applies to the -9 in Example 4, but only to the 9 in Example 5. Similarly, the exponent applies to the -6 in Example 6, but only to the 6 in Example 7. **Watch out for parentheses!**

At this time, I would like to mention that Property I, $a^m \cdot a^n = a^{m+n}$, holds whenever m and n are **any** two integers. For example, observe that $a^{-4} \cdot a^6 = \dfrac{1}{a^4} \cdot \dfrac{a^6}{1} = \dfrac{a^6}{a^4} = a^{6-4} = a^2$ which is the same as $a^{-4} \cdot a^6 = a^{(-4)+6} = a^2$. If both exponents are negative, then Property I still works. For example, notice that $a^{-5} \cdot a^{-2} = \dfrac{1}{a^5} \cdot \dfrac{1}{a^2} = \dfrac{1}{a^{5+2}} = \dfrac{1}{a^7} = a^{-7}$ which is the same as $a^{-5} \cdot a^{-2} = a^{(-5)+(-2)} = a^{-7}$.

Try These (Set 4): Evaluate or simplify. Each of your answers should contain positive exponents.

1) 3^{-2} 2) 5^{-3} 3) 2^{-1} 4) 11^{-2} 5) $(-2)^{-4}$

6) -2^{-4} 7) x^{-3}, $x \neq 0$ 8) y^{-8}, $y \neq 0$ 9) $(-4)^{-3}$ 10) -4^{-3}

PROPERTY V.   Let a be any real number and let m and n be integers. Then

$$(a^m)^n = a^{mn}.$$

Note that the only exception to this property is when $a = 0$ and either $m = 0$ or $n = 0$. In this case, we obtain 0^0 which is undefined.

Let's look at a demonstration of why this property should work. Consider the expression $(a^5)^4$. According to the property, the answer should be $a^{(5)(4)} = a^{20}$. Let's try it **without** using the property. Well, observe that $(a^5)^4 = \underbrace{(a^5)(a^5)(a^5)(a^5)}_{\text{by Property I}} = a^{5+5+5+5} = a^{20}$, which is what we expected.

Let's take a look at another demonstration. Observe that

$$(a^{-6})^3 = \left(\frac{1}{a^6}\right)^3 = \underbrace{\left(\frac{1}{a^6}\right)\left(\frac{1}{a^6}\right)\left(\frac{1}{a^6}\right)}_{\text{by Property I}} = \frac{1}{a^{6+6+6}} = \frac{1}{a^{18}} = a^{-18}$$

which is the same as $a^{(-6)(3)} = a^{-18}$. If both m and n are negative integers, then a demonstration of this property would require some knowledge of mixed quotients, which we will study later on. For example, $(a^{-3})^{-5} = a^{(-3)(-5)} = a^{15}$ and $(a^{-1})^{-1} = a^{(-1)(-1)} = a^1 = a$. At this time, we will take it for granted that it works.

Examples. Evaluate or simplify. Assume that all variables represent non-zero real numbers.

1) $(a^6)^3 = a^{(6)(3)} = a^{18}$ 2) $(x^5)^{-2} = x^{(5)(-2)} = x^{-10} = \frac{1}{x^{10}}$ 3) $(y^{-3})^{-2} = y^{(-3)(-2)} = y^6$

4) $(b^0)^8 = b^{(0)(8)} = b^0 = 1$ 5) $(2^3)^2 = 2^{(3)(2)} = 2^6 = 64$ 6) $\left[(-5)^2\right]^2 = (-5)^4 = 625$

Try These (Set 5): Simplify. Assume that all variables represent non-zero real numbers.

1) $(x^4)^4$ 2) $(y^7)^3$ 3) $(a^{-1})^{-9}$ 4) $(b^{10})^{-3}$ 5) $(t^0)^6$ 6) $(x^{-4})^9$

PROPERTY VI.   Let a and b be any two real numbers and let n be any integer. Then

$$(ab)^n = a^n b^n.$$

Notice that this property simply states that you can 'distribute the exponent' into the parentheses (not to be confused with the Distributive Property). The only exception to applying this property is when either $a = 0$ or $b = 0$ and $n = 0$. Such a situation produces 0^0 which is undefined.

Let's look at a demonstration of why this property should work. Let's consider $(ab)^3$. According to the property, the answer should be a^3b^3. Let's try it **without** using the property. Well, observe that $(ab)^3 = \underbrace{(ab)(ab)(ab)}_{\text{by the Associative Property}} = ababab = a^3b^3$ (obtained by commuting terms), which is what we expected. Let's look at another demonstration. Observe that

$$(ab)^{-3} = \underbrace{\left(\frac{1}{ab}\right)^3}_{\text{by Property IV}} = \underbrace{\left(\frac{1}{ab}\right)\left(\frac{1}{ab}\right)\left(\frac{1}{ab}\right) = \frac{1}{a^3b^3}}_{\text{by the Associative and Commutative Properties}} = a^{-3}b^{-3},$$

which is what the property yields. By the way, this property **doesn't** work if you are **adding** or **subtracting** in the parentheses.

 BEWARE: $(a+b)^n \neq a^n + b^n$ and $(a-b)^n \neq a^n - b^n$ (unless $n = 1$).

For example, $(9+3)^2 \neq 9^2 + 3^2$ and $(5-1)^2 \neq 5^2 - 1^2$.

Examples. Simplify.

1) $(xy)^7 = x^7 y^7$

2) $(ab)^2 = a^2 b^2$

3) $(4xy)^3 = 4^3 x^3 y^3 = 64 x^3 y^3$

4) $\left(-2a^4 b^{10}\right)^3 = (-2)^3 \left(a^4\right)^3 \left(b^{10}\right)^3 = -8a^{12} b^{30}$ (by Property V)

5) $\left(4x^2 y^3 z^8\right)^2 = 4^2 \left(x^2\right)^2 \left(y^3\right)^2 \left(z^8\right)^2 = 16 x^4 y^6 z^{16}$ (by Property V)

6) $\left(\frac{2}{5}m^5 n\right)^3 = \left(\frac{2}{5}\right)^3 \left(m^5\right)^3 (n)^3 = \frac{8}{125} m^{15} n^3$ (by Property V)

Try These (Set 6): Simplify. Assume that all variables represent non-zero real numbers.

1) $(ab)^5$

2) $(3xy)^2$

3) $\left(-4x^3 y^5\right)^2$

4) $\left(3x^5 y^5 z\right)^4$

5) $\left(-\frac{7}{4}a^3 b^8\right)^3$

6) $\left(2xy^5 z^2\right)^5$

PROPERTY VII. Let a be any real number, b be any non-zero real number, and n be any integer. Then

$$\left(\frac{a}{b}\right)^n = \frac{a^n}{b^n}.$$

Note that the only exception is when both $a = 0$ and $n \leq 0$. In this case, 0^n arises, which is undefined.

To demonstrate the validity of this property, let's simplify the expression $\left(\frac{a}{b}\right)^4$. Observe that $\left(\frac{a}{b}\right)^4 = \left(\frac{a}{b}\right)\left(\frac{a}{b}\right)\left(\frac{a}{b}\right)\left(\frac{a}{b}\right) = \frac{a^4}{b^4}$, which is what the property claimed to give us. The property also holds if the exponent is a negative integer, which will be taken for granted at the moment.

Examples. Evaluate or simplify. Assume that all variables represent non-zero real numbers.

1) $\left(\frac{2}{5}\right)^2 = \frac{2^2}{5^2} = \frac{4}{25}$

2) $\left(-\frac{3}{5}\right)^3 = -\frac{3^3}{5^3} = -\frac{27}{125}$

3) $\left(\frac{x}{y}\right)^8 = \frac{x^8}{y^8}$

4) $\left(\frac{9}{b^5}\right)^2 = \frac{9^2}{(b^5)^2} = \frac{81}{b^{10}}$ (by Property V)

5) $\left(\frac{x^3}{2y^4}\right)^5 = \frac{(x^3)^5}{(2y^4)^5} = \frac{x^{15}}{32y^{20}}$ (by Property V)

6) $\underbrace{\left(-\frac{3a^{11}}{10bc^5}\right)^2 = \frac{3^2(a^{11})^2}{10^2b^2(c^5)^2}}_{\text{by Properties VI and V}} = \frac{9a^{22}}{100b^2c^{10}}$

Try These (Set 7): Evaluate or simplify. Assume that all variables represent non-zero real numbers.

1) $\left(\frac{8}{3}\right)^2$
2) $\left(-\frac{1}{5}\right)^3$
3) $\left(\frac{y^5}{12}\right)^2$
4) $\left(\frac{4x^9}{y^4}\right)^3$
5) $\left(-\frac{x^7}{3y}\right)^2$
6) $\left(\frac{10m^0}{3n^6}\right)^3$

Let's do some examples which use more than one property. For now, we will focus on nonnegative integer exponents only. Negative integer exponents will be studied extensively in the next section.

Examples. Simplify. Assume that all variables represent non-zero real numbers.

1) $\underbrace{5x^2(2x)^2 = 5x^2(4x^2)}_{\text{by Properties VI and I}} = 20x^4$

2) $\underbrace{(9a^3)^0(-5a^{10}) = 1(-5a^{10})}_{\text{by Property III}} = -5a^{10}$

3) $\underbrace{(-2x^2y^3)^4(-3x^5y^2) = (16x^8y^{12})(-3x^5y^2)}_{\text{by Properties VI, V, and I}} = -48x^{13}y^{14}$

4) $\underbrace{\frac{7m^{10}}{2n^4}\left(\frac{2m^2}{5n^3}\right)^2 = \frac{7m^{10}}{\overset{}{\underset{1}{\cancel{2}}}n^4}\left(\frac{\overset{2}{\cancel{4}}m^4}{25n^6}\right)}_{\text{by Properties VII, VI, V, and I}} = \frac{14m^{14}}{25n^{10}}$

5) $\underbrace{\frac{7x^2(4x^5)^2}{-4x^9} = \frac{7x^2(16x^{10})}{-4x^9} = \frac{112x^{12}}{-4x^9}}_{\text{by Properties VI, V, II, and I}} = -28x^3$

42

6) $\underbrace{\left(-\dfrac{1}{4}x^3\right)^3 \left(\dfrac{3}{2x^0}\right)^2 = \left(-\dfrac{1}{64}x^9\right)\left(\dfrac{3}{2}\right)^2}_{\text{by Properties VI, V, and III}} = \left(-\dfrac{1}{64}x^9\right)\left(\dfrac{9}{4}\right) = -\dfrac{9}{256}x^9$

Try These (Set 8): Simplify. Assume that all variables represent non-zero real numbers.

1) $8x^7\left(3x\right)^2$

2) $\left(7x^3\right)^2\left(-10x^2\right)^0$

3) $\left(5x^2y\right)^2\left(-x^6y^{12}\right)^3$

4) $\left(\dfrac{-2x^8}{-3y^2}\right)^3\left(\dfrac{4x^3}{13y^8}\right)^0$

5) $\dfrac{9s^3\left(2s^3t^7\right)^2}{\left(4t\right)^2}$

6) $\dfrac{\left(7a^5\right)\left(-a^3\right)^2}{\left(5a^0\right)^3}$

Let's summarize all of the properties that we have learned so far. I will only summarize the properties in which the bases in each expression is non-zero. If we allow a base to equal zero, then we need to be careful with the exponents that we are using.

PROPERTY I. Let $a \neq 0$ be a real number and let m and n be any integers. Then

$$a^m \cdot a^n = a^{m+n}.$$

PROPERTY II. Let $a \neq 0$ be a real number and let m and n be any integers. Then

$$\frac{a^m}{a^n} = a^m \div a^n = a^{m-n}.$$

PROPERTY III. Let $a \neq 0$ be a real number. Then

$$a^0 = 1.$$

PROPERTY IV. Let $a \neq 0$ be a real number and let n be any integer. Then

$$a^{-n} = \frac{1}{a^n}.$$

PROPERTY V. Let $a \neq 0$ be a real number and let m and n be integers. Then

$$\left(a^m\right)^n = a^{mn}.$$

PROPERTY VI. Let $a \neq 0$ and $b \neq 0$ be two real numbers and let n be any integer. Then

$$\left(ab\right)^n = a^n b^n.$$

PROPERTY VII. Let $a \neq 0$ and $b \neq 0$ be two real numbers and n any integer. Then

$$\left(\frac{a}{b}\right)^n = \frac{a^n}{b^n}.$$

Exercise 2.1

In Exercises 1-16, write each product using exponents. State the exponent and the base.

1. 4×4

2. $7 \times 7 \times 7$

3. $8 \cdot 8 \cdot 8 \cdot 8$

4. $1 \cdot 1 \cdot 1$

5. $(-6)(-6)(-6)$

6. $(-12)(-12)$

7. $\left(\dfrac{2}{9}\right)\left(\dfrac{2}{9}\right)\left(\dfrac{2}{9}\right)\left(\dfrac{2}{9}\right)$

43

8. $\left(-\frac{3}{7}\right)\left(-\frac{3}{7}\right)\left(-\frac{3}{7}\right)\left(-\frac{3}{7}\right)$

9. $x \cdot x \cdot x \cdot x \cdot x$

10. $y \cdot y \cdot y$

11. $(a)(a)(a)(a)(a)$

12. $(b)(b)$

13. $(4n)(4n)$

14. $(10m)(10m)(10m)$

15. $\left(x^2y\right)\left(x^2y\right)\left(x^2y\right)\left(x^2y\right)$

16. $\left(2ab^3\right)\left(2ab^3\right)\left(2ab^3\right)\left(2ab^3\right)\left(2ab^3\right)$

In Exercises 17-59, evaluate.

17. 8^2

18. 5^2

19. $\left(\frac{3}{4}\right)^3$

20. $\left(\frac{9}{7}\right)^3$

21. $\left(-\frac{3}{11}\right)^2$

22. $(-7)^2$

23. -7^2

24. $\left(-\frac{1}{5}\right)^3$

25. $\left(-\frac{1}{2}\right)^5$

26. $(-1)^3$

27. -1^3

28. 4^4

29. 6^0

30. $\left(\frac{2}{15}\right)^0$

31. $(-12)^0$

32. -12^0

33. $\frac{9^6}{9^5}$

34. $\frac{4^8}{4^6}$

35. $\frac{(-3)^{12}}{(-3)^9}$

36. $\frac{(-2)^8}{(-2)^6}$

37. $\frac{6^5}{6^7}$

38. $\frac{8^3}{8^6}$

39. $\frac{(-4)^5}{(-4)^6}$

40. $\frac{(-10)^4}{(-10)^7}$

41. 11^{-1}

42. 3^{-3}

43. 3^{-2}

44. 2^{-4}

45. 5^{-3}

46. $(-7)^{-2}$

47. -7^{-2}

48. -8^{-3}

49. -8^{-3}

50. -2^{-1}

51. $(-2)^{-2}$

52. $\left(2^2\right)^3$

53. $\left(3^3\right)^2$

54. $\left(5^2\right)^{-1}$

55. $\left(3^4\right)^{-1}$

56. $\frac{33^3}{11^3}$

57. $\frac{800^2}{100^2}$

58. $\frac{(-100)^4}{100^4}$

59. $\frac{100^5}{(-100)^5}$

In Exercises 60-127, simplify each expression using the properties discussed in this section. Assume that all variables represent non-zero numbers. Make sure that all of your answers contain **only** positive exponents.

60. $x^7 \cdot x^2$

61. $y^2 \cdot y^5$

62. $a^9 \cdot a$

63. $s \cdot s^3$

64. $\left(x^5\right)\left(x^3\right)\left(x^4\right)$

65. $\left(a^5\right)\left(a^5\right)\left(a^2\right)$

66. $\left(4x^2\right)\left(8x^7\right)$

67. $\left(-2x^5\right)\left(6x^3\right)$

68. $\left(-8x^2y^{11}\right)\left(9xy^3\right)$

69. $\left(2x^3y\right)\left(x^9y^{12}\right)$

70. $\left(9s^3t^6\right)\left(2s^2t\right)$

71. $\left(4a^2b^2\right)\left(5a^{10}b^9\right)$

72. $\frac{x^7}{x^3}$

73. $\frac{x^{10}}{x^3}$

74. $\frac{a^7b^{18}}{-a^6b^{11}}$

75. $\frac{-35s^8t^5}{-5s^4t}$

76. $\frac{18x^7y^8}{-4x^3y^5}$

77. $\frac{25x^{18}y^{16}}{-10x^4y^5}$

78. $(3x)^0$

79. $3x^0$

80. $8x^4y^3 \left(5y^8\right)^0$ 81. $-12t^4 \left(10s^8t^{10}\right)^0$ 82. y^{-2} 83. y^{-3}

84. $-x^{-6}$ 85. $-x^{-5}$ 86. $a^{-3} \cdot a^{-1}$ 87. $x^{-6} \cdot x^{-2}$

88. $t^5 \cdot t^{-4}$ 89. $t^{-4} \cdot t^7$ 90. $\dfrac{x^5}{x^{-2}}$ 91. $\dfrac{y^9}{y^{-1}}$

92. $\dfrac{x^9y^{-1}}{xy^0}$ 93. $\dfrac{32x^0y^{-1}}{16x^5y^{-4}}$ 94. $\left(x^3\right)^6$ 95. $\left(x^9\right)^2$

96. $\left(t^{-4}\right)^4$ 97. $\left(s^8\right)^{-5}$ 98. $\left(a^0\right)^4$ 99. $\left(x^0\right)^{-7}$

100. $(2y)^2$ 101. $(3x)^4$ 102. $\left(-9a^3b^8\right)^2$ 103. $\left(-4x^7y^8\right)^3$

104. $(3x)^{-5}$ 105. $(7s)^{-3}$ 106. $\left(4xy^{10}\right)^{-1}$ 107. $\left(16x^4y\right)^{-1}$

108. $\left(\dfrac{1}{4}m^7n^2\right)^2$ 109. $\left(\dfrac{7}{3}a^2b^6\right)^2$ 110. $\left(\dfrac{a}{b}\right)^4$ 111. $\left(\dfrac{x}{y}\right)^9$

112. $\left(\dfrac{2}{x^3}\right)^2$ 113. $\left(-\dfrac{6}{a^7}\right)^2$ 114. $\left(\dfrac{4x}{y^2}\right)^3$ 115. $\left(\dfrac{5x^6}{y^5}\right)^4$

116. $\left(-\dfrac{2x^5}{yz^2}\right)^3$ 117. $\left(-\dfrac{m^7}{8n^3}\right)^2$ 118. $2x^6\left(-3x\right)^3$ 119. $-9a^3\left(2a^7\right)^2$

120. $\left(5a^6\right)^0\left(-4a^{10}\right)^2$ 121. $\left(13x^5\right)^2\left(2x^5\right)^0$ 122. $\left(-5a^3b^4\right)^2\left(2ab^3\right)^2$

123. $\left(m^2n^7\right)^3\left(-6mn^8\right)^3$ 124. $\left(\dfrac{7x^2}{-y^4}\right)^0 \cdot \left(\dfrac{7x^2}{12y^5}\right)^2$ 125. $\left(\dfrac{-11a^5}{3b^4}\right)^2 \cdot \dfrac{(-2a)^0}{11b^3}$

126. $\dfrac{14x^3\left(2x^8y^0\right)^2}{\left(6x^3y\right)^2} \cdot \left(-\dfrac{1}{9y^{12}}\right)^0$ 127. $\dfrac{\left(-9x^0y^{11}\right)^2}{-3\left(3x^2y\right)^3} \cdot \dfrac{\left(-5x^0y^4\right)^0}{(-2x)^3}$

Section 2.2 Negative Integer Exponents Revisited

In the previous section, we've studied several properties which integer exponents satisfy. We began with two natural properties (I and II) and then defined two new types of integer exponents, the zero exponent (III) and the negative exponent (IV). Recall that Property IV states that if a is any non-zero real number and n is any whole number, then

$$a^{-n} = \frac{1}{a^n}.$$

In this section, we will learn how to work with this property when negative exponents appear in a fraction and products are present in the numerator and/or denominator. The technique which we will apply will be referred to as the **flipping technique**. As it was mentioned in the introduction, the actual work which goes on in this technique will be overlooked since it involves doing computations with mixed quotients and we have not yet learned about these algebraic objects. When we do study mixed quotients, I will demonstrate why the flipping technique works. For now, we will use it freely.

I will now give a new property to add to our list of properties. This property can actually be obtained from Property IV and vice-versa.

PROPERTY VIII: Let a and b be any two non-zero real numbers and let n be any integer. Then

$$\left(\frac{a}{b}\right)^{-n} = \left(\frac{b}{a}\right)^{n} = \frac{b^n}{a^n}.$$

Notice that the negative exponent 'flips' (or takes the reciprocal of) the fraction $\frac{a}{b}$, giving us $\frac{b}{a}$. After flipping the fraction, the negative sign disappears. Observe that Property IV can be obtained from Property VIII in the following way:

$$a^{-n} = \underbrace{\left(\frac{a}{1}\right)^{-n} = \left(\frac{1}{a}\right)^{n}}_{\text{by Property VIII}} = \frac{1^n}{a^n} = \frac{1}{a^n}, \text{ provided that } a \neq 0.$$

Establishing Property VIII from Property IV requires more work which will be left for later. Let's see some examples with negative integer exponents.

Examples. Evaluate.

1) $\left(\dfrac{3}{2}\right)^{-1} = \left(\dfrac{2}{3}\right)^{1} = \dfrac{2}{3}$

2) $\left(\dfrac{1}{8}\right)^{-2} = \left(\dfrac{8}{1}\right)^{2} = 8^2 = 64$

3) $\left(\dfrac{3}{5}\right)^{-3} \cdot \left(\dfrac{5}{6}\right)^{-2} = \left(\dfrac{5}{3}\right)^{3} \cdot \left(\dfrac{6}{5}\right)^{2} = \dfrac{5^3}{3^3} \cdot \dfrac{6^2}{5^2} = \dfrac{\overset{5}{\cancel{125}}}{\underset{3}{\cancel{27}}} \cdot \dfrac{\overset{4}{\cancel{36}}}{\underset{1}{\cancel{25}}} = \dfrac{20}{3}$

4) $\left(\dfrac{8}{5}\right)^{-2} + 4^{-3} = \left(\dfrac{5}{8}\right)^{2} + \dfrac{1}{4^3} = \dfrac{25}{64} + \dfrac{1}{64} = \dfrac{\overset{13}{\cancel{26}}}{\underset{32}{\cancel{64}}} = \dfrac{13}{32}$

5) $\dfrac{7^{-2}}{3^1} = \dfrac{1 \cdot 7^{-2}}{3^1} = \dfrac{1}{3^1 \cdot 7^2} = \dfrac{1}{3\,(49)} = \dfrac{1}{147}$

Notice that the negative exponent *flips* the 7^{-2} into the denominator and the -2 becomes 2.

6) $\dfrac{4^3}{5^{-2}} = \dfrac{4^3}{1 \cdot 5^{-2}} = \dfrac{4^3 \cdot 5^2}{1} = \dfrac{16\,(25)}{1} = \dfrac{400}{1} = 400$

Notice that the negative exponent *flips* the 5^{-2} into the numerator and the -2 becomes 2.

7) $\dfrac{6^{-1} \cdot 3^2}{5^3 \cdot 2^{-2}} = \dfrac{3^2 \cdot 2^2}{6^1 \cdot 5^3} = \dfrac{9(4)}{6(125)} = \dfrac{\overset{6}{\cancel{36}}}{\underset{1}{\cancel{6}}(125)} = \dfrac{6}{125}$

Notice that 6^{-1} *flips* to the denominator, whereas the 2^{-2} *flips* to the numerator. Consequently, both exponents become positive.

46

Rules for Applying the Flipping Technique

Whenever you have a fraction whose numerator and denominator are factored, any factor in the numerator containing a negative exponent *flips* down to the denominator and any factor in the denominator containing a negative exponent *flips* up to the numerator. After the factor is *flipped*, the negative sign disappears. For example, we have (assuming all variables are non-zero)

$$\frac{a^{-m}}{b^n} = \frac{1}{a^m b^n}, \quad \frac{a^m}{b^{-n}} = \frac{a^m b^n}{1} = a^m b^n, \quad \frac{a^{-m} b^n}{c^p} = \frac{b^n}{a^m c^p}, \text{ and } \frac{a^m}{b^{-n} c^p} = \frac{a^m b^n}{c^p}.$$

8) $\dfrac{8^2 \cdot 3^{-1}}{4^2 \cdot 10^{-2}} = \dfrac{8^2 \cdot 10^2}{4^2 \cdot 3^1} = \dfrac{\overset{4}{\cancel{64}}(100)}{\underset{1}{\cancel{16}}(3)} = \dfrac{400}{3}$

9) $\dfrac{5^{-2} \cdot 2^{-1}}{5^{-3} \cdot 2^4} = \dfrac{5^3}{5^2 \cdot 2^4 \cdot 2^1} = \dfrac{\overset{1}{\cancel{5^3}}}{\underset{1}{\cancel{5^2}} \cdot 2^5} = \dfrac{5}{32}$

Note that the previous example can also be evaluated by using Property II. Observe that

$$\frac{5^{-2} \cdot 2^{-1}}{5^{-3} \cdot 2^4} = \frac{5^{-2}}{5^{-3}} \cdot \frac{2^{-1}}{2^4} = 5^{-2-(-3)} \cdot 2^{-1-4} = 5^1 \cdot 2^{-5} = \frac{5}{1} \cdot \frac{1}{2^5} = \frac{5}{32}.$$

In my opinion, the flipping technique is easier.

10) $\underbrace{\dfrac{-7^2 \cdot 8^{-1}}{3^2 \cdot 4^{-2} \cdot 9^0} = -\dfrac{7^2 \cdot 8^{-1}}{3^2 \cdot 4^{-2} \cdot 9^0}}_{\text{Pull out the negative sign to avoid confusion.}} = -\dfrac{7^2 \cdot 4^2}{3^2 \cdot 8^1 \cdot 9^0} = -\dfrac{49 \cdot \overset{2}{\cancel{16}}}{9 \cdot \underset{1}{\cancel{8}} \cdot 1} = -\dfrac{98}{9}$

The same rules for 'flipping' apply when we have algebraic expressions containing negative exponents.

Examples. Rewrite each expression **without** negative exponents.

1) $2(x+1)^{-1} = \underbrace{\dfrac{2(x+1)^{-1}}{1} = \dfrac{2}{(x+1)^1}}_{\text{Only } (x+1) \text{ flips.}} = \dfrac{2}{x+1}$

2) $4x^2(5x-2)^{-3} = \underbrace{\dfrac{4x^2(5x-2)^{-3}}{1} = \dfrac{4x^2}{(5x-2)^3}}_{\text{Only } (5x-2) \text{ flips.}}$

3) $\dfrac{6x^3}{(x-8)^{-1}} = \dfrac{6x^3(x-8)^1}{1} = 6x^3(x-8)$

4) $\dfrac{(y+3)^{-2}}{(7y+4)^3} = \dfrac{1}{(7y+4)^3(y+3)^2}$

5) $\dfrac{(t-1)^{-1}}{(2t+9)^{-4}} = \dfrac{(2t+9)^4}{(t-1)^1} = \dfrac{(2t+9)^4}{t-1}$

47

6) $\dfrac{4x^{-2}(x+2y)^2}{3^{-1}y^4(x-8y)^{-3}} = \dfrac{3\cdot 4(x+2y)^2(x-8y)^3}{x^2y^4} = \dfrac{12(x+2y)^2(x-8y)^3}{x^2y^4}$

Try These (Set 9): Evaluate.

1) $\left(\dfrac{1}{2}\right)^{-2}$ 2) $\left(\dfrac{3}{4}\right)^{-3}$ 3) $\left(\dfrac{4}{5}\right)^{-1} - \left(\dfrac{2}{7}\right)^{-2}$

4) $\dfrac{3^2}{9^{-1}}$ 5) $\dfrac{6^{-2}}{2^3}$ 6) $\dfrac{10^{-2}}{4^0}$

7) $\dfrac{3^3\cdot 4^{-2}}{3^{-1}\cdot 4^{-1}}$ 8) $\dfrac{6^0\cdot 8^{-1}}{2^{-4}\cdot 9^0}$ 9) $\dfrac{-3^2\cdot 5^{-1}}{(-10)^{-2}\cdot 2^3}$

Suppose that we are given an algebraic expression containing the zero exponent or negative exponents. We'll usually want to rewrite such an expression so that only positive exponents appear in the expression. We will do some examples which involve this rewriting process next.

Examples. Rewrite each expression as an expression with positive exponents only and simplify. Assume that all variables represent non-zero numbers.

1) $\underbrace{\left(\dfrac{3}{y}\right)^{-2} = \left(\dfrac{y}{3}\right)^2}_{\text{Property VIII}} = \dfrac{y^2}{3^2} = \dfrac{y^2}{9}$

2) $\underbrace{\left(\dfrac{x^2}{2}\right)^{-1} \cdot \left(\dfrac{x^5}{7}\right)^{-2} = \left(\dfrac{2}{x^2}\right)^1 \cdot \left(\dfrac{7}{x^5}\right)^2}_{\text{Property VIII}} = \left(\dfrac{2}{x^2}\right)\left(\dfrac{49}{x^{10}}\right) = \dfrac{98}{x^{12}}$

3) $\underbrace{a^4 b^{-4} = \dfrac{a^4 b^{-4}}{1}}_{\text{Create a fraction.}} = \dfrac{a^4}{b^4}$

4) $\underbrace{\left(a^4 b\right)^{-4} = \dfrac{\left(a^4 b\right)^{-4}}{1}}_{\text{Create a fraction.}} = \dfrac{1}{\left(a^4 b\right)^4} = \dfrac{1}{a^{16}b^4}$

5) $\underbrace{\left(7m^4 n^{-1}\right)^2 = 49m^8 n^{-2}}_{\text{by Properties VI and V}} = \dfrac{49m^8 n^{-2}}{1} = \dfrac{49m^8}{n^2}$

6) $\underbrace{\left(-6x^3 y^{-1}\right)^{-3} = \dfrac{\left(-6x^3 y^{-1}\right)^{-3}}{1}}_{\text{Create a fraction.}} = \underbrace{\dfrac{1}{\left(-6x^3 y^{-1}\right)^3} = \dfrac{1}{-216x^9 y^{-3}}}_{\text{by Properties VI and V}} = \dfrac{y^3}{-216x^9} \text{ or } -\dfrac{y^3}{216x^9}$

7) $\underbrace{\left(4a^{-6} b^{-8}\right)^3 = 64a^{-18} b^{-24}}_{\text{by Properties VI and V}} = \dfrac{64a^{-18} b^{-24}}{1} = \dfrac{64}{a^{18}b^{24}}$

48

$$\overbrace{\text{Flip } (-5x^4y^{-1}z^2)^{-1} \text{ and set } y^0=1.}$$

8) $(-5x^4y^{-1}z^2)^{-1} \cdot (2x^{-1}y^0z^{-5})^2 = \dfrac{\overbrace{(-5x^4y^{-1}z^2)^{-1} \cdot (2x^{-1}y^0z^{-5})^2}}{1} = \dfrac{(2x^{-1}(1)z^{-5})^2}{(-5x^4y^{-1}z^2)^1}$

$$= \underbrace{\dfrac{(2x^{-1}z^{-5})^2}{-5x^4y^{-1}z^2} = \dfrac{4x^{-2}z^{-10}}{-5x^4y^{-1}z^2}}_{\text{by Properties VI and V}} = \underbrace{\dfrac{4y^1}{-5x^2x^4z^2z^{10}}}_{\text{after flipping}} = -\dfrac{4y}{5x^6z^{12}}$$

9) $\dfrac{\left(5a^3b^{-7}\right)^2}{\left(6a^2b^{-3}\right)^0\left(-5a^{-1}b^{-4}\right)^3} = \underbrace{\dfrac{\left(5a^3b^{-7}\right)^2}{(1)\left(-5a^{-1}b^{-4}\right)^3} = \dfrac{\overset{1}{\cancel{25}}a^6b^{-14}}{\underset{5}{\cancel{-125}}a^{-3}b^{-12}}}_{\text{by Properties VI and V}} = \underbrace{-\dfrac{a^6a^3b^{12}}{5b^{14}}}_{\frac{b^{12}}{b^{14}}=b^{12-14}=b^{-2}=\frac{1}{b^2}} = -\dfrac{a^9}{5b^2}$

Try These (Set 10): Rewrite each expression as an expression with positive exponents only and simplify. Assume that all variables represent nonzero numbers.

1) $\left(\dfrac{x}{10}\right)^{-2}$ 　　 2) $\left(\dfrac{7}{x^3}\right)^{-2} \cdot \left(\dfrac{x^5}{2}\right)^{-3}$ 　　 3) $13a^6b^{-2}c^0$ 　　 4) $(-5x^{-3}y^{-8})^{-2}$

5) $(-9a^6bc^{-2})^0 \cdot (5a^{-6}b^4c^0)^{-3}$ 　　　　 6) $\dfrac{4x^3y^{-2}(5x)^2}{(15x^{-7}y)^0(8xy^{-2})^2}$

7) $\dfrac{\left(-s^{-3}t^5\right)^{-1}}{12s^2t^{-6}} \cdot 2st^4$ 　　　　 8) $\left[\left(x^4y^7\right)^{-1} \cdot \left(6x^{-1}y^0\right)\right]^{-2}$

Exercise 2.2

In Exercises 1-36, evaluate. Your answers should be simplified and without any exponents.

1. $\left(\dfrac{1}{4}\right)^{-1}$ 　　　 2. $\left(\dfrac{1}{2}\right)^{-1}$ 　　　 3. $\left(\dfrac{5}{3}\right)^{-1}$ 　　　 4. $\left(\dfrac{7}{6}\right)^{-1}$

5. $\left(\dfrac{7}{8}\right)^{-2}$ 　　　 6. $\left(\dfrac{3}{8}\right)^{-2}$ 　　　 7. $\left(\dfrac{2}{7}\right)^{-3}$ 　　　 8. $\left(\dfrac{9}{2}\right)^{-3}$

9. $\dfrac{2^2}{5^{-1}}$ 　　　 10. $\dfrac{5^2}{2^{-1}}$ 　　　 11. $\dfrac{2^{-2}}{4^2}$ 　　　 12. $\dfrac{6^{-2}}{3^2}$

13. $\dfrac{(-10)^{-2}}{(-3)^1}$ 　　 14. $\dfrac{(-8)^{-1}}{(-6)^2}$ 　　 15. $\dfrac{5^{-2}}{3^{-4}}$ 　　 16. $\dfrac{8^{-2}}{7^{-3}}$

17. $\dfrac{(-9)^{-2}}{-2^{-3}}$ 　　 18. $\dfrac{-3^{-2}}{(-2)^{-5}}$ 　　 19. $\dfrac{4^1 \cdot 3^{-2}}{4^{-1} \cdot 3^2}$ 　　 20. $\dfrac{6^{-3} \cdot 7^0}{6^{-2} \cdot 7^{-1}}$

21. $\dfrac{9^{-3} \cdot 2^0}{9^{-2} \cdot 2^{-5}}$ 　　 22. $\dfrac{3^{-2} \cdot 8^{-1}}{3^1 \cdot 8^{-2}}$ 　　 23. $5^0 \cdot 2^{-4} \cdot 6$ 　　 24. $4^3 \cdot 5^{-1} \cdot 10^0$

25. $\dfrac{12^0}{7^{-3}}$ 　　 26. $\dfrac{11^0}{3^{-5}}$ 　　 27. $\dfrac{6^{-2}}{16^0}$ 　　 28. $\dfrac{10^{-3}}{(-5)^0}$

29. $\dfrac{3^2 \cdot (-5)^{-1}}{(-4)^{-2} \cdot 2^{-1}}$ 　 30. $\dfrac{(-6)^{-2} \cdot (-2)^{-1}}{7^{-2} \cdot 6^0}$ 　 31. $\left(\dfrac{5}{2}\right)^{-2} + \left(\dfrac{2}{3}\right)^{-1}$ 　 32. $\left(\dfrac{2}{3}\right)^{-3} - \left(\dfrac{8}{9}\right)^{-1}$

33. $2\left(\dfrac{4}{5}\right)^{-2} + \left(\dfrac{2}{5}\right)^{-3}$ 　 34. $\left(\dfrac{3}{4}\right)^{-3} - 2\left(\dfrac{9}{2}\right)^{-1}$ 　 35. $\dfrac{7}{18}\left(\dfrac{5}{6}\right)^{-2} + \left(\dfrac{4}{7}\right)^0$ 　 36. $\left(\dfrac{1}{9}\right)^0 - \dfrac{7}{4}\left(\dfrac{3}{2}\right)^{-2}$

In Exercises 37-80, rewrite the given expression with positive exponents **only** and simplify. Assume that all variables represent non-zero numbers.

37. $\left(\dfrac{a}{6}\right)^{-1}$ 38. $\left(\dfrac{b}{3}\right)^{-1}$ 39. $\left(\dfrac{a}{7}\right)^{-2}$ 40. $\left(\dfrac{b}{4}\right)^{-3}$

41. $\left(\dfrac{7a}{5}\right)^{-2}$ 42. $\left(\dfrac{4}{3t}\right)^{-3}$ 43. $\left(\dfrac{9}{4x^2}\right)^{-3}$ 44. $\left(\dfrac{8}{7b^5}\right)^{-2}$

45. $\left(\dfrac{10m^2}{3n^{12}}\right)^{-2}$ 46. $\left(\dfrac{11p^8}{6q^2}\right)^{-2}$ 47. $13x^{-4}y^0z^5$ 48. $7x^3y^{-8}z^0$

49. $\left(5a^5b^{-1}\right)^{-2}$ 50. $\left(4a^{-5}b^2\right)^{-3}$ 51. $\left(\dfrac{a^{-3}}{b^6}\right)^{-2}$ 52. $\left(\dfrac{m^4}{n^{-8}}\right)^{-3}$

53. $\left(\dfrac{a^0}{b^{-7}}\right)^{-2}$ 54. $\left(\dfrac{a^3}{b^0}\right)^{-10}$ 55. $\left(\dfrac{3x^{-1}}{4x^0}\right)^{-1}$ 56. $\left(\dfrac{7t^0}{11t^{-5}}\right)^{-1}$

57. $\left(\dfrac{x^2}{6}\right)^{-2}\cdot\left(\dfrac{x^4}{2}\right)^{-1}$ 58. $\left(\dfrac{y^5}{5}\right)^{-1}\cdot\left(\dfrac{y^3}{3}\right)^{-3}$ 59. $\left(\dfrac{10}{m^3}\right)^{-3}\cdot\left(\dfrac{m^2}{100}\right)^{-1}$

60. $\left(\dfrac{12}{t^7}\right)^{-2}\cdot\left(\dfrac{t^5}{12}\right)^{-1}$ 61. $\dfrac{a^7b^4}{8}\cdot\dfrac{\left(ab^6\right)^{-1}}{4}$ 62. $\dfrac{\left(x^3y^5\right)^{-1}}{2}\cdot\dfrac{x^4y^9}{3}$

63. $\dfrac{\left(s^8t^{-1}\right)^{-1}}{s^2t^5}$ 64. $\dfrac{\left(a^3b^{-7}\right)^{-1}}{a^5b^9}$ 65. $\dfrac{x^3y^{-3}}{\left(x^{-3}y^7\right)^{-1}}$

66. $\dfrac{x^{-7}y^3}{\left(x^2y^{-4}\right)^{-1}}$ 67. $\dfrac{x^9y^{-8}}{\left(x^{-2}y^{10}\right)^{-1}}$ 68. $\dfrac{x^{-9}y^3}{\left(x^6y^{-3}\right)^{-1}}$

69. $6x^4y^{-5}(3xy^3)^2$ 70. $-3x^3y^{-7}(4xy)^2$ 71. $(3a^{-3}b^2)^0(9a^{-3}b^6)^2$

72. $(8x^4y^{-4})^0(-9xy^{-5})^2$ 73. $(16ab^{-2}c^6)^0(-2a^{-1}b^0c^4)^{-3}$ 74. $(x^0y^{-3}z^4)^{-5}(-8x^{-5}y^{-1}z^3)^0$

75. $\dfrac{\left(5x^8y^{-1}\right)^2\left(3x^0y\right)}{(xy^2)\left(-4x^6y^4\right)^0}$ 76. $\dfrac{\left(9x^{-13}y\right)\left(2x^5\right)^2}{\left(x^3y^5\right)^0\left(2x^2y\right)}$ 77. $\dfrac{\left(4x^5y^{-9}\right)^0}{\left(3x^2\right)^3\left(y^{-1}\right)^2}\cdot\dfrac{9x^5}{x^{-6}y^{-7}}$

78. $\dfrac{\left(s^3t^{-9}\right)^{-2}}{2s^5t^{-1}}\cdot\dfrac{4t^6}{\left(8s^3t^{-1}\right)^0}$ 79. $\left[\left(25x^3y^{-2}\right)^{-1}\left(5x^0y^{-5}\right)^3\right]^{-2}$ 80. $\left[\left(-4a^5b^{-2}\right)^{-3}\cdot\left(\dfrac{a^{-2}b^0}{8}\right)^{-1}\right]^2$

Section 2.3   Scientific Notation

When working with extremely large and extremely small positive terminating decimals like 7,120,301,000 and 0.00000061, it is convenient to express such a number as a product of two factors, one factor being a real number between 1 and 10 (this factor may equal 1 but never equals 10) and the other factoring of the form 10^p, where p is some integer. In fact, *any* positive terminating decimal can be expressed in the form $m \times 10^p$, where m is between 1 and 10 and p is some integer. When we express a positive terminating decimal in such a form, will say that it is written in **scientific notation**. We will begin this section by practicing converting back and forth between positive terminating decimals and their scientific notation. Afterwards, we will apply the properties of exponents to do computations with numbers written in scientific notation.

I) Converting a Positive Terminating Decimal to Scientific Notation

Suppose that n is a positive terminating decimal. I will describe the method which enables us to convert n into scientific notation. The procedure is divided into four cases.

Case 1. If $n < 1$, then you move the decimal point of your number to the **right** until it is to the right of the first **non-zero** digit. If this first non-zero digit, together with all other digits to the right of the moved decimal, is called m and if you've moved your decimal point p places to the right, then $n = m \times 10^{-p}$.

Examples. Write each number in scientific notation.

1) $0.4 = 4 \times 10^{-1}$ (Move the decimal point one place to the right.)

2) $0.163 = 1.63 \times 10^{-1}$ (Move the decimal point one place to the right.)

3) $0.000724 = 7.24 \times 10^{-4}$ (Move the decimal point four places to the right.)

4) $0.000000000862005 = 8.62005 \times 10^{-10}$ (Move the decimal point ten places to the right.)

5) $0.010101 = 1.0101 \times 10^{-2}$ (Move the decimal point two places to the right.)

6) $0.0067562 = 6.7562 \times 10^{-3}$ (Move the decimal point three places to the right.)

Case 2. If the number, n, is between 1 and 10, then we can always write it as $n = n \times 10^0$.

Examples. Write each number in scientific notation.

1) $9 = 9 \times 10^0$

2) $1.465 = 1.465 \times 10^0$

3) $3.14 = 3.14 \times 10^0$

Case 3. If $n = 10$, then $10 = 1.0 \times 10^1$ is in scientific notation. We can also write $10 = 1 \times 10^1$.

Case 4. If $n > 10$, then you move the decimal point of your number to the **left** until it is to the right of the first digit. If this first digit, together with all other digits to the right of the moved decimal, is called m and if you've moved your decimal point p places to the left, then $n = m \times 10^p$.

Examples. Write each number in scientific notation.

1) $261.781 = 2.61781 \times 10^2$ (Move the decimal point two places to the left.)

2) $42 = 42.0 = 4.2 \times 10^1$ (Move the decimal point one place to the left.)

3) $3,053,221.1123 = 3.0532211123 \times 10^6$ (Move the decimal point six places to the left.)

4) $10.80032 = 1.080032 \times 10^1$ (Move the decimal point one place to the left.)

5) $7,000,000,000 = 7.000000000000 \times 10^9$ or simply 7×10^9 (Move the decimal point nine places to the left.)

6) $982,001,123.16652 = 9.8200112316652 \times 10^8$ (Move the decimal point eight places to the left.)

II) Converting from Scientific Notation to a Positive Terminating Decimal

Next I will discuss the method for converting a number from scientific notation to a positive terminating decimal.

Case 1. Suppose that the given number is of the form $m \times 10^p$, where p is a positive integer. To begin with, you locate the decimal point in the number m. Starting from the decimal point, count p digits to the **right**, adding in additional zeros if necessary. After counting p digits to the right and placing the decimal point in the end position, you'll end up with your answer.

Examples. Write each number as a terminating decimal.

1) $1.2 \times 10^3 = 1.200 \times 10^3 = 1,200.0 = 1,200$ (Move the decimal point three places to the right.)

2) $8 \times 10^2 = 8.00 \times 10^2 = 800.0 = 800$ (Move the decimal point two places to the right.)

3) $9.602 \times 10^5 = 9.60200 \times 10^5 = 960,200$ (Move the decimal point five places to the right.)

4) $1.014 \times 10^7 = 1.0140000 \times 10^7 = 10,140,000$ (Move the decimal point seven places to the right.)

5) $7.0004 \times 10^1 = 70.004$ (Move the decimal point one place to the right.)

6) $3.994718 \times 10^4 = 39,947.18$ (Move the decimal point four places to the right.)

Case 2. Suppose that the given number is of the form $m \times 10^{-p}$, where p is a positive integer. To begin with, you locate the decimal point in the number m. Starting from the decimal point, count p digits to the **left**, adding in additional zeros if necessary. After counting p digits to the left and placing the decimal point in the end position, you'll end up with your answer.

Examples. Write each number as a terminating decimal.

1) $3.117 \times 10^{-2} = 0.03117$ (Move the decimal point two places to the left.)

2) $2 \times 10^{-4} = 2.0 \times 10^{-4} = 0.0002$ (Move the decimal point four places to the left.)

3) $1.0317 \times 10^{-1} = 0.10317$ (Move the decimal point one place to the left.)

4) $7.4093 \times 10^{-3} = 0.0074093$ (Move the decimal point three places to the left.)

5) $8.3 \times 10^{-4} = 0.00083$ (Move the decimal point four places to the left.)

6) $1 \times 10^{-9} = 1.0 \times 10^{-9} = 0.000000001$ (Move the decimal point nine places to the left.)

Try These (Set 11):

I) Convert each number into scientific notation.

1) $4,993$ 2) 528.901 3) 0.120026

4) $13,890.111$ 5) 0.077691 6) 1

II) Convert each number into a terminating decimal.

1) 6.8×10^2 2) 8.0012×10^4 3) 5.16×10^1

4) 6.34×10^{-3} 5) 7.5002×10^{-1} 6) 1×10^{-4}

Now that we have an understanding of how scientific notation works, let's see how our properties of exponents allow us to do computations when our expressions are in this notation.

Examples. Evaluate. Express the answer in scientific notation.

1) $\underbrace{\left(3 \times 10^4\right)\left(2 \times 10^3\right) = 6 \times 10^7}_{\text{by Property I}}$

2) $\underbrace{\left(7 \times 10^{-2}\right)\left(8 \times 10^{-2}\right) = 56 \times 10^{-4}}_{\text{by Property I}} = \underbrace{\left(5.6 \times 10^1\right) \times 10^{-4} = 5.6 \times 10^{-3}}_{\text{by the Associative Property and Property I}}$

3) $\dfrac{1.5 \times 10^{-1}}{1.5 \times 10^{12}} = \dfrac{1.5}{1.5} \times \dfrac{10^{-1}}{10^{12}} = \underbrace{1 \times \dfrac{10^{-1}}{10^{12}} = 1 \times 10^{-1-12}}_{\text{by Property II}} = 1 \times 10^{-13}$

4) $\dfrac{\overset{2}{\cancel{8}} \times 10^8}{\underset{1}{\cancel{4}} \times 10^{-6}} = \underbrace{\dfrac{2}{1} \times \dfrac{10^8}{10^{-6}} = 2 \times 10^{8-(-6)}}_{\text{by Property II}} = 2 \times 10^{14}$

5) $\underbrace{\left(5 \times 10^7\right)^2 = 25 \times 10^{14}}_{\text{by Properties VI and V}} = \underbrace{\left(2.5 \times 10^1\right) \times 10^{14} = 2.5 \times 10^{15}}_{\text{by the Associative Property and Property I}}$

6) $\underbrace{\left(6 \times 10^{-3}\right)^2 = 36 \times 10^{-6}}_{\text{by Properties VI and V}} = \underbrace{\left(3.6 \times 10^1\right) \times 10^{-6} = 3.6 \times 10^{-5}}_{\text{by the Associative Property and Property I}}$

7) $\underbrace{\dfrac{\left(3 \times 10^3\right)\left(2 \times 10^{-5}\right)^2}{6 \times 10^4} = \dfrac{\left(3 \times 10^3\right)\left(4 \times 10^{-10}\right)}{6 \times 10^4} = \dfrac{12 \times 10^{-7}}{6 \times 10^4}}_{\text{by Properties VI, V, and I}} = \dfrac{12}{6} \times \dfrac{10^{-7}}{10^4} = 2 \times 10^{-7-4} = 2 \times 10^{-11}$

Try These (Set 12): Evaluate. Express the answer in scientific notation.

1) $\left(1.2 \times 10^6\right)\left(5 \times 10^4\right)$　　2) $\dfrac{3.2 \times 10^{-5}}{0.8 \times 10^2}$　　3) $\left(8 \times 10^{10}\right)^3$

4) $\left(1 \times 10^{-14}\right)\left(1 \times 10^{-10}\right)$　　5) $\left(3 \times 10^3\right)\left(4 \times 10^{-1}\right)^3$　　6) $\dfrac{1 \times 10^{-2}}{\left(3 \times 10^4\right)\left(9 \times 10^{-4}\right)^{-1}}$

Exercise 2.3

In Exercises 1-24, write each number in scientific notation.

1. 0.2	2. 0.4	3. 0.00982	4. 0.0007802
5. 0.0010111001	6. 0.0001095	7. 6	8. 3
9. 4.23	10. 7.804	11. 3.14	12. 2.71828
13. 60	14. 98	15. 26.19	16. 42.61
17. 935.112	18. 202.14	19. 4,502	20. 8,103
21. 65,782.001	22. 11,099.53	23. 52,402,437.86	24. 410,130,612.0002

In Exercises 25-50, write each number as a terminating decimal.

25. 5×10^1 26. 6×10^1 27. 3.9×10^2 28. 9.3×10^2

29. 7.26×10^1 30. 3.86×10^1 31. 6.403×10^4 32. 1.1927×10^3

33. 4.82777×10^4 34. 9.145554×10^4 35. 7.0×10^5 36. 1.0×10^8

37. 3.0×10^8 38. 2.00×10^{14} 39. 2.53911×10^8 40. 9.830002×10^9

41. 7.16562×10^1 42. 6.0338×10^1 43. 8×10^{-1} 44. 2×10^{-1}

45. 1.113×10^{-2} 46. 7.3615×10^{-1} 47. 8.22762×10^{-3} 48. 2.002×10^{-4}

49. 1×10^{-9} 50. 1×10^{-12}

In Exercises 51-90, evaluate. Express the answer in scientific notation

51. $\left(3 \times 10^1\right)\left(3 \times 10^2\right)$

52. $\left(2 \times 10^2\right)\left(4 \times 10^7\right)$

53. $\left(2.5 \times 10^8\right)\left(5 \times 10^1\right)$

54. $\left(3 \times 10^7\right)\left(4.1 \times 10^2\right)$

55. $\left(5 \times 10^{-7}\right)\left(1 \times 10^{-1}\right)$

56. $\left(1 \times 10^{-6}\right)\left(4 \times 10^{-2}\right)$

57. $\left(6 \times 10^{-5}\right)\left(6 \times 10^{11}\right)$

58. $\left(8 \times 10^{-2}\right)\left(4 \times 10^6\right)$

59. $\left(7 \times 10^{-2}\right)\left(9 \times 10^{-6}\right)$

60. $\left(9 \times 10^7\right)\left(3 \times 10^{-1}\right)$

61. $\dfrac{8 \times 10^5}{4 \times 10^3}$

62. $\dfrac{9 \times 10^{13}}{3 \times 10^7}$

63. $\dfrac{150 \times 10^{12}}{15 \times 10^2}$

64. $\dfrac{450 \times 10^{14}}{50 \times 10^3}$

65. $\dfrac{65 \times 10^{-2}}{5 \times 10^6}$

66. $\dfrac{121 \times 10^{-8}}{11 \times 10^2}$

67. $\dfrac{144 \times 10^{-1}}{6 \times 10^{-9}}$

68. $\dfrac{360 \times 10^{-8}}{1 \times 10^{-13}}$

69. $\left(2 \times 10^4\right)^2$

70. $\left(3 \times 10^5\right)^2$

71. $\left(5 \times 10^4\right)^3$

72. $\left(6 \times 10^5\right)^3$

73. $\left(7 \times 10^{-4}\right)^2$

74. $\left(8 \times 10^{-3}\right)^2$

75. $\left(2 \times 10^{-2}\right)^{-2}$

76. $\left(2 \times 10^{-5}\right)^{-2}$

77. $\left(5 \times 10^2\right)\left(4 \times 10^6\right)^2$

78. $\left(2 \times 10^1\right)\left(4 \times 10^4\right)^3$

79. $\left(2 \times 10^4\right)^3\left(3 \times 10^{-7}\right)^2$

80. $\left(3 \times 10^{-11}\right)^2\left(1 \times 10^{-4}\right)^3$

81. $\dfrac{\left(4 \times 10^2\right)\left(5 \times 10^{-1}\right)^{-1}}{2 \times 10^0}$

82. $\dfrac{\left(6 \times 10^3\right)^{-1}\left(2 \times 10^{-5}\right)}{4 \times 10^0}$

83. $\dfrac{\left(2 \times 10^4\right)^2\left(9 \times 10^3\right)^1}{4 \times 10^4}$

84. $\dfrac{\left(5 \times 10^7\right)^1\left(4 \times 10^8\right)^2}{2 \times 10^9}$

85. $\dfrac{\left(2 \times 10^7\right)^{-2}}{\left(2 \times 10^5\right)^{-3}}$

86. $\dfrac{\left(2 \times 10^2\right)^{-3}}{\left(4 \times 10^4\right)^{-2}}$

87. $\dfrac{\left(1 \times 10^{10}\right)^{-2}}{1 \times 10^{-5}}$

88. $\dfrac{\left(1 \times 10^5\right)^{-2}}{1 \times 10^{-4}}$

89. $\dfrac{8 \times 10^4}{\left(7 \times 10^{-3}\right)^{-1}}$

90. $\dfrac{9 \times 10^3}{\left(3 \times 10^{-4}\right)^{-1}}$

END OF CHAPTER 2   QUIZ

1. $(-5)^2 =$
   a) 25   b) -25 c) 10   d) -10 e) -52

2. $4^3 =$
   a) 12   b) 81   c) 64   d) 43   e) 7

3. $\left(-\dfrac{1}{2}\right)^3 - \left(\dfrac{1}{2}\right)^3 =$
   a) 0   b) $\dfrac{1}{4}$ c) $-\dfrac{3}{8}$ d) $-\dfrac{1}{4}$ e) $-\dfrac{1}{8}$

4. $x^3 \cdot x^4 =$
   a) x^{12} b) $2x^7$ c) x^7 d) $2x^{12}$ e) x^{14}

5. $\left(4^3\right)\left(4^7\right) =$
   a) 4^{10} b) 16^{10} c) 4^{21} d) 16^{21} e) 336

6. $\dfrac{y^{19}}{y^{14}} =$
   a) y^{33} b) y^5 c) 1   d) 0   e) 5

7. $\left(x^{12}\right)^4 =$
   a) x^{48} b) x^{16} c) x^3 d) $4x^{12}$ e) x^{96}

8. $3a^7b^{-6} =$
   a) $\dfrac{1}{3a^7b^6}$ b) $\dfrac{3}{a^7b^6}$ c) $\dfrac{1}{(3a^7b)^6}$ d) $\dfrac{b^6}{3a^7}$ e) $\dfrac{3a^7}{b^6}$

9. $x^6\left(x^2y^3\right)^{-4} =$
   a) x^2y^{12} b) $\dfrac{x^2}{y^2}$ c) $\dfrac{y^2}{x^2}$ d) $\dfrac{1}{x^2y^{12}}$ e) $\dfrac{1}{y^{12}}$

10. $\dfrac{a^{-2}b^3}{a^{-9}b^8} =$
    a) a^7b^5 b) $\dfrac{a^7}{b^5}$ c) $\dfrac{a^{11}}{b^5}$ d) $\dfrac{1}{a^7b^5}$ e) $\dfrac{1}{a^{11}b^5}$

11. $\left(\dfrac{7}{4x^5}\right)^2 =$
    a) $\dfrac{49}{16x^7}$ b) $\dfrac{49}{8x^{10}}$ c) $\dfrac{49}{16x^{10}}$ d) $\dfrac{49}{4x^5}$ e) $\dfrac{7}{4x^{10}}$

12. $\left(\dfrac{8}{9}\right)^{-2} \cdot \left(\dfrac{4}{3}\right)^{3} =$

    a) 3 b) $\dfrac{4,096}{2,187}$ c) $\dfrac{1}{3}$ d) $\dfrac{3}{2}$ e) -3

13. $\left(m^3 n^{-2}\right)^{-3} \left(m^{-1} n^3\right)^0 =$

    a) 1 b) $\dfrac{1}{n^5}$ c) $\dfrac{m^9}{n^6}$ d) $\dfrac{n^6}{m^9}$ e) $\dfrac{n^9}{m^{10}}$

14. $\left(\dfrac{4a}{3b^2}\right)^3 \cdot \dfrac{3b}{(4a)^3} =$

    a) $\dfrac{9}{b^5}$ b) $\dfrac{64a^3}{9b^5}$ c) $9b^5$ d) $\dfrac{27}{9b^5}$ e) $\dfrac{1}{9b^5}$

15. $\dfrac{5^{-2} \cdot x^3}{4^2 \cdot x^{-9}} =$

    a) $\dfrac{1}{400x^2}$ b) $\dfrac{x^{12}}{400}$ c) $\dfrac{400}{x^{12}}$ d) $\dfrac{16x^2}{25}$ e) $\dfrac{-25x^{12}}{16}$

16. $\dfrac{u^{-4} v^{-3} w^0}{u^0 v^8 w^{-9}} =$

    a) $\dfrac{u^4 v^{11}}{w^9}$ b) $\dfrac{v^{11} w^9}{u^4}$ c) $\dfrac{u^4 w^9}{v^{11}}$ d) $\dfrac{w^9}{u^4 v^{11}}$ e) $\dfrac{1}{u^4 v^{11} w^9}$

17. $\left(-6x^{-2} y^7 z^0\right)^{-2} =$

    a) $-\dfrac{1}{36x^4 y^{14}}$ b) $\dfrac{y^{14}}{36x^4}$ c) $\dfrac{x^4}{36y^{14}}$ d) $\dfrac{x^4 z}{36y^{14}}$ e) $\dfrac{-36x^4}{y^{14}}$

18. $\left(3 \times 10^8\right) \times \left(2 \times 10^{-5}\right) =$

    a) 6×10^{13} b) 60×10^3 c) 6×100^3 d) 6×100^{13} e) 6×10^3

19. $7,314.118 =$

    a) $7,314 \times 10^3$ b) 7.314118×10^3 c) $7,314,118 \times 10^3$

    d) 7.314118×10^4 e) 7.314118×10^{-3}

20. $\dfrac{2 \times 10^{-9}}{4 \times 10^{-2}} =$

    a) 0.5×10^{-8} b) 50×10^{-8} c) 5×10^{-8} d) 5×10^{-7} e) 5×10^{-10}

ANSWERS FOR QUIZ 2   1. a   2. c   3. d   4. c   5. a

    6. b   7. a   8. e   9. d   10. b

    11. c   12. a   13. d   14. e   15. b

    16. d   17. c   18. e   19. b   20. c

Chapter 3:   Polynomials

This chapter is devoted to the study of algebraic objects known as **polynomials**. A polynomial is a sum and/or difference of **monomials**, the 'building blocks' of a polynomial. As we shall see later in this book, many algebraic expressions such as rational expressions and radical expressions are constructed from polynomials.

In Section 3.1, we will develop a vocabulary list of new words and phrases which are often used when discussing polynomials. To help us adapt to this new algebraic language, many examples are provided. Sections 3.2, 3.3, and 3.4 discuss how to do algebraic manipulations with polynomials. These operations include addition, subtraction, multiplication, and division. In Section 3.5, we will learn how to factor a polynomial.

Section 3.1   Definitions and Examples of Polynomials

We begin this section with some definitions relating to the 'building blocks' of polynomials called monomials.

Definition 1: A **monomial** is either a real number (called a **constant monomial**) or a product of a real number with variable(s).

Any real number is a monomial (a constant). For example, the numbers 6, -1, 3.2817, 0, $-\frac{3}{28}$, and π are all constant monomials. The expressions $8x$, $-3x^2$, $7a^3b^6$, $\frac{9}{17}t^3$, $10.28ab^2$, and πx^5 are all monomials since each is a product of a real number with variables.

Monomials are named according to the number of variables they contain. For example, the monomial $8x$ is called a **monomial in one variable**, x, and the monomial $7a^3b^6$ is called a **monomial in two variables**, a and b. Notice that the expressions $\frac{2x^5}{7}$ and $\frac{y^3}{9}$ are also monomials because we can rewrite them as $\frac{2x^5}{7} = \frac{2}{7}x^5$ and $\frac{y^3}{9} = \frac{1}{9}y^3$. However, the expressions $\frac{1}{x^2}$ and $-\frac{5}{t^3}$ are NOT monomials because they cannot be expressed as a product of a number with variables. Notice that we can rewrite $\frac{1}{x^2} = x^{-2}$ and $-\frac{5}{t^3} = -5t^{-3}$. Both of the exponents of the variables are negative integers which cannot occur in a monomial. In fact, the exponents of the variables in a monomial **must** be positive integers. Therefore, $3a^5b^2c^6$ is a monomial, but $4x^5y^8z^{-2}$ is not a monomial.

Definition 2: The number part of a monomial is called the **coefficient** of the monomial. The variable part of a monomial will be referred to simply as the **variable part**.

Examples. Find the coefficient and variable part of each monomial.

1) $7x$ has the coefficient 7 and the variable part x.

2) $-13a^3$ has the coefficient -13 and the variable part a^3.

3) $\frac{4}{5}x^7y^2$ has the coefficient $\frac{4}{5}$ and variable part x^7y^2.

4) 16 has the coefficient 16 and no variable part (or an **empty** variable part).

5) y^9 has the coefficient 1 (since $y^9 = 1y^9$) and the variable part y^9.

6) $-x^3y^2$ has the coefficient -1 (since $-x^3y^2 = -1x^3y^2$) and the variable part x^3y^2.

7) $\dfrac{3a^4b}{19}$ has the coefficient $\dfrac{3}{19}$ and the variable part a^4b.

Definition 3: The sum of the exponents of the variables of a monomial is called the **degree** of the monomial.

Any constant monomial (except for 0) has the degree 0. The monomial 0 has no degree (or undefined degree).

Examples. Find the degree of each monomial.

1) $7x$ has the degree 1 since $7x = 7x^1$.

2) $-13a^3$ has the degree 3.

3) $\dfrac{4}{5}x^7y^2$ has the degree $9\,(=7+2)$.

4) $\dfrac{3a^4b}{19} = \dfrac{3}{19}a^4b^1$ has the degree $5\,(=4+1)$.

5) $x^6yz^2 = x^6y^1z^2$ has the degree $9\,(=6+1+2)$.

6) 16 has the degree 0 since it is a constant monomial.

You should notice from the examples above that the degree just tells us how many variables are multiplying together. For example, notice that $\dfrac{4}{5}x^2y^6 = \dfrac{4}{5} \cdot \underbrace{x \cdot x \cdot y \cdot y \cdot y \cdot y \cdot y \cdot y}_{\text{8 variables altogether}}$. Observe that a constant monomial (other than 0) doesn't contain any variables, so its degree is 0. Moreover, the degree of a monomial in one variable is simply the exponent. Hence, the degree of $5x^4$ is 4 and the degree of $9.142a^3$ is 3.

We are now ready to define a polynomial and other mathematical words and phrases related to it. For now, we will focus **only** on polynomials in one variable. We will look at some definitions for polynomials in several variables afterwards.

Definition 4: A **polynomial in one variable** is a sum of monomials, each containing the same variable. We call each monomial in a polynomial a **term** of the polynomial.

Note that the definition also allows differences to appear in a polynomial since every difference can be expressed as a sum. Put another way, we have

$$a - b = a + (-b)$$

for any monomials a and b.

Some examples of polynomials in one variable are

$$7x + 1,\; 4x^2 + 2x - 9,\; -t^5 + 6 - 2t^2 + t^3,\; \frac{-3}{4}y^3 + 7.002y^2 - 8.14,\; \text{and } x^4 + 3x.$$

Notice that every monomial can be thought of as a polynomial. For example, we can write the monomial $7x$ as $7x + 0$, making it a polynomial with two terms. Furthermore, in order for an algebraic expression to be a polynomial, each of its 'building blocks' **must** be a monomial. Hence, the expression $5x^2 - x + \dfrac{2}{x^3}$ is not a polynomial since $\dfrac{4}{x^8}$ is not a monomial. However, the expression $3x^2 - 2x + \dfrac{x^3}{8}$ is a polynomial since $\dfrac{x^3}{8} = \dfrac{1}{8}x^3$ is, in fact, a monomial.

Sometimes we may be given a polynomial which does not appear to be a polynomial. For example, $\dfrac{7x^2 + 21x - 2}{7}$ is a polynomial since

$$\frac{7x^2 + 21x - 2}{7} = \frac{7}{7}x^2 + \frac{21}{7}x - \frac{2}{7} = x^2 + 3x - \frac{2}{7}.$$

We will encounter such expressions as we go along. Let's now look at some definitions.

Definition 5: A polynomial in one variable is in **descending order** if the degrees of its terms are decreasing when the polynomial is read from left to right.

As we will see in the next examples, every polynomial in one variable can be written in descending order.

Examples. Write the polynomials in descending order.

1) $7x + 1$ is already in descending order since $7x + 1 = \underbrace{7x^1}_{\text{degree 1}} + \underbrace{1}_{\text{degree 0}}$ and the degrees are decreasing.

2) $4x^2 + 2x - 9$ is already in descending order since $4x^2 + 2x - 9 = \underbrace{4x^2}_{\text{degree 2}} + \underbrace{2x^1}_{\text{degree 1}} + \underbrace{(-9)}_{\text{degree 0}}$ and the degrees are decreasing.

3) $-t^5 + 6 - 2t^2 + t^3$ is not in descending order since the terms of $\underbrace{-t^5}_{\text{degree 5}} + \underbrace{6}_{\text{degree 0}} + \underbrace{(-2t^2)}_{\text{degree 2}} + \underbrace{t^3}_{\text{degree 3}}$ do not have degrees which are decreasing. However, by the Commutative Property, we can rewrite our polynomial as $-t^5 + t^3 - 2t^2 + 6$ and obtain descending order.

4) $\dfrac{1}{2}y^2 - 8y^3 + 9$ is not in descending order since $\underbrace{\dfrac{1}{2}y^2}_{\text{degree 2}} + \underbrace{(-8y^3)}_{\text{degree 3}} + \underbrace{9}_{\text{degree 0}}$ and the degrees are not decreasing. By commuting the first two terms, we get $-8y^3 + \dfrac{1}{2}y^2 + 9$. And now the polynomial is in descending order.

Observe that when a polynomial is written in descending order, the exponents of the terms decrease from left to right. This happens because the degree of a monomial in one variable is just the exponent of the variable part.

Definition 6: A polynomial is **simplified** if its terms have different variable parts.

For example, $5x^2 - 6x$ is simplified since the variable parts of the terms, x^2 and x, are different. The polynomial $7a^3 + 3a^3 - 2a$ is not simplified since the terms $7a^3$ and $3a^3$ have the same variable parts, a^3.

Definition 7: The left-most (non-zero) term of a simplified polynomial written in descending order is called the **leading term** of the polynomial.

Examples. Find the leading term of each polynomial.

1) $7x + 1$ has the leading term $7x$.

2) $9x^2 - 2x + 1$ has the leading term $9x^2$.

3) $\underbrace{-t^5 - 7 + 4t^2 + t^3}_{\text{not descending}} = \underbrace{-t^5 + t^3 + 4t^2 - 7}_{\text{is descending}}$ has the leading term $-t^5$.

4) $\underbrace{\frac{1}{2}y^2 - 8y^3 + 7}_{\text{not descending}} = \underbrace{-8y^3 + \frac{1}{2}y^2 + 7}_{\text{is descending}}$ has the leading term $-8y^3$.

5) $0x^5 - 4x^4 + 7x - 2 = -4x^4 + 7x - 2$ has the leading term $-4x^4$.

Notice that the leading term of a polynomial in one variable is just the term in the polynomial containing the largest exponent. Moreover, the leading term of a monomial is just the monomial itself. Hence, the leading term of $8a^2$ is $8a^2$ and the leading term of -1 is -1. By convention, the leading term of 0 is 0.

Definition 8: The coefficient of the leading term of a polynomial in one variable is called the **leading coefficient** of the polynomial.

Examples. Find the leading coefficient of each polynomial.

1) $7x + 1$ has the leading coefficient 7.

2) $5x^2 - 3x + 1$ has the leading coefficient 5.

3) $-t^5 + t^3 + 4t^2 - 7$ has the leading coefficient -1 since $-t^5 = -1t^5$.

4) $x^3 + 2x^2 - 7$ has the leading coefficient 1 since $x^3 = 1x^3$.

Definition 9: The **degree** of a polynomial in one variable is the degree of its leading term.

Examples. Find the degree of each polynomial.

1) $\underbrace{2x}_{\text{degree 1}} + 1$ has the degree 1.

2) $\underbrace{9x^2}_{\text{degree 2}} - 2x + 1$ has the degree 2.

3) $\underbrace{-t^5}_{\text{degree 5}} + t^3 + 4t^2 - 7$ has the degree 5.

4) $\underbrace{x^3}_{\text{degree 3}} + 2x^2 - 7$ has the degree 3.

You may have noticed that the degree of a polynomial is simply the largest of the degrees (or exponents) of the terms of the polynomial.

Definition 10: A polynomial in one variable is in **ascending order** if the degrees of its terms are increasing when the polynomial is read from left to right.

For example, the polynomials $6+x$, $3-y-4y^2$, $5a-3a^2+9a^4$, and $-4x-x^3+7x^4$ are in ascending order. We can always express a polynomial in one variable in ascending order by commuting terms if necessary. We've seen this done before when we've rewritten polynomials in descending order.

Definition 11: A **binomial** is a polynomial with two terms.

For example, the polynomials $x+1$, $-5y+3$, $2.01x^2 - 10.431$, $\frac{6}{5}a^4 + 7a$, and $-t^2 - \frac{9}{20}$ are binomials. Notice that the prefix of the word 'binomial' is 'bi', meaning two.

Definition 12: A **trinomial** is a polynomial with three terms.

For example, the polynomials $2x^2 + 3x + 9$, $-5y^2 + 4 - y$, $\frac{9}{5}x^4 - \frac{3}{5}x^3 - \frac{6}{5}$, $a^4 + 5.001a^5 + 0.162$, and $-t^2 - 9t + 2$ are trinomials. Notice that the prefix of the word 'trinomial' is 'tri', meaning three.

Definition 13: A polynomial of degree one is called **linear**.

For example, the polynomials x, $5t$, $4x - 3$, $7 + 14b$, $\frac{4}{11}t + 1$, and $-12 - \frac{5}{3}y$ are linear polynomials. Notice that the number of terms in a polynomial does not determine whether or not it is linear. For instance, x is a monomial, whereas $4x - 3$ is a binomial. Nevertheless, they are both linear. Examples of polynomials which are **not** linear are x^2, $5x^3 - 7$, and $-3x^4 + x^2 - 9x + 1$.

Definition 14: A polynomial of degree two is called **quadratic**.

For example, the polynomials x^2, $3y^2 - 5y$, $4t^2 + 8t - 1$, $4 + 12a - a^2$, $\frac{-2}{7}x^2 - \frac{6}{5}x + 1$, and $-\frac{15}{16} - 9.01y^2$ are quadratic polynomials. Notice that the number of terms in a polynomial does not determine whether or not it is quadratic. For instance, x^2 is a monomial, $3y^2 - 5y$ is a binomial, and $4t^2 + 8t - 1$ is a trinomial. However, they are all quadratic. Examples of polynomials which are **not** quadratic are x, $-4x^3 + 6x^2 + 12$, and $a^4 - 5a^2 - 6$.

Let's list a few definitions relating to polynomials in several variables.

Definition 15: A **polynomial in several variables** is a sum of monomials with move than one variable, If no two terms of a polynomial have the same variable part, then the polynomial is **simplified**.

Examples.

1) $7x^2 + 3xy - y^2$ is a polynomial in two variables, x and y. It is simplified because the terms $7x^2$, $3xy$, and $-y^2$ have different variable parts.

2) $-a^3b + 8b^2c^3 + 2a^3b + 10c$ is a polynomial in three variables, a, b, and c. It is **not** simplified since the terms $-a^3b$ and $2a^3b$ have the same variable part, a^3b.

3) $5x - \frac{2}{9}y - z - \frac{5}{2}xy + 3yz - 8xz + \frac{3}{10}wxyz$ is a polynomial in four variables, w, x, y, and z. It is simplified.

4) $2x^2y^2 - \frac{6x}{y}$ is not a polynomial in two variables since $\frac{6x}{y}$ is not a monomial.

Some of the definitions that we've learned for polynomials in one variable do not make sense for several variables. For instance, there is no such thing as 'descending order' for a polynomial in several variables. Observe, for example, that there is no unique way of writing the polynomial

$$x^2 + xy - y^2 = \underbrace{x^2 + x^1y^1 - y^2}_{\text{Each term has the degree 2.}}$$

in 'descending order' as we did before. The reason is that all three terms of the polynomial have the same degree, so there is no unique way of rearranging the terms so that the degrees decrease from left to right. Therefore, there is no such thing as 'descending order' for polynomials in several variables. This implies that there is no leading term and leading coefficient as well. However, there is a way of defining the degree of such a polynomial.

Definition 16: The **degree** of any simplified polynomial is equal to the largest of the degrees of its terms. If it so happens that some of the terms of a polynomial have the same largest degree, say n, then the degree of the polynomial is n.

Examples. Find the degree of each polynomial.

1) $4x^3 - 5xz^2 - z^4 = \underbrace{4x^3}_{\text{degree 3}} - \underbrace{5x^1z^2}_{\text{degree 3}} - \underbrace{z^4}_{\text{degree 4}}$ has the degree 4.

2) $9a - 4a^3b^2 + b^2 - 9a^4b^2 = \underbrace{9a^1}_{\text{degree 1}} - \underbrace{4a^3b^2}_{\text{degree 5}} + \underbrace{b^2}_{\text{degree 2}} - \underbrace{9a^4b^2}_{\text{degree 6}}$ has the degree 6.

3) $x^2 + xy - y^2 = \underbrace{x^2 + x^1y^1 - y^2}_{\text{Each term has the degree 2.}}$ has the degree 2.

4) $-12x^5 + 3x^4 + \dfrac{7}{8}x - 1$ has the degree 5.

Exercise 3.1

In Exercises 1-12, find the coefficient and the degree of each monomial.

1. 2 　　　　　2. -5 　　　　　3. $-6x$ 　　　　4. $8t$ 　　　　5. $9y^2$

6. $13a^5$ 　　　7. $7x^3y^5$ 　　　8. $-s^4t^3$ 　　　9. $\dfrac{15x^3}{14}$ 　　10. $\dfrac{4a^8}{11}$

11. $-\dfrac{2y^{10}}{7}$ 　　12. $\dfrac{-x^5}{4}$

In Exercises 13-24, determine whether or not the expression is a polynomial. For those expressions which are polynomials, find the coefficient of each term.

13. $8a^3 - a^2$ 　　　　　14. $3x^2 + 5x - 6$ 　　　　15. $\dfrac{3x}{13} + \dfrac{x^2}{12} - \dfrac{1}{2}$ 　　　　16. $\dfrac{y^2}{9} - \dfrac{7y}{3} + 8$

17. $\dfrac{9}{x^4} + 12 - 3x$ 　　18. $-5t^4 + \dfrac{1}{t^2}$ 　　　19. $\dfrac{3xy}{4} - \dfrac{4x^8}{5y}$ 　　　20. $\dfrac{2x + 9}{8}$

21. $\dfrac{12x^2 - 5}{3}$ 　　22. $\dfrac{5}{2ab^4} + \dfrac{5ab^4}{2}$ 　　23. $\dfrac{x^2 + 12y^2 - 24}{12}$ 　　24. $\dfrac{-5a + b + 10c}{5}$

In Exercises 25-36, write the polynomial in descending order. Find the leading term, the leading coefficient, and the degree of each.

25. $7 + 2x$ 　　　　　26. $3 + 5x$ 　　　　　27. $8 - 3x$ 　　　　　28. $12 - x$

29. $2x^2 + 12 - 5x$ 　　30. $-a + 9a^2 - 16$ 　　31. $t^2 - 6t^3 + \dfrac{2}{9}$ 　　32. $8x^2 - \dfrac{1}{3}x^6 + x$

33. $-\dfrac{14}{13} + 9t - 2t^2$ 　　34. $6 - \dfrac{8}{3}x - x^2$ 　　35. $\dfrac{-x^2}{3} - \dfrac{1}{4}x^5 + x^3$ 　　36. $\dfrac{8x^4}{13} + 3x - \dfrac{1}{10}x^3$

In Exercises 37-56, find the degree of each polynomial and decide whether the polynomial is linear, quadratic, or neither.

37. $-8x$

38. $5t$

39. $3a$

40. $-b$

41. $5x^2$

42. $6t^2$

43. $2x - 5$

44. $-11a + 3$

45. $6 - 11x$

46. $-2 - 8x$

47. $13x + 2$

48. $-x + 5$

49. $y^2 + 5y - 1$

50. $-2a^2 + a + 8$

51. $8 + 8x^2$

52. $4x^2 + 8x + 9x^3$

53. $2t + 5t^3$

54. $b - 7b^3 + 4b^2$

55. $\dfrac{3a^4 + 12a^2 - 2a}{3}$

56. $\dfrac{2x^2 - 8x + 1}{2}$

In Exercises 57-66, find the degree of each polynomial.

57. $4y + 7x + 6y^2$

58. $x + 5y - 4x^2$

59. $6y^4 - x^3 - 8x$

60. $a^2 + b^5 - 3a^5$

61. $x^2 + 2x^2y - y^3$

62. $5a^3b + ab^3 + 12b$

63. $12x^7 - 5xy^3 + 3x^2y^3$

64. $2s^4 + 8s^3t^3 + 9t^4$

Section 3.2   Addition and Subtraction of Polynomials

Now that we know what a polynomial is, let's start doing some algebraic manipulations with them. In this section, we will do some addition and subtraction of polynomials. We'll begin with addition and subtraction of monomials. Afterwards, we'll see how some of our properties from Chapter 1 allow us to add and subtract polynomials.

Suppose we want to add two monomials, say $5x$ and $4x$, into a single monomial. The first question to answer is "When can we add two monomials?". Well, the answer to this question depends on the variable parts of our monomials. If the two monomials have the same variable parts, they can be combined into a single monomial.

Definition: Two or more monomials are called **like terms** if they have the same variable parts.

In our example, $5x$ and $4x$ are like terms. Observe that $5x + 4x = (5 + 4)x = 9x$ which is just an application of the Distributive Property (read from right to left). Let's look at some examples.

Examples. Combine into a single monomial (if possible).

1) $\underbrace{8a + 2a}_{\text{like terms}} = (8 + 2)a = 10a$

2) $\underbrace{-9xy + 5xy}_{\text{like terms}} = (-9 + 5)xy = -4xy$

3) $\underbrace{-6x^5y^2 - 19x^5y^2}_{\text{like terms}} = (-6 - 19)x^5y^2 = -25x^5y^2$

4) $\underbrace{-15st^2 + \left(-19st^2\right) = -15st^2 - 19st^2}_{\text{Remember that } a+(-b)=a-b.} = (-15 - 19)\, st^2 = -34st^2$

5) $8a^2 - 12a^2 + 17a^2 = (8 - 12 + 17)a^2 = 13a^2$

6) $-12x^3y - 2x^3y + 6x^3y + 8x^3y = (-12 - 2 + 6 + 8)x^3y = 0x^3y = 0$

7) $2ab^2 - 5a^2b^4$ don't combine into a single monomial (the terms aren't like terms).

Now, suppose we want to add the binomials $(8x + 1) + (-2x + 3)$. Well, by the Associative Property for addition, we can disregard the parentheses. Moreover, by the Commutative Property, we can collect like terms. By doing this, we'd obtain

$$8x + 1 + (-2x) + 3 = 8x + (-2x) + 1 + 3 = 6x + 4.$$

Examples. Combine.

1) $\underbrace{(2x - 3) + (7x + 1) = 2x - 3 + 7x + 1}_{\text{by the Associative Property}} = 9x - 2$

2) $\underbrace{(-4x^2 + 5x - 7) + (6x^2 - 13x + 18) = -4x^2 + 5x - 7 + 6x^2 - 13x + 18}_{\text{by the Associative Property}} = 2x^2 - 8x + 11$

3) $(5a^2 + 12b^2 - 2) + (-a^2 + 19ab + 6b^2) = 5a^2 + 12b^2 - 2 + (-a^2) + 19ab + 6b^2$

$$= 4a^2 + 18b^2 - 2 + 19ab$$

4) $(2y^3 - 7y^2 - 3) + (-9y^2 + 8y) + (8y^3 + 5y^2 - 7y) = 2y^3 - 7y^2 - 3 + (-9y^2) + 8y + 8y^3 + 5y^2 - 7y$

$$= 10y^3 - 11y^2 + y - 3$$

5) $\left(\dfrac{2}{3}x^2 - 6x + \dfrac{3}{8}\right) + \left(\dfrac{1}{9}x^2 + 13x + \dfrac{7}{12}\right) = \dfrac{2}{3}x^2 - 6x + \dfrac{3}{8} + \dfrac{1}{9}x^2 + 13x + \dfrac{7}{12}$

$$= \left(\dfrac{2}{3} + \dfrac{1}{9}\right)x^2 + (-6 + 13)x + \left(\dfrac{3}{8} + \dfrac{7}{12}\right)$$

$$= \left(\dfrac{6}{9} + \dfrac{1}{9}\right)x^2 + 7x + \left(\dfrac{9}{24} + \dfrac{14}{24}\right)$$

$$= \dfrac{7}{9}x^2 + 7x + \dfrac{23}{24}$$

Notice that the above problems were done while written horizontally. You can also add polynomials by writing the problem vertically. The way that you'd do this is by writing your polynomials one above the other so that the 'columns' contain like terms. For example, let's add $7x^2 + 6x - 8$ and $3x^2 + x - 7$ vertically. Well, we need to rewrite the problem and add the columns up as follows:

$$\begin{array}{r} 7x^2 + 6x - 8 \\ +\quad\underline{3x^2 +\ x - 7} \\ 10x^2 + 7x - 15 \end{array}$$

64

By the Commutative Property for addition, it doesn't matter which polynomial goes on top:

$$\begin{array}{r} 3x^2 + \ x - 7 \\ + \ \underline{7x^2 + 6x - 8} \\ 10x^2 + 7x - 15 \end{array}$$

Let's see some more examples like this.

Examples. Add.

1) $8x - 2$ and $3x + 7$

$$\begin{array}{r} 8x - 2 \\ + \ \underline{3x + 7} \\ 11x + 5 \end{array}$$

2) $-4x^2 + 3xy + y^2$ and $7x^2 - 10xy - 8y^2$

$$\begin{array}{r} -4x^2 + \ 3xy + \ y^2 \\ + \ \underline{7x^2 - 10xy - 8y^2} \\ 3x^2 - \ 7xy - 7y^2 \end{array}$$

3) $8a^2 - 3$ and $4a^2 + 15a - 7$

$$\begin{array}{r} 8a^2 \qquad - 3 \\ + \ \underline{4a^2 + 15a - 7} \\ 12a^2 + 15a - 10 \end{array}$$

4) $5xy^2 + 10x^2 + 14$ and $6y^2 - 12x^2 + 2y - 14$

$$\begin{array}{r} 5xy^2 + 10x^2 + 14 \\ + \ \underline{6y^2 \qquad - 12x^2 - 14 + 2y} \\ 6y^2 + 5xy^2 - 2x^2 \qquad + 2y \end{array}$$

5) $4a + 2b$, $-a + 7b$, and $-4b - 10a$

$$\begin{array}{r} 4a + 2b \\ -a + 7b \\ + \ \underline{-10a - 4b} \\ -7a + 5b \end{array}$$

You can add polynomials either by writing the problem either horizontally or vertically. Pick the method that you are comfortable with. Both techniques will be used, so make sure you get enough practice with each of them.

Definition: The **additive inverse** of a polynomial, P, is $-P$.

Observe that the sum of a polynomial and its additive inverse is 0 since $P + (-P) = 0$.

For example, the additive inverse of $8x - 5$ is $-(8x - 5) = -8x + 5$ and the additive inverse of $-6x^2 + 8x - 1$ is $-(-6x^2 + 8x - 1) = 6x^2 - 8x + 1$.

65

Try These (Set 1): Combine using any technique.

1) $(3y + 11) + (-2y + 2)$

2) $(9x^2 - x + 8) + (2x^2 + 7x + 13)$

3) $(7x^2 + 6xy - 2y^2) + (-x^2 - 10xy + 12y^2)$

4) $(4a + ab - 2) + (-6ab + a^2 - 8a)$

5) $(-13x^2 - 10) + (7x - 2)$

6) $\left(\dfrac{1}{3}t^2 + \dfrac{2}{5}t - 1\right) + \left(-\dfrac{4}{3}t^2 - \dfrac{4}{25}t - \dfrac{7}{6}\right)$

Try These (Set 2): Find the additive inverse of each polynomial.

1) $5x$ 2) $3x^2 - 2x + 1$ 3) $-8a^2 + 7ab^2$ 4) $x^2 - 3y$ 5) $\dfrac{-x}{6} + \dfrac{8x^2}{11}$

Let's look at the example $(2x - 5) - (7x - 6)$. Subtraction of polynomials works differently than addition because there is no Associative Property for subtraction. Consequently, we can't just throw away the parentheses. Instead, we need to distribute the negative sign into the second pair of parentheses. This will change the signs of all of the terms in the second pair of parentheses. Once this is done, we may toss out all parentheses and combine like terms. In other words, we have:

$$(2x - 5) - (7x - 6) = \underbrace{2x - 5 - 7x + 6}_{7x \text{ became } -7x \text{ and } -6 \text{ became } 6.} = -5x + 1$$

By the way, this can be done because $(2x - 5) - (7x - 6)$ is really the same as $(2x - 5) + (-1)(7x - 6)$ and the -1 may be distributed into the second pair of parenthesis.

Examples. Combine.

1) $\underbrace{(5y + 3) - (2y + 7) = 5y + 3 - 2y - 7}_{\text{Distribute the } - \text{ sign and change the signs of } 2y \text{ and } 7.} = 3y - 4$

2) $\underbrace{(-6x^2 + 4x - 9) - (3x^2 - 7x + 2) = -6x^2 + 4x - 9 - 3x^2 + 7x - 2}_{\text{Distribute the } - \text{ sign and change the signs of } 3x^2, -7x, \text{ and } 2.} = -9x^2 + 11x - 11$

3) $\underbrace{(10a^2 - ab + 12b^2) - (-8a^2 + 2ab - b^2) = 10a^2 - ab + 12b^2 + 8a^2 - 2ab + b^2}_{\text{Distribute the } - \text{ sign and change the signs of } -8a^2, 2ab, \text{ and } -b^2.} = 18a^2 - 3ab + 13b^2$

4) $\underbrace{(14s + 2st^2 - 10t^3) - (-9s^2 - 3s + t^3 + 7) = 14s + 2st^2 - 10t^3 + 9s^2 + 3s - t^3 - 7}_{\text{Distribute the } - \text{ sign and change the signs of } -9s^2, -3s, t^3, \text{ and } 7.}$

$$= 17s + 2st^2 - 11t^3 + 9s^2 - 7$$

As with addition, there is a way of subtracting two polynomials by aligning them up vertically in such a way that the columns consist of like terms. The major difference between addition and subtraction is that when subtracting, all of the terms in the second polynomial **change signs** and the subtraction problem **turns into** an addition problem. This is due to the fact that the -1 multiplies the second polynomial, similar to the above 'horizontal technique'. Before doing some subtraction problems 'vertically', let's review how to subtract one number from another. We know how to do subtraction when the problem is given to us mathematically, but sometimes it is given to us verbally. For example, suppose we want to subtract 3 from 12. We would write the subtraction problem as $12 - 3$ (not $3 - 12$). Notice that the second number, 12, goes first and the 3 goes second. If we wanted to write this 'vertically', we would write:

$$\begin{array}{r} 12 \\ -3 \\ \hline \end{array}$$

The same thing happens when subtracting polynomials. For example, let's subtract $5x - 7$ from $12x - 3$. If we were to do this problem 'horizontally', then the subtraction problem would be written as $(12x - 3) - (5x - 7)$. To do this 'vertically', we write:

$$
\begin{array}{r}
12x - 3 \\
- \quad 5x - 7 \\
\hline
\end{array}
\qquad \text{becomes} \qquad
\begin{array}{r}
12x - 3 \\
+ \quad -5x + 7 \\
\hline
7x + 4
\end{array}
$$

Notice that the subtraction problem turned into an addition problem and the signs of the terms of $5x - 7$ changed ($5x$ became $-5x$ and -7 became 7). Let's see some examples using this method.

Examples.

1) Subtract $6a + 1$ from $-a + 7$.

$$
\begin{array}{r}
-a + 7 \\
- \quad 6a + 1 \\
\hline
\end{array}
\qquad \text{becomes} \qquad
\begin{array}{r}
-a + 7 \\
+ \quad -6a - 1 \\
\hline
-7a + 6
\end{array}
$$

2) Subtract $-5x^2 - 9x$ from $3x^2 + x$.

$$
\begin{array}{r}
3x^2 + x \\
- \quad -5x^2 - 9x \\
\hline
\end{array}
\qquad \text{becomes} \qquad
\begin{array}{r}
3x^2 + x \\
+ \quad 5x^2 + 9x \\
\hline
8x^2 + 10x
\end{array}
$$

3) Subtract $4y^2 - 11y + 3$ from $7y^2 - 18$.

$$
\begin{array}{r}
7y^2 \quad - 18 \\
- \quad 4y^2 - 11y + 3 \\
\hline
\end{array}
\qquad \text{becomes} \qquad
\begin{array}{r}
7y^2 \quad - 18 \\
+ \quad -4y^2 + 11y - 3 \\
\hline
3y^2 + 11y - 21
\end{array}
$$

4) Subtract $-9t^2 + 15t$ from $15t^2 + 21$.

$$
\begin{array}{r}
15t^2 \quad + 21 \\
- \quad -9t^2 + 15t \\
\hline
\end{array}
\qquad \text{becomes} \qquad
\begin{array}{r}
15t^2 \quad + 21 \\
+ \quad 9t^2 - 15t \\
\hline
24t^2 - 15t + 21
\end{array}
$$

5) Subtract $-5x^2 - 3y^2$ from $8y^2 - 9xy$.

$$
\begin{array}{r}
8y^2 - 9xy \\
- \quad -3y^2 \quad - 5x^2 \\
\hline
\end{array}
\qquad \text{becomes} \qquad
\begin{array}{r}
8y^2 - 9xy \\
+ \quad 3y^2 \quad + 5x^2 \\
\hline
11y^2 - 9xy + 5x^2
\end{array}
$$

We will see that both methods come in handy. You should get to know how to do each of them.

Try These (Set 3): Subtract.

1) $(9x + 2y) - (-x + 11y)$

2) $\left(-8a^2 + 3ab - b^2\right) - \left(-3a^2 - 6ab + 11b^2\right)$.

3) $\left(s^2 - 5t^2\right) - \left(3s^2 + 8st - 2t^2\right)$

4) Subtract $4x^2 + 12xy - 9$ from $3x^2 - 8xy - 6$.

5) Subtract $5a^2 - a + 6$ from $-9a^2 + 16$.

6) Subtract $m - 3mn$ from $n - 3nm$.

Exercises 3.2

In Exercises 1-48, combine.

1. $9x + 7x$ 2. $2y + 5y$ 3. $-12y^2 + 7y^2$ 4. $-a^2 + 8a^2$

5. $-6x - 6x$ 6. $-3p - 13p$ 7. $6ab^3 + (-11ab^3)$ 8. $(-14x^2y) + 5x^2y$

9. $(-18ab) - (-4ab)$ 10. $(-2st) - (-4st)$ 11. $-6a^2b^2 - a^2b^2 + 9a^2b^2$ 12. $4x^2 + 6x^2 - 13x^2$

13. $7q + 14q - 8q + q$ 14. $3n - 7n + n + 9n$

15. $(11a + 3) + (-8a + 4)$ 16. $(6b - 1) + (b + 15)$

17. $\left(a^2 - 4a - 3\right) + \left(8a^2 - 2a + 7\right)$ 18. $\left(x^2 + 9x + 3\right) + \left(4x^2 - 7x - 2\right)$

19. $\left(-x^2 - 2xy - 8y^2\right) + \left(-x^2 + 2xy + 15y^2\right)$ 20. $\left(7m^2 - m + 6\right) + \left(-3m^2 + m - 13\right)$

21. $(p + 3q - 5) + (7 + 9p + 4pq)$ 22. $(4a - 5b - 2) + (12b - 6ab + 4)$

23. $\left(9x^2 - z^2\right) + \left(4z^2 - 12xz + 9x^2\right)$ 24. $\left(a^2 - b^2\right) + \left(a^2 + 11ab + b^2\right)$

25. $(8x + 1) - (3x + 7)$ 26. $(6a + b) - (9a + 8b)$

27. $(-3a + 8b) - (4a - b)$ 28. $(-2p + 2q) - (7p - q)$

29. $\left(-x^2 + 5x + 8\right) - \left(3x^2 - 2x - 6\right)$ 30. $\left(14a^2 - a - 8\right) - \left(3a^2 + 5a - 9\right)$

31. $\left(8a^2 - 4ab + b^2\right) - \left(-2a^2 + 10b^2\right)$ 32. $\left(-s^2 - 2st^2 + t^2\right) - \left(s^2 - 7t^2\right)$

33. $(12p + pq - q) - \left(-3p + 2pq - 9q^2\right)$ 34. $\left(8x^2 - 13xy - 15x\right) - \left(2xy - x - 6xy^2\right)$

35. $\left(-6x^2 + 10\right) - \left(18 - 8x^2 + 3y^2\right)$ 36. $\left(p^2 - 5\right) - \left(-q^2 + 13p^2 + 14\right)$

37. $(6x + 2y) + (9x - 3y) + (-7x + y)$ 38. $(3a - 14) + (14a + 9) + (a - 7)$

39. $\left(5x^2 - 9x\right) + \left(-8x^2 + 2\right) + (x + 15)$ 40. $\left(2s^2 - 3\right) + \left(-t^2 + 12s^2\right) + \left(6s^2 + 14\right)$

41. $(7m + 4) + (12m - 3) - (-7m + 8)$ 42. $(-x + 4) + (3x - 17) - (3x + 9)$

43. $\left(x^2 + 9\right) + \left(x^2 - 5x\right) - (-7x + 14)$ 44. $\left(4a^2 - a\right) + \left(-a^2 + 9\right) - (2a + 7)$

45. $\left(2y^2 - 5\right) - \left(4y^2 + 2y - 2\right) + (y + 8)$ 46. $\left(3b^2 + 5b\right) - \left(9b^2 - 12b + 10\right) + (2b - 5)$

47. $\left(6t^2 + 12\right) - \left(-t^2 - 11t\right) - (7t - 14)$ 48. $\left(2x^2 - 8y\right) - (3xy - 6y) - \left(2x^2 + 15xy\right)$

In Exercises 49-56, find the additive inverse of the given polynomial.

49. $8x$ 50. $-7a^2$ 51. $6n - 7$ 52. $-9x + 10$

53. $-a^2 - 6a + 4$ 54. $7y^2 + y - 1$ 55. $-x^2 - 9xy + 4y^2$ 56. $8t^2 + 3st - s^2$

Section 3.3   Multiplication of Polynomials

In this section, we will learn how to multiply polynomials together. We will begin by studying multiplication of a monomial by a polynomial. Afterwards, we will look at the product of two binomials, followed by the product of any two polynomials.

1. <u>Monomial × Monomial</u>

We have already learned how to multiply two monomials (see Chapter 2). Let's look at few examples for review.

Examples. Multiply.

1) $\left(6x^3y\right)\left(3x^3y^8\right) = 18x^{3+3}y^{1+8} = 18x^6y^9$

2) $\left(-7a^2b^5\right)\left(7ab^4\right) = -49a^{2+1}b^{5+4} = -49a^3b^9$

3) $\left(-\dfrac{2}{\overset{9}{\cancel{9}}_{1}}x^7y^2z\right)\left(-\dfrac{\overset{2}{\cancel{18}}}{5}xy^4z^2\right) = \dfrac{4}{5}x^{7+1}y^{2+4}z^{1+2} = \dfrac{4}{5}x^8y^6z^3$

4) $\left(5x^2yz^3\right)\left(-9x^4y\right) = -45x^{2+4}y^{1+1}z^3 = -45x^6y^2z^3$

Try These (Set 4): Multiply.

1) $\left(-a^3\right)\left(-10a^3\right)$ 2) $\left(-4x^2y^9\right)\left(-3x^3y\right)$ 3) $\left(\dfrac{2}{7}x^4\right)\left(\dfrac{21}{8}x^2y^8\right)$ 4) $\left(\dfrac{4}{5}m^2n^2\right)\left(-15m^5n^4\right)$

2. <u>Monomial × Polynomial</u>

To multiply a monomial by a polynomial, we'll use the Distributive Property.

Examples. Multiply.

1) $4a^2\left(8a-2\right) = 4a^2\left(8a\right) + 4a^2\left(-2\right) = 32a^3 - 8a^2$

2) $5\left(5x^2 - 4x + 2\right) = 5\left(5x^2\right) + 5\left(-4x\right) + 5(2) = 25x^2 - 20x + 10$

3) $2y\left(y^2 + 7y - 2\right) = 2y\left(y^2\right) + 2y(7y) + 2y(-2) = 2y^3 + 14y^2 - 4y$

4) $-3x^2\left(9x^2 - 6x - 17\right) = -3x^2\left(9x^2\right) - 3x^2\left(-6x\right) - 3x^2\left(-17\right) = -27x^4 + 18x^3 + 51x^2$

5) $-9p^5q^3\left(-5p^2 + 12pq^4\right) = -9p^5q^3\left(-5p^2\right) - 9p^5q^3\left(12pq^4\right) = 45p^7q^3 - 108p^6q^7$

6) $-7a^3b^4\left(-3a^2b^2 - 4ab^2 + 7a^2b\right) = -7a^3b^4\left(-3a^2b^2\right) - 7a^3b^4\left(-4ab^2\right) - 7a^3b^4\left(7a^2b\right)$
$$= 21a^5b^6 + 28a^4b^6 - 49a^5b^5$$

In the next set of examples, the Distributive Property is used to simplify each expression.

Examples. Simplify.

1) $2(6x+1) - 9 = 12x + 2 - 9 = 12x - 7$

2) $3a^2(-a+4) + 18a^3 = -3a^3 + 12a^2 + 18a^3 = 15a^3 + 12a^2$

3) $4(x-4) + 7(3x-8) = 4x - 16 + 21x - 56 = 25x - 72$

4) $a(11+2a) - 4a(6-7a) = 11a + 2a^2 - 24a + 28a^2 = -13a + 30a^2$

5) $-3x(8x+3y) + 12y(2x-3y) = \underbrace{-24x^2 - 9xy + 24yx - 36y^2 = -24x^2 + 15xy - 36y^2}$

Note that $xy=yx$ by the Commutative Property.

6) $8k^2(9k^2+2k+5) - 3k(-6k+12) + 7k^4 - 3k = 72k^4 + 16k^3 + 40k^2 + 18k^2 - 36k + 7k^4 - 3k$
$$= 79k^4 + 16k^3 + 58k^2 - 39k$$

Try These (Set 5): Multiply.

1) $3x(x-8)$

2) $-5y^2(3y^2 - y + 6)$

3) $6a(3a^2 - 2ab - b^2)$

4) $-7p^2q^7(-2pq^2 + 3p^2q^2 + 8pq)$

Try These (Set 6): Simplify.

1) $3x(2x-1) + 7x(x+3)$

2) $-4a(a^2+2a+4) + 3a(2a^2-3a-2)$

3) $5y^2(4y+2x-12) - 5x^2(-2y+x-11)$

4) $-x(2x+3) - 3x(7x+2) + x(x-4)$

5) $3a(6a-3b) + 5b(-7a+b) - ab(b-2)$

6) $8(-2+8x+5y) - 5(-1+3y-x) - 12(x+3)$

3. Binomial × Binomial

To multiply two binomials, say $(A+B)(C+D)$, we distribute both A and B into the second pair of parentheses. We obtain

$$(A+B)(C+D) = A(C+D) + B(C+D) = \underbrace{AC}_{\text{First terms}} + \underbrace{AD}_{\text{Outer terms}} + \underbrace{BC}_{\text{Inner terms}} + \underbrace{BD}_{\text{Last terms}}.$$

This method of multiplying two binomials is referred to as the **FOIL method.** It gets this name by taking the first initial of the name of each of the above products and putting them next to each other.

Examples. Multiply.

1) $(x+1)(x+2) = \underbrace{x(x)}_{\text{First}} + \underbrace{x(2)}_{\text{Outer}} + \underbrace{1(x)}_{\text{Inner}} + \underbrace{1(2)}_{\text{Last}} = x^2 + \underbrace{2x + x}_{\text{Combine.}} + 2 = x^2 + 3x + 2$

2) $(x-2)(x+9) = \underbrace{x(x)}_{\text{First}} + \underbrace{x(9)}_{\text{Outer}} + \underbrace{(-2)(x)}_{\text{Inner}} + \underbrace{(-2)(9)}_{\text{Last}} = x^2 + \underbrace{9x - 2x}_{\text{Combine.}} - 18 = x^2 + 7x - 18$

3) $(3y - 5)(2y - 1) = 3y(2y) + 3y(-1) + (-5)(2y) + (-5)(-1) = 6y^2 - 3y - 10y + 5 = 6y^2 - 13y + 5$

4) $(4 + 7x)(3 - x^2) = 4(3) + 4(-x^2) + 7x(3) + 7x(-x^2) = \underbrace{12 - 4x^2 + 21x - 7x^3}_{\text{Nothing combines.}}$

5) $(3a - 5b)(-a - 2b) = 3a(-a) + 3a(-2b) + (-5b)(-a) + (-5b)(-2b)$
$$= -3a^2 - 6ab + 5ba + 10b^2$$
$$= -3a^2 - ab + 10b^2$$

6) $(-4x + 7xy)(4y - 8xy) = -4x(4y) + (-4x)(-8xy) + 7xy(4y) + 7xy(-8xy)$
$$= -16xy + 32x^2y + 28xy^2 - 56x^2y^2$$

7) $(7x + 9)(7x - 9) = 7x(7x) + 7x(-9) + 9(7x) + 9(-9) = 49x^2 - 63x + 63x - 81 = 49x^2 - 81$

8) $(6a + 5)^2 = (6a + 5)(6a + 5) = 6a(6a) + 6a(5) + 5(6a) + 5(5) = 36a^2 + 30a + 30a + 25 = 36a^2 + 60a + 25$

Next I will list some special products which often appear. You can check these by using the FOIL method.

Special Products

I. The Difference of Two Squares: $(A + B)(A - B) = A^2 - B^2$

II. The Square of a Sum: $(A + B)^2 = (A + B)(A + B) = A^2 + 2AB + B^2$

III. The Square of a Difference: $(A - B)^2 = (A - B)(A - B) = A^2 - 2AB + B^2$

Some common mistakes which frequently occur involve the last two products. Let me tell you what they are:

   BEWARE: $(A + B)^2 \neq A^2 + B^2$, $(A - B)^2 \neq A^2 + B^2$, and $(A - B)^2 \neq A^2 - B^2$.

To avoid making these mistakes, I suggest that you remember how the products are written rather than memorizing the identities. After you get enough practice, you should then memorize them.

Examples. Multiply.

1) $\underbrace{(x + 3)(x - 3) = (x)^2 - (3)^2}_{\text{By Special Product I, letting } A = x \text{ and } B = 3.} = x^2 - 9$

Note that if we did this without the formula, we'd get the same answer:

$$(x + 3)(x - 3) = x^2 \underbrace{- 3x + 3x}_{0} - 9$$
$$= x^2 + 0 - 9$$
$$= x^2 - 9$$

71

2) $\underbrace{(y-6)(y+6) = (y)^2 - (6)^2}$ $= y^2 - 36$

By Special Product I, letting $A=y$ and $B=6$.

3) $\underbrace{(2y+9)(2y-9) = (2y)^2 - (9)^2}$ $= 4y^2 - 81$

By Special Product I, letting $A=2y$ and $B=9$.

4) $\underbrace{(3a-10)(3a+10) = (3a)^2 - (10)^2}$ $= 9a^2 - 100$

By Special Product I, letting $A=3a$ and $B=10$.

5) $(x+4)^2 = (x+4)(x+4) = x^2 + 4x + 4x + 16 = x^2 + 8x + 16$

6) $(b-7)^2 = (b-7)(b-7) = b^2 - 7b - 7b + 49 = b^2 - 14b + 49$

7) $(2t+6)^2 = (2t+6)(2t+6) = 4t^2 + 12t + 12t + 36 = 4t^2 + 24t + 36$

8) $(5-11x)^2 = (5-11x)(5-11x) = 25 - 55x - 55x + 121x^2 = 25 - 110x + 121x^2$

9) $\underbrace{(3x+1)^2 = (3x)^2 + 2(3x)(1) + (1)^2}$ $= 9x^2 + 6x + 1$

By Special Product II, letting $A=3x$ and $B=1$.

10) $\underbrace{(3a-10b)^2 = (3a)^2 - 2(3a)(10b) + (10b)^2}$ $= 9a^2 - 60ab + 100b^2$

By Special Product III, letting $A=3a$ and $B=10b$.

Try These (Set 7): Multiply.

1) $(x+2)(x-8)$ 2) $(4a-3)(4a-5)$ 3) $(y^2 + 2y)(3y - 8)$

4) $(11-2x)(3-x)$ 5) $(2y+7)(2y-7)$ 6) $(2a+12)^2$

4. Polynomial × Polynomial

It's time for the grand finale: how do we multiply **any** two polynomials? Well, it turns out that the Distributive Property is the thing to use, just as for the monomial × polynomial and binomial × binomial cases. Let's see how this works.

Examples. Multiply.

1) $(x+3)(x^2 + 2x - 3) = \underbrace{x\left(x^2\right) + x(2x) + x(-3) + 3\left(x^2\right) + 3(2x) + 3(-3)}$

Distribute both the x and the 3 into the 2nd parenthesis.

$= x^3 + 2x^2 - 3x + 3x^2 + 6x - 9 = x^3 + 5x^2 + 3x - 9$

2) $(4a^2 - 5)(3a^2 - 2a + 6) = 4a^2\left(3a^2\right) + 4a^2(-2a) + 4a^2(6) + (-5)\left(3a^2\right) + (-5)(-2a) + (-5)(6)$

$= 12a^4 - 8a^3 + 24a^2 - 15a^2 + 10a - 30$

$= 12a^4 - 8a^3 + 9a^2 + 10a - 30$

3) $(x + 2y - 1)(x - 3y - 1)$

$= \underbrace{x(x) + x(-3y) + x(-1) + 2y(x) + 2y(-3y) + 2y(-1) + (-1)(x) + (-1)(-3y) + (-1)(-1)}$

Distribute the x, $2y$, and -1 into the 2nd parenthesis.

$= x^2 - 3xy - x + 2yx - 6y^2 - 2y - x + 3y + 1$

$= x^2 - xy - 2x - 6y^2 + y + 1$

72

4) $(4y - 1)^3 = \underbrace{(4y - 1)(4y - 1)}(4y - 1) = (16y^2 - 8y + 1)(4y - 1)$

FOIL the first pair, $(4y-1)(4y-1)$.

$$= 16y^2(4y) + 16y^2(-1) + (-8y)(4y) + (-8y)(-1) + 1(4y) + 1(-1)$$
$$= 64y^3 - 16y^2 - 32y^2 + 8y + 4y - 1$$
$$= 64y^3 - 48y^2 + 12y - 1$$

5) $\underbrace{(6t + 1)(2t - 2)(t + 3) = (12t^2 - 10t - 2)(t + 3)} = 12t^3 + 36t^2 - 10t^2 - 30t - 2t - 6$

FOIL $(6t+1)(2t-2)$ first.

$$= 12t^3 + 26t^2 - 32t - 6$$

6) $(3x + 1)^2 (3x - 1) = (3x + 1) \underbrace{(3x + 1)(3x - 1)}_{\text{Use Special Product I.}} = \underbrace{(3x + 1)(9x^2 - 1) = 27x^3 - 3x + 9x^2 - 1}_{\text{Use the FOIL method.}}$

The previous examples could've been done by setting the problem up **vertically**. Let's see how this method works.

7) $(a + 2)(a^2 + 4a - 1) =$

$$
\begin{array}{r}
a^2 + 4a - 1 \\
a + 2 \\
\hline
2a^2 + 8a - 2 \\
a^3 + 4a^2 - a \\
\hline
a^3 + 6a^2 + 7a - 2
\end{array}
$$

$\longleftarrow$ 2 times $a^2 + 4a - 1$

$\longleftarrow$ a times $a^2 + 4a - 1$

8) $(3y - 7)(-4y^3 - 5y^2 + 3) =$

$$
\begin{array}{r}
-4y^3 - 5y^2 + 3 \\
3y \quad - 7 \\
\hline
28y^3 + 35y^2 \quad - 21 \\
-12y^4 - 15y^3 \quad + 9y \\
\hline
-12y^4 + 13y^3 + 35y^2 + 9y - 21
\end{array}
$$

$\longleftarrow$ -7 times $-4y^3 - 5y^2 + 3$

$\longleftarrow$ $3y$ times $-4y^3 - 5y^2 + 3$

9) $(x + 2y - 3)(2x - 3y + 5) =$

$$
\begin{array}{r}
x + 2y - 3 \\
2x - 3y + 5 \\
\hline
5x + 10y - 15 \\
-3xy - 6y^2 \quad + 9y \\
2x^2 + 4xy \quad - 6x \\
\hline
2x^2 + xy - 6y^2 - x + 19y - 15
\end{array}
$$

$\longleftarrow$ 5   times $x + 2y - 3$

$\longleftarrow$ $-3y$ times $x + 2y - 3$

$\longleftarrow$ $2x$ times $x + 2y - 3$

You could choose whichever method you'd like. Both of them will be used from this point on. The next thing that I'd like to to mention two special products which will arise later on. They are numbered as a continuation of the previous set of special products.

73

Let's verify Special Product IV using the vertical method:

$$
\begin{array}{r}
A^2 - AB + B^2 \\
A + B \\
\hline
A^2B - AB^2 + B^3 \\
A^3 - A^2B + AB^2 \\
\hline
A^3 \qquad\qquad\qquad + B^3
\end{array}
$$

I'll leave it for you to verify Special Product V.

Try These (Set 8): Multiply.

1) $(x+2)\left(x^2 + 4x - 1\right)$

2) $(2y-1)\left(y^2 - 5y + 3\right)$

3) $(5a+b)\left(2a^2 - ab - 3b^2\right)$

4) $(x+5)^2 (x-5)$

5) $(2t-3)^3$

6) $\left(m^2 - 2m - 1\right)^2$

Exercise 3.3

In Exercises 1-86, multiply and simplify.

1. $\left(4x^2\right)\left(5x^3\right)$ 2. $\left(-2x^3\right)\left(9x^3\right)$ 3. $\left(-9a^5\right)\left(-7a^6\right)$ 4. $\left(3t^4\right)(-12t)$

5. $\left(-\dfrac{5}{6}y^5\right)\left(\dfrac{12}{25}y^7\right)$ 6. $\left(\dfrac{4}{7}t^4\right)\left(-\dfrac{14}{9}t^3\right)$ 7. $(-8y^2)\left(\dfrac{-9}{16}y^8\right)$ 8. $\left(\dfrac{2}{13}p^3\right)\left(26p^7\right)$

9. $\left(3a^{13}b^{16}\right)\left(-ab^{12}\right)$ 10. $\left(-5s^{12}t^{10}\right)\left(-3s^2t^8\right)$ 11. $\left(\dfrac{9x^5y^{12}}{8}\right)\left(\dfrac{-24xy^{11}}{5}\right)$ 12. $\left(\dfrac{-6m^8n^2}{7}\right)\left(\dfrac{-9mn^{13}}{12}\right)$

13. $5a(4a+7)$ 14. $7y(6y+8)$ 15. $9x^4(8x^3 - 2x)$ 16. $4t^5(5t^4 - 3t^3)$

17. $-2p^3(-12p + 8p^3)$ 18. $-3x^5(8x^2 - 10x^4)$ 19. $6x^3y^4(2x^2y^5 - 5xy^2)$ 20. $7x^2y^8(-3xy^3 + 4x^5y^2)$

21. $5(2a^2 + 7a - 1)$ 22. $4(t^2 - 7t + 10)$ 23. $8x^2(5x^3 - 4x^2 - 15)$ 24. $2n^3(-7n^3 - n^4 + 1)$

25. $-2x^5y^3(5x^4 - 8x^2y^2 + y^2)$ 26. $6x^2y^8(2x^3 - 7xy + 3y^2)$ 27. $9a^3b^2(-a^2b^4 + 3a^5b^2 - 4a^6b^7)$

28. $-7p^2q^8(2p^4q - 8p^3q^3 - p^{12}q^{15})$ 29. $5xy^2z^9(x^3y + 7xy^6 - 2yz^{13})$ 30. $-6x^5y^2z(12x^5y - 3z^6 - 5x^3yz^8)$

31. $(x+2)(x+3)$ 32. $(x+7)(x+6)$ 33. $(y-8)(y+3)$ 34. $(a+2)(a-9)$

35. $(t-8)(t-7)$ 36. $(b-4)(b-10)$ 37. $(2x+1)(5x+3)$ 38. $(2y+5)(3y+1)$

39. $(5t+9)(3t-4)$ 40. $(6x-7)(2x+3)$ 41. $(3-4n)(11+3n)$ 42. $(7+6a)(3-2a)$

43. $(2-7t)(3-2t)$ 44. $(1-9x)(1-4x)$ 45. $\left(5x^2 + 2x\right)(3x+1)$ 46. $\left(y^2 - 8y\right)(3y+2)$

47. $\left(4t^2 - 7t\right)\left(-5t + 5\right)$ 48. $\left(-6a^2 + 3\right)\left(8a - 3\right)$ 49. $\left(n^3 - 7n\right)\left(6n - 2\right)$ 50. $\left(2p^3 + 5p\right)\left(-p + 7\right)$

51. $(x + 1)(x - 1)$ 52. $(x - 2)(x + 2)$ 53. $(8 - y)(8 + y)$ 54. $(11 + a)(11 - a)$

55. $(4x + 3)(4x - 3)$ 56. $(5p + 4)(5p - 4)$ 57. $(10a - 9b)(10a + 9b)$ 58. $(2x - 7y)(2x + 7y)$

59. $(x + 2)^2$ 60. $(y + 4)^2$ 61. $(p - 8)^2$ 62. $(x - 13)^2$ 63. $(2y + 3)^2$

64. $(7n + 4)^2$ 65. $(8x - 5y)^2$ 66. $(3m + 7n)^2$ 67. $(4 - 13x)^2$ 68. $(5 - 12p)^2$

69. $(x + 3)\left(x^2 + 2x - 2\right)$ 70. $(x - 1)\left(x^2 - 3x + 4\right)$ 71. $(2y - 3)\left(y^2 - y - 3\right)$

72. $(5a + 1)\left(a^2 - 2a + 6\right)$ 73. $(4b + 2)\left(16b^2 - 8b + 4\right)$ 74. $(3y - 4)\left(9y^2 + 12y + 16\right)$

75. $(x + 2y + 5)(6x - 5)$ 76. $(8a - b + 3)(2b + 4)$ 77. $(t + 2)^3$

78. $(x - 4)^3$ 79. $(2m - 3n)^3$ 80. $(5p + 2q)^3$ 81. $(x + 3)^2(x - 3)$

82. $(y - 6)^2(y + 6)$ 83. $(a + 2)(3a - 2)(2a + 1)$ 84. $(5s - 1)(s + 4)(3s - 2)$

85. $(2x - 3y + 1)^2$ 86. $(-m + 3n + 8)^2$

In Exercises 87-107, simplify.

87. $8(3x + 3) + 2(2x - 1)$ 88. $-3(5y - 4) + 6(y + 2)$ 89. $-x^2(8x + 2) - 2x^2(9x - 3)$

90. $-7a^2(a - 5) + 6a^2(3a + 1)$ 91. $3p^2(-p^2 + 5p - 1) - 6p(p^2 - 4p)$

92. $4t(8t^2 - 2t + 7) + 6t^2(-t^2 + 3t - 2)$ 93. $6x(4x - 1) + 5x(-x + 2) - 10(x^2 - 5)$

94. $-9y(2 - 5y) + 8y^2(y + 1) - 7(2y^2 + 3)$ 95. $(x + 1)(x - 2) + (x + 2)(x + 8)$

96. $(t + 1)(t + 4) + (t - 2)(t - 4)$ 97. $(2a - 3)(a + 1) - (a + 2)(2a - 5)$

98. $(n + 5)(2n + 1) - (4n - 1)(2n - 3)$ 99. $(y + 5)(y - 5) + (y + 9)(y - 9)$

100. $(x + 6)(x - 6) + (x - 7)(x + 7)$ 101. $(3b - 2)(3b + 2) - (7 + 3b)(7 - 3b)$

102. $(x + 2)^2 + (x - 4)^2$ 103. $(r + 3)^2 + (r - 7)^2$ 104. $(y - 5)^2 - (y + 1)^2$

105. $(x + 6)^2 - (x - 1)^2$ 106. $(y - 13)^2 + (y + 8)(y - 3)$ 107. $(2x + 5)^2 - (x - 1)(x + 4)$

Section 3.4   Division of Polynomials

In this section, we will learn how to divide two polynomials. The section begins with a look at how to divide a monomial by a monomial. Afterwards, we will learn how to divide a polynomial by a monomial, followed by the quotient of any two polynomials. We will also learn about the remainder of a quotient of two polynomials. As we will see, dividing two polynomials is just like dividing two integers.

1. **Monomial $\div$ Monomial**

We have already learned how to divide two monomials (see Chapter 2). Let's look at few examples for review. Recall that a division problem can be written in different ways. Notice that the following all mean the same thing:

$$a \div b = \frac{a}{b} = b\overline{)\,a\,}$$

Examples. Divide.

1) $(12x^9) \div (3x^2) = \underbrace{\dfrac{12x^9}{3x^2}}_{\text{Rewrite as a fraction.}} = 4x^7$

2) $(-36a^4b^8) \div (4ab^5) = \dfrac{-36a^4b^8}{4ab^5} = -9a^3b^3$

3) $(-42x^5y^{15}) \div (-6xy^9) = \dfrac{-42x^5y^{15}}{-6xy^9} = 7x^4y^6$

4) $(-35mn^7) \div (5mn^2) = \dfrac{-35mn^7}{5mn^2} = -7n^5$

5) $(8x^5y^9z^3) \div (28x^4y^2z) = \dfrac{\overset{2}{\cancel{8}}x^5y^9z^3}{\underset{7}{\cancel{28}}x^4y^2z} = \dfrac{2}{7}xy^7z^2$

Notice that all of the above answers are monomials. However, it is NOT always the case that the quotient of two monomials is a monomial. For example, notice that

$$(-16x^2) \div (8x^5) = \frac{-16x^2}{8x^5} = -\frac{2}{x^3}.$$

And this is not a monomial since the denominator contains a variable.

Try These (Set 9): Divide.

1) $(14x^9) \div (2x^6)$ 2) $(24a^9b^3) \div (-4a^8b)$ 3) $(-32x^{16}y^{15}) \div (-4x^7y)$

4) $(15st^6) \div (-3s^4t^2)$ 5) $(42m^{10}n^3) \div (6m^{11}n^5)$ 6) $(54x^2yz^3) \div (-9x^2yz^9)$

2. **Polynomial ÷ Monomial**

To divide a polynomial by a monomial, we will use the following:

$$\frac{A+B}{C} = \frac{A}{C} + \frac{B}{C} \quad \text{and} \quad \frac{A-B}{C} = \frac{A}{C} - \frac{B}{C}$$

Examples. Divide.

1) $(18x^6 + 21x^4) \div (3x) = \dfrac{18x^6 + 21x^4}{3x} = \dfrac{\overset{6}{\cancel{18}}x^6}{\cancel{3}x} + \dfrac{\overset{7}{\cancel{21}}x^4}{\cancel{3}x} = 6x^5 + 7x^3$

2) $(30y^2 + 20y) \div (-5y) = \dfrac{30y^2 + 20y}{-5y} = \dfrac{\overset{6}{\cancel{30}}y^2}{\cancel{-5}y} + \dfrac{\overset{4}{\cancel{20}}y}{\cancel{-5}y} = -6y + (-4) = -6y - 4$

76

3) $\left(-6x^4y^6 - 8x^2y^{10}\right) \div \left(-6x^2y^4\right) = \dfrac{-6x^4y^6 - 8x^2y^{10}}{-6x^2y^4} = \dfrac{-\overset{}{\cancel{6}}x^4y^6}{\cancel{-6}x^2y^4} - \dfrac{\overset{4}{\cancel{8}}x^2y^{10}}{\underset{3}{\cancel{-6}}x^2y^4}$

$$= x^2y^2 - \left(-\dfrac{4}{3}y^6\right) = x^2y^2 + \dfrac{4}{3}y^6$$

4) $\left(-32a^6b^5 + 12a^9b^{14} - 10a^8b\right) \div \left(12a^4b\right) = \dfrac{-32a^6b^5 + 12a^9b^{14} - 10a^8b}{12a^4b} = \dfrac{-\overset{8}{\cancel{32}}a^6b^5}{\underset{3}{\cancel{12}}a^4b} + \dfrac{\cancel{12}a^9b^{14}}{\cancel{12}a^4b} - \dfrac{\overset{5}{\cancel{10}}a^8b}{\underset{6}{\cancel{12}}a^4b}$$

$$= -\dfrac{8}{3}a^2b^4 + a^5b^{13} - \dfrac{5}{6}a^4$$

Observe that all of the answers above are polynomials. As for the case of monomial $\div$ monomial, the quotient does NOT have to be a polynomial. For example, observe that

$$\left(20a^2 + 3\right) \div (4a) = \frac{20a^2 + 3}{4a} = \frac{20a^2}{4a} + \frac{3}{4a} = 5a + \frac{3}{4a}\,.$$

And the answer, $5a + \dfrac{3}{4a}$, is NOT a binomial since $\dfrac{3}{4a}$ is NOT a monomial. What does the expression $\dfrac{3}{4a}$ represent? Well, to understand this a little bit better, let's recall how we divide whole numbers. Suppose we want to divide $18 \div 7$. What we'd usually do is to rewrite the example as either $7\overline{)\,18}$ (often seen when doing **long division**) or as $\dfrac{18}{7}$ (which is called an **improper fraction**). Let's take a look at $7\overline{)\,18}$. To compute this, we begin by figuring out the largest whole number, q, for which $7q$ is less than or equal to 18. Notice that $7\,(2) = 14$, but $7\,(3) = 21$ which is larger than 18. Therefore, our **quotient** is 2. Now, observe that $18 - 7\,(2) = 18 - 14 = 4$, so the **remainder** is 4. We usually write '2 R 4' to represent the fact that the quotient is 2 and the remainder is 4. In terms of long division, we have:

$$
\begin{array}{r}
2\ \text{R}\ 4 \\
7\overline{)\,18} \\
-14 \\
\hline
4
\end{array}
$$

As for $\dfrac{18}{7}$, recall that we evaluate it by dividing the denominator into the numerator and express our improper fraction as a **mixed number.** We write the quotient as a whole number and the remainder as the numerator of a fraction whose denominator is the **divisor,** namely 7. We obtain the following:

$$\frac{18}{7} = 2 + \frac{4}{7} = 2\frac{4}{7}$$

No matter how it is written, the quotient and remainder are the same. Furthermore, we know that we can check our answer as follows:

$$18 = \underbrace{7\,(2) + 4}_{\text{divisor} \times \text{quotient} + \text{remainder}}$$

Now, let's return to our example $\dfrac{20a^2 + 3}{4a} = 5a + \dfrac{3}{4a}$. In the expression $\dfrac{3}{4a}$, the numerator 3 is the remainder of our division problem and the term $5a$ is the quotient. We can also express this as:

$$
\begin{array}{r}
5a\ \text{R}\ 3 \\
4a\overline{)\,20a^2 + 3} \\
-\,20a^2 \\
\hline
3
\end{array}
$$

77

As before, we can check our answer by verifying that

$$20a^2 + 3 = 4a(5a) + 3$$

which is true. To summarize, whenever you do a division problem (in fraction form) and end up with a fraction whose denominator (after simplifying) contains a variable, then the numerator of the fraction (before simplifying) is the remainder of the problem.

Try These (Set 10): Divide.

1) $(9x^2 + 15x) \div (3x)$ 2) $(25a^3 - 15a^2) \div (5a)$ 3) $(-35x^8y^6 - 14x^5y^9 + 7x^9y^2) \div (-7x^5y)$
4) $(44m^{12} - 24m^6 + 7m^5) \div (-4m^6)$ 5) $(8y^2 - 14y^4 + y^5) \div (4y^3)$

3. Polynomial ÷ Polynomial

The method of dividing two polynomials is just like dividing two integers. The first example is done in detail.

Examples. Divide.

1) $(x^2 + 4x + 2) \div (x + 3)$

We'll begin by rewriting the example in long division format. If both polynomials are in one (and the same) variable, make sure that they are written in descending order. We obtain:

$$x + 3 \overline{) \; x^2 + 4x + 2}$$

Now, we divide the leading term of the dividend, $x^2 + 4x + 2$, by the leading term of the divisor, $x + 3$. We obtain $\dfrac{x^2}{x} = x$ Put this on top of the division symbol as follows:

$$
\begin{array}{r}
x \phantom{{} + 4x + 2} \\
x + 3 \overline{) \; x^2 + 4x + 2}
\end{array}
$$

Next, we will multiply the divisor, $x+3$, by x and put the answer beneath the dividend, x^2+4x+2. After doing so, we subtract and obtain the following (remember to change the signs of the terms of the polynomial which is being subtracted):

$$
\begin{array}{r}
x \phantom{{} + 4x + 2} \\
x + 3 \overline{) \; x^2 + 4x + 2} \\
- x^2 + 3x \phantom{{} + 2} \\
\hline
x \phantom{{} + 2}
\end{array}
$$

As with division of integers, we will carry down the term(s) in the next column(s), $+2$ in our example, and repeat the process. We divide the leading term of $x+2$ by the leading term of $x+3$ and get $\dfrac{x}{x} = 1$. Put the $+1$ on top of the division symbol next to the x. We get:

$$
\begin{array}{r}
x + 1 \phantom{{} + 2} \\
x + 3 \overline{) \; x^2 + 4x + 2} \\
- x^2 + 3x \phantom{{} + 2} \\
\hline
x + 2
\end{array}
$$

78

Now we multiply $x + 3$ by 1, put the answer beneath $x + 2$, and subtract. By doing so, we get:

$$
\begin{array}{r}
x + 1 \\
x + 3 \overline{)\, x^2 + 4x + 2} \\
- x^2 + 3x \\
\hline
x + 2 \\
- x + 3 \\
\hline
-1
\end{array}
$$

Notice that there are no more terms to carry down, and if we divided the leading term of $x + 3$ by the leading term of -1, we'd have $\dfrac{-1}{x}$. Since this is not a monomial, we see that -1 is the remainder. Therefore, we write:

$$
\begin{array}{r}
x + 1 \ \ \text{R} \ \ -1 \\
x + 3 \overline{)\, x^2 + 4x + 2} \\
- x^2 + 3x \\
\hline
x + 2 \\
- x + 3 \\
\hline
-1
\end{array}
$$

In order to check this answer, we need to verify that $\underbrace{x^2 + 4x + 2}_{\text{dividend}} = \underbrace{(x + 3)(x + 1) + (-1)}_{\text{divisor} \times \text{quotient} + \text{remainder}}$. Well, by applying the FOIL method, we obtain:

$$(x + 3)(x + 1) + (-1) = x^2 + 3x + x + 3 + (-1) = x^2 + 4x + 2$$

And so the answer checks out. Notice that we can express the division problem in fractional form as

$$\frac{x^2 + 4x + 2}{x + 3} = x + 1 + \frac{-1}{x + 3} = x + 1 - \frac{1}{x + 3}.$$

2) $\left(2y^2 - y - 8\right) \div (y + 5)$

$$
\begin{array}{r}
2y - 11 \ \ \text{R} \ \ 47 \\
y + 5 \overline{)\, 2y^2 - y - 8} \\
- 2y^2 + 10y \\
\hline
-11y - 8 \\
- -11y - 55 \\
\hline
47
\end{array}
$$

Once again, we can check this answer by verifying that

$$2y^2 - y - 8 = (y + 5)(2y - 11) + 47.$$

Notice that we can also write

$$\frac{2y^2 - y - 8}{y + 5} = 2y - 11 + \frac{47}{y + 5}.$$

3) $(3x^2 + 5x + 1) \div (3x - 7)$

$$\begin{array}{r} x + 4 \ \text{R} \ \ 27 \\ 3x - 7{\overline{\smash{\big)}\,3x^2 + 5x - 1}} \\ -\underline{3x^2 - 7x} \\ 12x - 1 \\ -\underline{12x - 28} \\ 27 \end{array}$$

4) $(14a^3 - 14a^2 - 2a + 8) \div (7a^2 - 7a)$

$$\begin{array}{r} 2a \ \text{R} \ \ -2a + 8 \\ 7a^2 - 7a{\overline{\smash{\big)}\,14a^3 - 14a^2 - 2a + 8}} \\ -\underline{14a^3 - 14a^2} \\ -2a + 8 \end{array}$$

Observe that $-2a + 8$ is the remainder since $\dfrac{-2a}{7a^2} = \dfrac{-2}{7a}$ contains a variable in the denominator. This means that we can't divide $-2a + 8$ by $7a^2 - 7a$ without a remainder. In fractional form, this division problem can be written as $\dfrac{14a^3 - 14a^2 - 2a + 8}{7a^2 - 7a} = 2a + \dfrac{-2a + 8}{7a^2 - 7a}$

5) $(5x^2 + 1) \div (x - 8)$

$$\begin{array}{r} 5x + 40 \ \text{R} \ \ 321 \\ x - 8{\overline{\smash{\big)}\,5x^2 + 0x + 1}} \\ -\underline{5x^2 - 40x} \\ 40x + 1 \\ -\underline{40x - 320} \\ 321 \end{array}$$

Notice that an 'x-term' column was added into the binomial $5x^2 + 1$. This is done just in case an 'x-term' appears as we work out the problem. Observe that this column was put in the middle of the terms $5x^2$ and 1 so that descending order is preserved. I usually call such a column a **ghost column**.

6) $(-2y^3 + 5y - 7) \div (2y + 3)$

Observe that there is no y^2 term in the dividend, $-2y^3 + 5y - 7$. Let's begin by creating a ghost column for the missing y^2. We will then divide.

$$\begin{array}{r} -y^2 + \dfrac{3}{2}y + \dfrac{1}{4} \ \text{R} \ \ -\dfrac{31}{4} \\ 2y + 3{\overline{\smash{\big)}\,-2y^3 + 0y^2 + 5y - 7}} \\ -\underline{-2y^3 - 3y^2} \\ 3y^2 + 5y - 7 \\ -\underline{3y^2 + \dfrac{9}{2}y} \\ \dfrac{1}{2}y - 7 \\ -\underline{\dfrac{1}{2}y + \dfrac{3}{4}} \\ -\dfrac{31}{4} \end{array}$$

7) $\left(14x^4 - 10x^2 + x\right) \div \left(7x^2 - 3\right)$

This time, two ghost columns are needed (one for the 'x^3-term' and one for the constant term).

$$
\begin{array}{r}
2x^2 - \dfrac{4}{7} \ \text{R} \ x - \dfrac{12}{7} \\[2pt]
7x^2 - 3{\overline{\smash{\big)}\, 14x^4 + 0x^3 - 10x^2 + x + 0}} \\
\underline{-14x^4 \qquad\qquad - 6x^2} \\
- 4x^2 + x + 0 \\
\underline{- \qquad\qquad - 4x^2 \qquad + \dfrac{12}{7}} \\
x - \dfrac{12}{7}
\end{array}
$$

Notice that the 'x^3-term' column was not needed here. However, it is better to be safe than sorry.

8) $\left(8x^3 + 27\right) \div (2x + 3)$

Insert two ghost columns, one for the 'x^2-term' and one for the 'x-term'.

$$
\begin{array}{r}
4x^2 - 6x + 9 \\
2x + 3{\overline{\smash{\big)}\, 8x^3 + \ 0x^2 + \ 0x + 27}} \\
\underline{- \qquad 8x^3 + 12x^2} \\
- 12x^2 + \ 0x + 27 \\
\underline{- \qquad\quad - 12x^2 - 18x} \\
18x + 27 \\
\underline{- \qquad\qquad\qquad 18x + 27} \\
0
\end{array}
$$

Here, both of the ghost columns were used. I'm glad we put them in there before getting ourselves into trouble! Notice that, in fractional form, we have $\dfrac{8x^3 + 27}{2x + 3} = 4x^2 - 6x + 9$.

Try These (Set 11): Divide.

1) $\left(y^2 - 3y + 1\right) \div (y + 2)$ 2) $\left(4x^2 + 7x + 5\right) \div (4x - 1)$

3) $\left(x^3 + 6x^2 - 4x + 3\right) \div (x + 3)$ 4) $\left(3x^2 + 2\right) \div (x - 7)$

5) $\left(a^4 + 2a^2 + 3a - 1\right) \div \left(a^2 + 3a - 1\right)$

Exercise 3.4

Divide.

1. $\left(24x^5\right) \div \left(3x^4\right)$ 2. $\left(4x^5\right) \div \left(2x^2\right)$ 3. $\left(-20b^8\right) \div \left(4b^3\right)$ 4. $\left(-16a^8\right) \div \left(4a^5\right)$

5. $\left(-20y^{16}\right) \div \left(-5y^8\right)$ 6. $\left(-32y^{20}\right) \div \left(-4y^9\right)$ 7. $\left(54x^{14}y^5\right) \div \left(9xy^2\right)$ 8. $\left(42x^2y^8\right) \div \left(7xy^3\right)$

9. $\left(8m^{15}n^{18}\right) \div \left(-2m^4n^9\right)$ 10. $\left(28s^7t^6\right) \div \left(-7s^2t^3\right)$ 11. $\left(-2x^6y^{10}\right) \div \left(8x^2y^8\right)$

12. $\left(-7x^3y^7\right) \div \left(14x^3y^5\right)$ 13. $\left(-8a^2b^2\right) \div \left(-18a^8b\right)$ 14. $\left(-12x^5y^4\right) \div \left(-8x^3y\right)$

15. $\left(-32a^3b^4\right) \div \left(40a^2b^7\right)$ 16. $\left(-25xy^6\right) \div \left(30x^7y^4\right)$ 17. $(12x + 21) \div 3$

18. $(16x + 40) \div 8$

19. $(12x^2 - 4x) \div (4x)$

20. $(-36a^2 + 12a) \div (6a)$

21. $(8x^3 - 24x) \div (-4x)$

22. $(-12y^4 + 36y^2) \div (-6y)$

23. $(28x^3 - 16x^2 + 20x) \div (4x)$

24. $(42x^3 + 18x^2 - 12x) \div (6x)$

25. $(-24a^5 - 30a^4 + 6a^2) \div (-3a^2)$

26. $(-14b^7 + 22b^6 - 6b^3) \div (-2b^2)$

27. $(24x^2 + 13x) \div (8x)$

28. $(45x^3 - 11x) \div (9x)$

29. $(6x^3 + 8x^2 - 12x) \div (-6x)$

30. $(-5t^4 - 12t^3 + 25t^2) \div (-5t^2)$

31. $(-36x^6y^9 + 16x^4y^5 - 24x^{11}y^8) \div (-12x^3y^4)$

32. $(9a^4b^{13} + 24a^8b^4 - 30a^6b^7) \div (-6a^4b^3)$

33. $(16s^4t^5 - 18s^6t^{10} - 24s^4t^9) \div (8s^{12}t^9)$

34. $(-44x^6y^2 + 28xy^{14} - 6x^8y^{10}) \div (4x^{14}y)$

35. $(x^2 + 4x + 3) \div (x + 1)$

36. $(x^2 + 5x + 6) \div (x + 2)$

37. $(x^2 + x - 6) \div (x + 3)$

38. $(x^2 + 3x - 28) \div (x + 7)$

39. $(x^2 + 4x - 45) \div (x - 5)$

40. $(x^2 + 8x - 20) \div (x - 2)$

41. $(x^2 + 4x + 2) \div (x + 1)$

42. $(x^2 + 5x + 2) \div (x + 3)$

43. $(y^2 - 12y + 3) \div (y + 5)$

44. $(y^2 - 8y + 4) \div (y + 4)$

45. $(a^2 - 7a - 9) \div (a + 4)$

46. $(b^2 - 14b - 3) \div (b + 7)$

47. $(x^2 + 10x - 6) \div (x - 3)$

48. $(x^2 + 6x - 11) \div (x - 4)$

49. $(p^2 - 4p - 14) \div (p + 4)$

50. $(t^2 - 7t - 20) \div (t + 2)$

51. $(3x^2 + 2x + 1) \div (x + 5)$

52. $(3x^2 + 2x + 2) \div (x + 2)$

53. $(7y^2 + 3y - 1) \div (y + 3)$

54. $(4k^2 - k + 7) \div (k + 4)$

55. $(8m^2 - 2m - 5) \div (m - 2)$

56. $(12n^2 - 7n - 1) \div (n - 3)$

57. $(2x^2 - 3x + 4) \div (2x + 1)$

58. $(4x^2 - 7x + 2) \div (4x + 3)$

59. $(3a^2 - 6a + 5) \div (3a - 4)$

60. $(6a^2 - 5a - 2) \div (6a - 2)$

61. $(5t^2 - 10t - 6) \div (5t - 2)$

62. $(2y^2 - 3y - 8) \div (2y - 7)$

63. $(4y^2 + 2y + 3) \div (4y - 1)$

64. $(9x^2 - 2x + 2) \div (9x - 1)$

65. $(6y^2 - y + 4) \div (3y - 1)$

66. $(12p^2 + 2p - 4) \div (4p - 1)$

67. $(x^3 + 3x^2 - 2x + 1) \div (x + 4)$

68. $(x^3 + 4x^2 - 7x + 2) \div (x + 3)$

69. $(y^3 - y^2 - 7y + 3) \div (y + 5)$

70. $(y^3 - 8y^2 - y + 2) \div (y + 3)$

71. $(x^3 - 4x^2 + 3x - 2) \div (x - 2)$

72. $(x^3 - 8x^2 - x + 5) \div (x - 3)$

73. $(5a^3 - 3a^2 + a + 2) \div (a - 3)$

74. $(-3b^3 + 6b^2 - 4b - 1) \div (b - 3)$

75. $(y^2 + 5) \div (y - 3)$

76. $(x^2 - 11) \div (x + 6)$

77. $(-3t^2 + 4t) \div (t + 6)$

78. $(8t^2 + 2t) \div (t - 4)$

79. $(x^2 + 5x) \div (x^2 + 6)$

80. $(y^2 + 4y) \div (y^2 - 8)$

81. $(9p^2 + 1) \div (p^2 - 8p)$

82. $(2p^2 - 3) \div (p^2 - 7)$

83. $(4x^2 + 1) \div (x^2 - 5x)$

84. $(3x^2 - 2) \div (x^2 + 5x)$

85. $(y^3 - 4y^2 + 2) \div (y - 3)$

86. $(x^3 - 3x + 4) \div (x - 2)$

87. $(a^3 + 2a^2 + 4) \div (a + 5)$

88. $(a^3 + 9a - 4) \div (a - 3)$

89. $(4b^3 + b^2 - 3b) \div (b^2 + 3)$

90. $(7x^3 - x^2 + 2x) \div (x^2 - 2)$

91. $(x^4 - 5x^2 + 9) \div (x^2 - 1)$

92. $(t^4 - 8t^2 - 1) \div (t^2 + 4)$

82

93. $\left(64x^3 + 1\right) \div (4x + 1)$ 94. $\left(8y^3 + 1\right) \div (2y + 1)$ 95. $\left(64a^3 - 27\right) \div (4a - 3)$

96. $\left(125a^3 - 8\right) \div (5a - 2)$

Section 3.5   Factoring Polynomials

In this section, we will learn how to factor a polynomial. Roughly speaking, to factor a polynomial means to express it as a product of other polynomials. There are several techniques available for factoring a polynomial, depending on what the polynomial looks like. We will study a few techniques in this section. To begin with, let's review some definitions which are used when factoring natural numbers.

Definition: The **factors** (or **divisors**) of a natural number, n, are those natural numbers which divide into n without a remainder.

For example, the set of factors of 6 is $\{1, 2, 3, 6\}$, and the set of factors of 32 is $\{1, 2, 4, 8, 16, 32\}$. Notice that every natural number has at least two factors. For example, 4 has three factors, 1, 2, and 4, while the number 17 has two factors, 1 and 17.

Definition: A natural number is called **factorable** (or **composite**) if it has factors other than 1 and itself. If a natural number has only the factors 1 and itself, it is called **prime**.

Notice that a factorable number can be written as a product of natural numbers other than 1 and itself, while a prime number can **only** be written as the product of 1 and itself. For example, $6 = 3 \times 2$, so 6 is factorable. The number 18 is also factorable since it can be written as $18 = 2 \times 9 = 3 \times 6$. However, the number 23 is prime since $23 = 1 \times 23$ and this is the only way that 23 can be written as a product of two natural numbers. By convention, we consider the number 1 to be composite.

The definitions and examples given above should be familiar to you already. We will generalize these definitions for polynomials. **We are only considering factors of a polynomial whose terms have integer coefficients.** I'll explain what I mean in the next set of examples.

Definition: The **factors** of a polynomial, P, are those polynomials which divide into P without remainder.

Every polynomial has factors -1, 1, and itself. If these are the only factors, then it is called **prime**. If it has other factors besides -1, 1, and itself, then it is called **factorable**.

Examples.

1) $4x^2 + 2x$ is factorable since $4x^2 + 2x = 2x(2x + 1)$. The factors of $4x^2 + 2x$ are $2x$ and $2x + 1$.

2) $x^2 + 6x + 5$ is factorable since $x^2 + 6x + 5 = (x + 1)(x + 5)$. The factors of $x^2 + 6x + 5$ are $x + 1$ and $x + 5$.

In both of these examples, notice that the terms of each of the factors have integer coefficients. The method of factoring a polynomial into a product of other polynomials which have integer coefficients is called **factoring over the integers.** For the most part, we will only be concerned with factoring over the integers On occasion, however, we will encounter examples which demonstrate how a polynomial may be prime over the integers, but is **factorable over the rationals or the irrationals.** For example, the polynomial $x^2 + 4$ is prime over the integers, meaning that the only two ways to write it as a product whose factors contain integer coefficients is

$$x^2 + 4 = 1(x^2 + 4) \quad \text{or} \quad x^2 + 4 = -1(-x^2 - 4).$$

83

If we allow rational numbers or irrational numbers to appear as coefficients of the factors, then there would be **infinitely many ways** to factor $x^2 + 4$. For example,

$$\frac{1}{2}(2x^2 + 8), \frac{3}{4}\left(\frac{4}{3}x^2 + \frac{16}{3}\right), \text{ and } \pi\left(\frac{1}{\pi}x^2 + \frac{4}{\pi}\right)$$

are factorizations of $x^2 + 4$.

3) $x^2 - 5$ is not factorable over the integers. However, if we factor over the irrationals, then

$$x^2 - 5 = \left(x + \sqrt{5}\right)\left(x - \sqrt{5}\right)$$

is a factorization of $x^2 - 5$ and both $x + \sqrt{5}$ and $x - \sqrt{5}$ are factors. In the next chapter, we will learn how to deal with square roots.

Our task is to learn how to factor a polynomial. Let's begin by recalling the definition of the greatest common factor of two or more natural numbers. Afterwards, we will generalize this definition for monomials and see how it helps us factor certain polynomials.

1. **The Greatest Common Factors**

Definition: The **greatest common factor** (**GCF**) of two or more natural numbers is the largest number which is a factor of each of the given numbers.

For example, let's find the GCF of 6 and 15. Well, the set of factors of 6 is $\{1, 2, 3, 6\}$ and the set of factors of 15 is $\{1, 3, 5, 15\}$. Notice that 1 and 3 are factors of both numbers, but 3 is the larger of the two. This means that the GCF is 3. An easier way to find the GCF of 6 and 15 is to take each factor of 6 and divide it into 15. The largest one which doesn't give a remainder is the GCF. Observe that **any** two natural numbers have a GCF. For example, the GCF of 7 and 19 is 1 since the factors of 7 are 1 and 7 and the factors of 19 are 1 and 19.

Definition: The **greatest common factor** (**GCF**) of two or more monomials is the 'largest' monomial which is a factor of each of the given monomials.

We need to understand what it means to be the 'largest' monomial. Suppose that we want the GCF of the monomials $5x^3$ and $10x^2$. Let's write down all of the factors of each monomial. Well, the set of factors of $5x^3$ is $\{1, 5, x, x^2, x^3, 5x, 5x^2, 5x^3\}$ and the set of factors of $10x^2$ is $\{1, 2, 5, 10, x, x^2, 2x, 5x, 10x, 2x^2, 5x^2, 10x^2\}$. The 'largest' monomial in common will be the monomial whose coefficient is the largest possible and whose variables are of largest degree among all of the common factors. In our example, this monomial is $5x^2$.

There is a simpler way to find the GCF of monomials. Rather than write down all of the factors of the monomials (which can take forever when the monomials have large degrees), all that we have to do to find the GCF is to find the GCF of the coefficients and choose the **smallest** exponent of all of the exponents for each variable that appears in the monomials. For example, the GCF of $8x^4y^7$ and $20x^3y^{12}$ is $4x^3y^7$ since the GCF of 8 and 20 is 4, the smallest exponent of the x variable (x^4 and x^3) is 3, and the smallest exponent of the y variable (y^{12} and y^7) is 7. Let's do some examples.

Examples.

1) The GCF of $8x^2$ and $6x^5$ is $2x^2$.

2) The GCF of $9y^5$ and $3y^{12}$ is $3y^5$.

3) The GCF of $16a^5b^2$ and $24ab^4$ is $8ab^2$.

4) The GCF of $20a^2b^3$ and $15b^6$ is $5b^3$.

5) The GCF of $7x^2y^6$ and $15x^8$ is x^2.　　　6) The GCF of $12x^5$, $9x^7$, and $21x^2$ is $3x^2$.

So, why do we need GCF's? Well, suppose we want to factor the binomial $5x^3 + 10x^2$. Remember that to factor means to express our polynomial as a product of other polynomials (with natural numbers as coefficients). Notice that the GCF of $5x^3$ and $10x^2$ is $5x^2$. This means that we can write our binomial as

$$5x^3 + 10x^2 = 5x^2 (x + 2).$$

Note that $x + 2$ is obtained by dividing the terms $5x^3$ and $10x^2$ by $5x^2$. Hence, $\dfrac{5x^3}{5x^2} = x$ and $\dfrac{10x^2}{5x^2} = 2$. Let's look at some examples.

Examples. Factor.

1) $3x + 15 = 3(x + 5)$ since the GCF of $3x$ and 15 is 3.

2) $16x^3 - 6x^2 = 2x^2 (8x - 3)$ since the GCF of $6x^2$ and $16x^3$ is $2x^2$.

3) $7y^4 + 21y^2 = 7y^2 (y^2 + 3)$ since the GCF of $7y^4$ and $21y^2$ is $7y^2$.

4) $24a^2b^5 + 16a^5b^3 = 8a^2b^3 (3b^2 + 2a^3)$ since the GCF of $24a^2b^5$ and $16a^5b^3$ is $8a^2b^3$.

5) $15mn^4 - 9m^2 = 3m (5n^4 - 3m)$

6) $x^3 + 8x^2 - 10x = x (x^2 + 8x - 10)$

7) $4a^3 - 12a^5 - 18a^2 = 2a^2 (2a - 6a^3 - 9)$

8) $20a^4b^4 + 15a^2b^3 - 25ab^5 = 5ab^3 (4a^3b + 3a - 5b^2)$

9) $\underbrace{x(x + 1) + 4(x + 1)}_{\text{Factors just like } xy+4y=y(x+4).} = (x + 1)(x + 4)$

10) $\underbrace{x^2(x - 2)^2 + 5(x - 2)}_{\text{Factors just like } x^2y^2+5y=y(x^2y+5).} = (x - 2)\underbrace{\left[x^2(x - 2) + 5\right]}_{\text{Simplify.}} = (x - 2)(x^3 - 2x^2 + 5)$

Sometimes we want to factor out a GCF whose coefficient is negative. When you factor out a negative coefficient, the terms which appear in the parentheses will have different signs than in the original polynomial.

Examples. Factor out a negative coefficient.

1) $-7x + 14 = -7(x - 2)$ 　　　　　　2) $-3a^3 - 9a^2 + 15 = -3(a^3 + 3a^2 - 5)$

3) $-10y - 30 = -10(y + 3)$ 　　　　　4) $-16t^2 + 32t + 96 = -16(t^2 - 2t - 6)$

Try These (Set 12): Factor.

1) $16x^4 + 20x^3$ 　　　2) $12a^3 - 11a$ 　　3) $y^5 - 6y^2 + 2y$ 　　4) $16x^4y^3 - 10xy^6$

5) $21st^8 - 7s^3t^4 + 14s^2t^2$ 　6) $x^2y + xy^2 - xy$ 　7) $x(x + 5) - 4(x + 5)$ 　8) $4(x - 3) + (x - 3)^2$

2. **Difference of Two Squares**

Whenever you have a polynomial which is a difference of two squares, you can factor it. The formula which tells us how to do this is already familiar to us from Section 3.3, namely:

Formula I: 　　$A^2 - B^2 = (A + B)(A - B)$

85

Before factoring these types of polynomials, it is good to have a list of perfect squares. Recall that a perfect square is a natural number which is the square of another natural number. The numbers on the left-hand side of each equals sign below are the perfect squares. I've listed the perfect squares which are frequently seen. You can find others on your own.

LIST OF SOME PERFECT SQUARES

$1 = 1^2$	$49 = 7^2$
$4 = 2^2$	$64 = 8^2$
$9 = 3^2$	$81 = 9^2$
$16 = 4^2$	$100 = 10^2$
$25 = 5^2$	$121 = 11^2$
$36 = 6^2$	$144 = 12^2$

Let's factor some differences of squares. In each of these examples, the GCF is 1.

Examples. Factor.

1) $x^2 - 1 = \underbrace{(x)^2 - (1)^2}_{\text{Let } A=x \text{ and } B=1 \text{ in Formula I.}} = (x+1)(x-1)$

2) $y^2 - 4 = \underbrace{(y)^2 - (2)^2}_{\text{Let } A=y \text{ and } B=2 \text{ in Formula I.}} = (y+2)(y-2)$

3) $64 - t^2 = \underbrace{(8)^2 - (t)^2}_{\text{Let } A=8 \text{ and } B=t \text{ in Formula I.}} = (8+t)(8-t)$

4) $9x^2 - 25 = \underbrace{(3x)^2 - (5)^2}_{\text{Let } A=3x \text{ and } B=5 \text{ in Formula I.}} = (3x+5)(3x-5)$

5) $81a^2 - 100b^2 = \underbrace{(9a)^2 - (10b)^2}_{\text{Let } A=9a \text{ and } B=10b \text{ in Formula I.}} = (9a+10b)(9a-10b)$

6) $16m^2n^2 - 1 = \underbrace{(4mn)^2 - (1)^2}_{\text{Let } A=4mn \text{ and } B=1 \text{ in Formula I.}} = (4mn+1)(4mn-1)$

7) $t^4 - 36 = \underbrace{(t^2)^2 - (6)^2}_{\text{Let } A=t^2 \text{ and } B=6 \text{ in Formula I.}} = (t^2+6)(t^2-6)$

8) $\underbrace{(x+1)^2 - y^2}_{\text{Let } A=x+1 \text{ and } B=y \text{ in Formula I.}} = [(x+1)+y][(x+1)-y] = (x+y+1)(x-y+1)$

9) $121x^2 - \dfrac{25}{4} = \underbrace{(11x)^2 - \left(\dfrac{5}{2}\right)^2}_{\text{Let } A=11x \text{ and } B=\frac{5}{2} \text{ in Formula I.}} = \left(11x + \dfrac{5}{2}\right)\left(11x - \dfrac{5}{2}\right)$

Even though the difference of two squares always factors, the sum of two squares may not.

Theorem: If A is a linear monomial whose coefficient is an integer, B is a non-zero integer, and the GCF of A and B is 1, then $A^2 + B^2$ is prime.

For example, the binomials $x^2 + 1$, $y^2 + 4$, $16a^2 + 9$, and $49x^2 + 100$ are all prime. However, the binomial $x^4 + 4$ is a sum of squares and **does** factor. In fact, we have $x^4 + 4 = \left(x^2 + 2x + 2\right)\left(x^2 - 2x + 2\right)$. Notice that the term x^4 is **not** the square of a linear monomial, but rather the square of a **quadratic** monomial, $\left(x^2\right)^2$. Consequently, the theorem does not apply to $x^4 + 4$.

Try These (Set 13): Factor. (if possible). If a polynomial doesn't factor, state that it is prime.

1) $a^2 - 4$ 2) $b^2 - 25$ 3) $144x^2 - 1$ 4) $25 - 169y^2$

5) $s^2 - 36t^2$ 6) $81x^2 - \frac{100}{121}y^2$ 7) $x^2 + 9$ 8) $81m^2 + 4$

3. Sum / Difference of Two Cubes

Now we will learn how to factor a sum of two cubes and a difference of two cubes. The formulas which tell us how to do this is already familiar to us from Section 3.3, namely:

$$\textbf{Formula II:} \qquad A^3 + B^3 = (A + B)\left(A^2 - AB + B^2\right)$$

$$\textbf{Formula III:} \qquad A^3 - B^3 = (A - B)\left(A^2 + AB + B^2\right)$$

Notice that the two formulas are pretty much identical, except for the signs of the terms.

Let's write a list of frequently used perfect cubes. Recall that a perfect cube is a natural number which is the cube of another natural number.

LIST OF SOME PERFECT CUBES

$1 = 1^3$	$216 = 6^3$
$8 = 2^3$	$343 = 7^3$
$27 = 3^3$	$512 = 8^3$
$64 = 4^3$	$729 = 9^3$
$125 = 5^3$	$1,000 = 10^3$

Examples. Factor.

1) $x^3 + 1 = \underbrace{(x)^3 + (1)^3 = (x + 1)\left(x^2 - (x)(1) + (1)^2\right)}_{\text{Let } A=x \text{ and } B=1 \text{ in Formula II.}} = (x + 1)\left(x^2 - x + 1\right)$

2) $y^3 - 8 = \underbrace{(y)^3 - (2)^3 = (y - 2)\left(y^2 + (y)(2) + (2)^2\right)}_{\text{Let } A=y \text{ and } B=2 \text{ in Formula III.}} = (y - 2)\left(y^2 + 2y + 4\right)$

3) $27 + t^3 = \underbrace{(3)^3 + (t)^3 = (3 + t)\left((3)^2 - (3)(t) + t^2\right)}_{\text{Let } A=3 \text{ and } B=t \text{ in Formula II.}} = (3 + t)\left(9 - 3t + t^2\right)$

4) $64a^3 - 27 = \underbrace{(4a)^3 - (3)^3 = (4a - 3)\left((4a)^2 + (4a)(3) + (3)^2\right)}_{\text{Let } A=4a \text{ and } B=3 \text{ in Formula III.}} = (4a - 3)\left(16a^2 + 12a + 9\right)$

5) $125m^3 + 8n^3 = \underbrace{(5m)^3 + (2n)^3 = (5m + 2n)\left((5m)^2 - (5m)(2n) + (2n)^2\right)}_{\text{Let } A=5m \text{ and } B=2n \text{ in Formula II.}}$

$\qquad = (5m + 2n)\left(25m^2 - 10mn + 4n^2\right)$

87

6) $27a^3 - \dfrac{1}{216} = (3a)^3 - \left(\dfrac{1}{6}\right)^3 = \left(3a - \dfrac{1}{6}\right)\left((3a)^2 + (3a)\left(\dfrac{1}{6}\right) + \left(\dfrac{1}{6}\right)^2\right) = \left(3a - \dfrac{1}{6}\right)\left(9a^2 + \dfrac{a}{2} + \dfrac{1}{36}\right)$

Try These (Set 14): Factor.

1) $x^3 - 1$ 2) $a^3 + 8$ 3) $64y^3 - 1$

4) $27x^3 + y^3$ 5) $216 + 125t^3$ 6) $x^3 - \dfrac{1}{8}$

Next we will factor some polynomials which contain more than two factors in their factorizations. The key thing to remember is that whenever you want to factor a polynomial, you **look for the GCF first.**

Examples. Factor completely.

1) $2x^2 - 8 = \underbrace{2(x^2 - 4)}_{\text{The GCF is 2.}} = 2\underbrace{(x+2)(x-2)}_{x^2-4 \text{ factored}}$

2) $x^4 - x^2 = \underbrace{x^2(x^2 - 1)}_{\text{The GCF is } x^2.} = x^2\underbrace{(x+1)(x-1)}_{x^2-1 \text{ factored}}$

3) $3xy^3 - 27xy = \underbrace{3xy(y^2 - 9)}_{\text{The GCF is } 3xy^2.} = 3xy\underbrace{(y+3)(y-3)}_{y^2-9 \text{ factored}}$

4) $32m^3n^3 + 4m^3 = \underbrace{4m^3(8n^3 + 1)}_{\text{The GCF is } 4m^3.} = 4m^3\underbrace{(2n+1)(4n^2 - 2n + 1)}_{8n^3+1 \text{ factored}}$

5) $4x^2 - 64 = \underbrace{4(x^2 - 16)}_{\text{The GCF is 4.}} = 4\underbrace{(x+4)(x-4)}_{x^2-16 \text{ factored}}$

Notice that if you don't factor out the GCF first, you'll obtain

$$\underbrace{4x^2}_{(2x)^2} - \underbrace{64}_{(8)^2} = (2x + 8)(2x - 8)$$

which is **not** factored completely since both $2x + 8$ and $2x - 8$ can be factored further. By continuing this, we obtain

$$4x^2 - 64 = (2x + 8)(2x - 8) = 2(x + 4) \cdot 2(x - 4) = 4(x + 4)(x - 4).$$

And we have now factored it completely. If you forget to factor out the GCF first, you may not realize that the polynomial is not factored completely. Be careful!

6) $\underbrace{x^4 - 16}_{\text{GCF is 1.}} = \underbrace{\left(x^2\right)^2 - (4)^2 = \overbrace{\left(x^2 + 4\right)}^{\text{prime}}(x^2 - 4)}_{\text{Use Formula I.}} = \left(x^2 + 4\right)\underbrace{(x+2)(x-2)}_{x^2-4 \text{ factored}}$

7) $x^6 - y^6 = \underbrace{\left(x^3\right)^2 - \left(y^3\right)^2}_{\text{Use Formula I.}} = (x^3 + y^3)(x^3 - y^3) = \underbrace{(x + y)\left(x^2 - xy + y^2\right)}_{x^3+y^3 \text{ factored}}\underbrace{(x - y)(x^2 + xy + y^2)}_{x^3-y^3 \text{ factored}}$

Observe that, if we factor $x^6 - y^6$ as a difference of two cubes rather than two squares, we'll obtain

$$x^6 - y^6 = \underbrace{\left(x^2\right)^3 - \left(y^2\right)^3}_{\text{Use Formula III.}} = (x^2 - y^2)(x^4 + x^2y^2 + y^4) = \underbrace{(x + y)(x - y)}_{x^2-y^2 \text{ factored}}(x^4 + x^2y^2 + y^4).$$

By comparing this factorization to the one in Example 7, we see that factoring $x^6 - y^6$ as a difference of two squares gives us a more complete factorization than factoring it as a difference of two cubes. This idea is useful to keep in mind.

If a binomial is both a difference of two squares and a difference of two cubes, factor it as a difference of two squares.

Try These (Set 15): Factor completely.

1) $6x^2 - 24$ 2) $5y^3 - 80y$ 3) $a^2y^3 - 27a^2$

4) $9s^2t^4 - 72s^2t$ 5) $x^4 - 256$ 6) $y^6 - 1$

4. Quadratic Trinomials

Recall that a quadratic polynomial is a polynomial of degree 2. We will learn how to factor quadratic trinomials which are of the form $ax^2 + bx + c$, where a, b, and c are non-zero real numbers. To begin with, let us focus on those quadratic trinomials whose leading coefficient is 1, namely $x^2 + bx + c$. The first thing to observe is that any such trinomial comes from multiplying two binomials by the FOIL method. For example, recall that

$$
(x+4)(x-7) = \overbrace{x^2}^{\text{F}} + \overbrace{(-7x)}^{\text{O}} + \overbrace{4x}^{\text{I}} + \overbrace{(-28)}^{\text{L}}
$$
$$
= \underbrace{x^2}_{\text{F}} \underbrace{-3x}_{\text{O+I}} \underbrace{-28}_{\text{L}}
$$

and the trinomial $x^2 - 3x - 28$ is a quadratic one. What's important to notice is that the last term, -28, comes from multiplying the numbers in the factorization, $+4$ and -7, whereas the coefficient of the term obtained by adding the outer and inner terms, -3, comes from adding the numbers $+4$ and -7. This provides us with a strategy for factoring a quadratic trinomial whose leading coefficient is 1. When factoring $x^2 + bx + c$, try to find two integers which multiply to c and add up to b. If two such integers can be found (call them p and q), then $x^2 + bx + c$ can be factored as

$$
x^2 + bx + c = (x+p)(x+q), \text{ where } p+q = b \text{ and } pq = c.
$$

If no such integers p and q can be found, then the trinomial $x^2 + bx + c$ is prime. This method of finding the numbers which yield the factorization is known as the **Reverse FOIL Method.** We will only look at polynomials for which p and q are integer valued. It is possible to have a quadratic trinomial which has factors whose coefficients are not integers. For example, notice that $(x+4)\left(x+\frac{1}{2}\right) = x^2 + \frac{9}{2}x + 2$. Going in the opposite direction, we have $x^2 + \frac{9}{2}x + 2 = (x+4)\left(x+\frac{1}{2}\right)$. And so the factor $x + \frac{1}{2}$ has a term with a rational coefficient of $\frac{1}{2}$. We will not be looking at polynomials which factor in this way. **We will only be concerned with factoring polynomials whose factors contain terms with integer coefficients.**

For example, let's factor the trinomial $x^2 + 7x + 12$. Observe that the leading coefficient is 1, so the Reverse FOIL Method requires us to find two numbers, say p and q, such that $pq = +12$ and $p + q = +7$. What we should do is to think about all possible pairs of numbers which multiply to $+12$. For starters, notice that both numbers **must** be positive since their product is positive and their sum is positive. Now, observe that

$$
\begin{aligned}
12 = 12 \times 1 \quad & \text{and} \quad 12 + 1 = 13, \quad \text{no good} \\
= 6 \times 2 \quad & \text{and} \quad 6 + 2 = 8, \quad \text{no good} \\
= 4 \times 3 \quad & \text{and} \quad 4 + 3 = 7, \quad \text{GOOD.}
\end{aligned}
$$

And so $x^2 + 7x + 12 = (x+4)(x+3)$. Notice that the Commutative Property allows us to write the answer as $x^2 + 7x + 12 = (x+3)(x+4)$ as well.

Examples. Factor.

1) $x^2 + 3x + 2 = (x + 2)(x + 1)$ since $2 \times 1 = 2$ and $2 + 1 = 3$.

2) $a^2 + 11a + 30 = (a + 6)(a + 5)$ since $6 \times 5 = 30$ and $6 + 5 = 11$.

3) $y^2 - 8y + 15 = (y - 3)(y - 5)$ since $(-3)(-5) = 15$ and $(-3) + (-5) = -8$.

4) $x^2 + 4x - 45 = (x - 5)(x + 9)$ since $(-5)(9) = -45$ and $(-5) + 9 = 4$.

5) $t^2 + 8t - 33 = (t + 11)(t - 3)$ since $(11)(-3) = -33$ and $11 + (-3) = 8$.

6) $x^2 + 2x + 1 = (x + 1)(x + 1) = (x + 1)^2$

7) $y^2 + 4y + 4 = (y + 2)(y + 2) = (y + 2)^2$

8) $m^2 - 20m + 100 = (m - 10)(m - 10) = (m - 10)^2$

9) $k^2 - 10k + 25 = (k - 5)(k - 5) = (k - 5)^2$

10) $x^2 + 6x + 2$ is prime since there are no two integers, p and q, for which $pq = 2$ and $p + q = 6$.

11) $a^2 - 3a - 9$ is prime since there are no two integers, p and q, for which $pq = -3$ and $p + q = -9$.

12) $y^2 + 25 = y^2 + 0y + 25$ is prime since there are no two integers, p and q, for which $pq = 25$ and $p + q = 0$.

Notice that each of the trinomials $x^2 + 2x + 1$, $y^2 + 4y + 4$, $m^2 - 20m + 100$, and $k^2 - 10k + 25$ factor into the square of another polynomial. These types of trinomials are special and will be useful later on.

Definition: A trinomial square is a trinomial which can be factored into the square of a polynomial.

There's a simple way of determining whether or not a trinomial is a trinomial square. If the first and last terms of the trinomial are squares of two monomials, say A and B, we look and see if the middle term is $2AB$. If it is, then the trinomial is a trinomial square. Otherwise, it isn't. This is a consequence of the formulas

$$A^2 + 2AB + B^2 = (A + B)^2 \qquad \text{and}$$
$$A^2 - 2AB + B^2 = (A - B)^2.$$

Examples. Factor.

1) $\underbrace{x^2}_{(x)^2} + \underbrace{2x}_{2(x)(1)} + \underbrace{1}_{(1)^2} = (x + 1)^2$

2) $\underbrace{y^2}_{(y)^2} + \underbrace{4y}_{2(y)(2)} + \underbrace{4}_{(2)^2} = (y + 2)^2$

3) $\underbrace{m^2}_{(m)^2} - \underbrace{20m}_{2(m)(10)} + \underbrace{100}_{(10)^2} = (m - 10)^2$ *To do*

4) $\underbrace{k^2}_{(k)^2} - \underbrace{10k}_{2(k)(5)} + \underbrace{25}_{(5)^2} = (k - 5)^2$

Try These (Set 16): Factor. If a trinomial not factorable, state that it is prime.

1) $x^2 + 6x + 8$ 2) $k^2 + 14k + 49$ 3) $y^2 - 9y + 20$

4) $x^2 - 3x + 12$ 5) $y^2 - 16y + 20$ 6) $m^2 + 24m + 144$

7) $y^2 + y - 30$ 8) $n^2 + 11n - 42$ 9) $x^2 - 22x + 121$

90

Now we will now learn how to factor quadratic trinomials whose leading coefficient is positive and not equal to 1, namely $ax^2 + bx + c$ with $a \neq 1$ and $a > 0$. As before, notice that any trinomial of this form comes from multiplying two binomials by the FOIL method. For example, recall that:

$$(2x + 7)(x - 3) = \overbrace{2x^2}^{F} + \overbrace{(-6x)}^{O} + \overbrace{7x}^{I} + \overbrace{(-21)}^{L}$$
$$= \underbrace{2x^2}_{F} + \underbrace{x}_{O+I} \underbrace{-21}_{L}$$

And the trinomial $2x^2 + x - 21$ is a quadratic one whose leading coefficient is 2. Notice that the first term, $2x^2$, comes from multiplying the first terms, $2x$ and x, whereas the last term, -21, comes from multiplying the numbers in the factorization, $+7$ and -3. Unlike the case where the leading coefficient is 1, the numbers $+7$ and -3 **do not** add up to the coefficient of the middle term, $+1$. This means that we cannot use the Reverse FOIL Method from before. There are two methods which we will learn about that will allow us to factor these types of polynomials. The first one is called the **Trial and Error Method** and the second is called the **Grouping Method.** Let me say a little bit about the Trial and Error Method. Roughly speaking, you choose two terms which multiply to first term of the trinomial and choose two numbers which multiply to the last term of the trinomial. Afterwards, check to see whether or not the outer and inner terms combine to the middle term in the trinomial. If so, you are done. If not, try out the other possible combinations.

To demonstrate how the Trial and Error Method works, let's factor $2x^2 + 5x - 3$. We begin by thinking of two monomials (each containing x) which multiply to $2x^2$. There is only one possibility, namely $2x$ and x. These will be the 'F' terms in FOIL. Now we think of two numbers which multiply to -3. The possibilities are $\{-1, 3\}$ and $\{1, -3\}$. The numbers in one of these sets of possibilities will (hopefully) be the 'L' terms in FOIL. Let's try the different possibilities of factoring:

$(2x + 3)(x - 1)$ fails since $O + I = (2x)(-1) + 3(x) = +x$ and we want $+5x$.
$(2x + 1)(x - 3)$ fails since $O + I = (2x)(-3) + 1(x) = -5x$ and we want $+5x$.

However,

$(2x - 1)(x + 3)$ works since $O + I = (2x)(3) + (-1)(x) = 5x$ which is what we want.

Notice that our second attempt, $(2x + 1)(x - 3)$, was close to what we wanted except for the signs. When this happens, just change the signs of your numbers and it will work. Moreover, you should realize that it DOES matter where your numbers go (unlike before when the leading coefficient is 1).

Let's do another example in detail. Let's factor $4y^2 + 17y + 15$. As before, we'll begin by thinking of two monomials (each containing y) which multiply to $4y^2$. There are two possibilities, namely $\{2y, 2y\}$ and $\{4y^2, y\}$. Now let's think of two numbers which multiply to 15. Both numbers must be positive since their product has to be $+15$ and the middle term of the trinomial is $+17y$. This means that we have $\{3, 5\}$ and $\{15, 1\}$. We now try the different possibilities:

$(2y + 3)(2y + 5)$ fails since $O + I = (2y)(5) + 3(2y) = +16y$ and we want $+17y$.
$(2y + 15)(2y + 1)$ fails since $O + I = (2y)(1) + 15(2y) = +32y$ and we want $+17y$.
$(4y + 3)(y + 5)$ fails since $O + I = (4y)(5) + 3(y) = +23y$ and we want $+17y$.

However,

$(4y + 5)(y + 3)$ works since $O + I = (4y)(3) + 5(y) = +17y$.

If it turned out that none of the possibilities work, then the polynomial would be prime. It may get frustrating when there are many possibilities to check until you reach the right answer. As you do more examples, you will start to see patterns in the numbers which will enable you to get the right answer quickly.

Let me give you some examples. Try them out **without** looking at the answers. Afterwards, compare your results to mine.

Examples. Factor using the Trial and Error Method.

1) $2x^2 + 7x + 3 = \underbrace{(2x+1)\,(x+3)}_{O+I=(2x)(3)+1(x)=7x}$

2) $3y^2 - 13y + 4 = \underbrace{(3y-1)\,(y-4)}_{O+I=(3y)(-4)+(-1)(y)=-13y}$

3) $5t^2 - 2t - 7 = \underbrace{(5t-7)\,(t+1)}_{O+I=(5t)(1)+(-7)(t)=-2t}$

4) $4a^2 + 20a + 21 = \underbrace{(2a+3)\,(2a+7)}_{O+I=(2a)(7)+3(2a)=20a}$

5) $16x^2 - 30x - 25 = \underbrace{(8x+5)\,(2x-5)}_{O+I=(8x)(-5)+5(2x)=-30x}$

6) $20p^2 - 31p + 12 = \underbrace{(4p-3)\,(5p-4)}_{O+I=(4p)(-4)+(-3)(5p)=-31p}$

7) $2y^2 - y + 8$ is prime since none of the possibilities work.

8) $12b^2 + 5b + 2$ is prime since none of the possibilities work.

The other method of factoring a trinomial $ax^2 + bx + c$ is called the **Grouping Method**. Let me demonstrate how this works by factoring $2x^2 + 5x + 2$ (which we've already done in Example 1). The idea is to split up the monomial $5x$ into two monomials. The coefficients of these two monomials are obtained in the following way:

$$\text{Find two numbers which multiply to } \overbrace{(2)(2)}^{\text{`F' and `L'}} = 4 \text{ and add up to } \overbrace{5}^{O+I} .$$

Well, the numbers 4 and 1 do the trick since $(4)(1) = 4$ and $4 + 1 = 5$. Now we rewrite our trinomial as

$$2x^2 + 5x + 2 = 2x^2 \underbrace{+4x + 1x}_{\text{Split up } 5x.} + 2 .$$

Next, we factor the GCF from the first two and the last two terms and get

$$2x^2 + 4x + 1x + 2 = 2x\underline{(x + 2)} + 1\underline{(x + 2)} .$$

The final step is to factor out the polynomial in the parenthesis and obtain

$$2x^2 + 5x + 2 = 2x^2 + 4x + 1x + 2 = 2x\underline{(x + 2)} + 1\underline{(x + 2)} = (x + 2)(2x + 1).$$

If you have trouble with this, think of the $(x + 2)$ as a letter, say y. Then $2x(x+2)+1(x+2)$ is the same as $2xy + 1y$, which factors as $y(2x + 1)$. Replacing y with $(x + 2)$ gives us the factorization $(x + 2)(2x + 1)$ as before. Let's take a look at some examples. Try them out **without** looking at the answers. Afterwards, check your work.

Examples. Factor using the Grouping Method.

1) $2x^2 - x - 6$

Notice that the coefficients of the first term, the last term, and the outer + inner term are 2, −6, and −1, respectively. We want to find two numbers which multiply to $(2)(-6) = -12$ and add up to −1. Observe that $(-4)(3) = -12$ and $-4 + 3 = -1$, so the numbers that we need are −4 and 3. We write the trinomial as

$$2x^2 - x - 6 = 2x^2 - 4x + 3x - 6$$

and now use the Grouping Method. We obtain:

$$2x^2 - x - 6 = 2x^2 - 4x + 3x - 6$$
$$= 2x(x - 2) + 3(x - 2)$$
$$= \underline{(x - 2)(2x + 3)}$$

92

2) $5y^2 - 17y + 6 = \underbrace{5y^2 - 15y - 2y + 6}_{(-15)(-2)=30 \text{ and } -15+(-2)=-17} = 5y\underline{(y-3)} - 2\underline{(y-3)} = \underline{(y-3)}(5y-2)$

3) $6t^2 + 7t - 20 = \underbrace{6t^2 + 15t - 8t - 20}_{(15)(-8)=-120 \text{ and } 15+(-8)=7} = 3t\underline{(2t+5)} - 4\underline{(2t+5)} = \underline{(2t+5)}(3t-4)$

As Example 3 demonstrates, the process of finding the two numbers can be quite tedious since there may be many possibilities for the two numbers to multiply to the one you want (here, it is $(6)(-20) = -120$). For this reason, I prefer to use the Trial and Error Method instead of the Grouping Method. You can use whichever method you'd like. Let's do some more.

4) $12a^2 + 29a + 15 = \underbrace{12a^2 + 9a + 20a + 15}_{(9)(20)=180 \text{ and } 9+20=29} = 3a\underline{(4a+3)} + 5\underline{(4a+3)} = \underline{(4a+3)}(3a+5)$

5) $6x^2 - 13x + 6 = \underbrace{6x^2 - 9x - 4x + 6}_{(-9)(-4)=36 \text{ and } (-9)+(-4)=-13} = 3x\underline{(2x-3)} - 2\underline{(2x-3)} = \underline{(2x-3)}(3x-2)$

6) $14n^2 + 43n + 20 = \underbrace{14n^2 + 35n + 8n + 20}_{(35)(8)=280 \text{ and } 35+8=43} = 7n\underline{(2n+5)} + 4\underline{(2n+5)} = \underline{(2n+5)}(7n+4)$

7) $25y^2 - 60y + 36 = \underbrace{25y^2 - 30y - 30y + 36}_{(-30)(-30)=900 \text{ and } (-30)+(-30)=-60} = 5y\underline{(5y-6)} - 6\underline{(5y-6)} = \underline{(5y-6)}(5y-6)$

$= (5y-6)^2.$

Notice that the trinomial $25y^2 - 60y + 36$ is a trinomial square since $25y^2 = (5y)^2$, $(6)^2 = 36$, and $60y = 2(5y)(6)$. Therefore, by using the formula $A^2 - 2AB + B^2 = (A-B)^2$ with $A = 5y$ and $B = 6$, we'll obtain the answer in a simpler way.

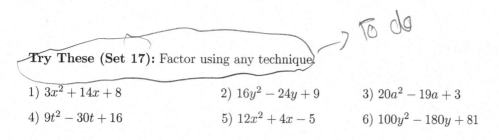

To do

Try These (Set 17): Factor using any technique.

1) $3x^2 + 14x + 8$ 2) $16y^2 - 24y + 9$ 3) $20a^2 - 19a + 3$

4) $9t^2 - 30t + 16$ 5) $12x^2 + 4x - 5$ 6) $100y^2 - 180y + 81$

5. Polynomials With Four Terms

Is we've seen in the previous examples, one method of factoring a quadratic trinomial is the **Grouping Method**. We will now apply this method to factor polynomials containing four terms. Suppose we want to factor $x^3 + 2x^2 + 5x + 10$. As before, we'll group the first two and last two terms. Next, we'll factor the GCF from each group. If the remaining polynomials in the parentheses are the same, we'll then factor it out and we are done. Following this routine, we have

$$x^3 + 2x^2 + 5x + 10 = (x^3 + 2x^2) + (5x + 10)$$
$$= x^2(x + 2) + 5(x + 2)$$
$$= (x + 2)(x^2 + 5).$$

And the polynomial is factored. Let's try some examples.

93

Examples. Factor.

1) $x^3 + 2x^2 + x + 2 = (x^3 + 2x^2) + (x + 2) = x^2(x + 2) + 1(x + 2) = (x + 2)(x^2 + 1)$

2) $2y^3 + 10y^2 - y - 5 = (2y^3 + 10y^2) + (-y - 5) = 2y^2(y + 5) - 1(y + 5) = (y + 5)(2y^2 - 1)$

3) $5n^3 - 35n^2 + 4n - 28 = (5n^3 - 35n^2) + (4n - 28) = 5n^2(n - 7) + 4(n - 7) = (n - 7)(5n^2 + 4)$

4) $a^5 - 3a^3 + 2a^2 - 6 = (a^5 - 3a^3) + (2a^2 - 6) = a^3(a^2 - 3) + 2(a^2 - 3) = (a^2 - 3)(a^3 + 2)$

5) $3p^6 + 9p^4 - 2p^2 - 6 = (3p^6 + 9p^4) + (-2p^2 - 6) = 3p^4(p^2 + 3) - 2(p^2 + 3) = (p^2 + 3)(3p^4 - 2)$

6) $3x^2y - 8x^2 + 6y - 16 = (3x^2y - 8x^2) + (6y - 16) = x^2(3y - 8) + 2(3y - 8) = (3y - 8)(x^2 + 2)$

There are polynomials which factor by grouping the first three terms, rather than the first and last two terms. For example, notice that

$$x^2 + 2x + 1 - y^2 = (x^2 + 2x + 1) - y^2 = (x + 1)^2 - y^2 = (x + 1 + y)(x + 1 - y)$$

by applying the formula $A^2 - B^2 = (A + B)(A - B)$ with $A = x + 1$ and $B = y$.

7) $a^2 - 6a + 9 - b^2 = (a^2 - 6a + 9) - b^2 = (a - 3)^2 - b^2 = (a - 3 + b)(a - 3 - b)$

8) $4y^2 + 4y + 1 - 25x^2 = (4y^2 + 4y + 1) - 25x^2 = (2y + 1)^2 - (5x)^2 = (2y + 1 + 5x)(2y + 1 - 5x)$

Note that if a polynomial with four terms doesn't factor using the Grouping Method, that doesn't mean that it is prime. It just means that the method which we are using is not going to give us the factorization (if there is one). For example, if we try to factor $8x^4 - 3x^3 - 2x^2 - 3$ using the methods mentioned above, we will not succeed. However, $8x^4 - 3x^3 - 2x^2 - 3$ does factor into $(x - 1)(8x^3 + 5x^2 + 3x + 3)$, so it is not prime.

Try These (Set 18): Factor.

1) $t^3 + 3t^2 + 2t + 6$ 2) $x^4 - 3x^3 + 7x - 21$ 3) $2y^3 - 10y^2 - y + 5$

4) $18a^4 + 27a^3 + 4a + 6$ 5) $8p^5 - 6p^3 + 20p^2 - 15$ 6) $x^2 + 14x + 49 - 100y^2$

6. **Putting it All Together**

Examples. Factor completely.

1) $3x^2 + 6x + 3 = \underbrace{3(x^2 + 2x + 1)}_{\text{The GCF first}} - \underbrace{3(x + 1)(x + 1)}_{x^2 + 2x + 1 \text{ factors}} = 3(x + 1)^2$

2) $5x^4 + 35x^3 + 30x^2 = \underbrace{5x^2(x^2 + 7x + 6)}_{\text{The GCF first}} = \underbrace{5x^2(x + 6)(x + 1)}_{x^2 + 7x + 6 \text{ factors}}$

3) $3a^4b^2 + 3a^3b^2 - 60a^2b^2 = 3a^2b^2(a^2 + a - 20) = 3a^2b^2(a + 5)(a - 4)$

4) $20y^5 + 22y^4 - 12y^3 = 2y^3(10y^2 + 11y - 6) = 2y^3(5y - 2)(2y + 3)$

5) $36a^4b + 56a^3b - 32a^2b = 4a^2b(9a^2 + 14a - 8) = 4a^2b(9a - 4)(a + 2)$

6) $-24p^2 - 28p + 20 = -4(6p^2 + 7p - 5) = -4(3p + 5)(2p - 1)$

7) $72 - y - y^2 = -1(y^2 + y - 72) = -1(y + 9)(y - 8)$

8) $y^4 - 2y^2 + 1 = \underbrace{(y^2 - 1)(y^2 - 1)}_{\text{Using Reverse FOIL.}} = (y + 1)(y - 1)(y + 1)(y - 1) = (y + 1)^2(y - 1)^2$

9) $t^6 + 11t^3 + 24 = \underbrace{(t^3 + 3)(t^3 + 8)}_{\text{Using Reverse FOIL.}} = \overbrace{(t^3 + 3)}^{\text{prime}} \underbrace{(t + 2)(t^2 - 2t + 4)}_{t^3 + 8 \text{ in factored form}}$

10) $12a^2 + 5ab - 2b^2 = \underbrace{(4a - b)(3a + 2b)}_{\text{Using Reverse FOIL.}}$

11) $6m^5n^3 + 14m^4n^4 + 4m^3n^5 = \underbrace{2m^3n^3(3m^2 + 7mn + 2n^2)}_{\text{The GCF first}} = 2m^3n^3\underbrace{(3m + n)(m + 2n)}_{\text{Using Reverse FOIL.}}$

$\rightarrow$ To do

Try These (Set 19): Factor completely.

1) $3x^3 + 15x^2 + 12x$ 2) $8y^2 - 24y - 14$ 3) $-24x^5 + 33x^4 + 30x^3$

4) $x^4 - 27x^2 + 50$ 5) $7y^7 + 14y^6 - 7y^4 - 14y^3$ 6) $32a^2 + 52ab + 15b^2$

Exercise 3.5

In Exercises 1-21, factor the GCF from each polynomial.

1. $2x + 18$ 2. $3y + 9$ 3. $4a^2 + 12$ 4. $8b^2 + 8$

5. $10x^2 + 5x - 20$ 6. $4t^2 + 12t - 28$ 7. $6x^2 + 24x$ 8. $18y^2 + 9y$

9. $15x^3 - 9x^2$ 10. $11p^3 + 5p^2$ 11. $7q^2 + 16q^5$ 12. $32y^4 - 16y^3 + 8y^2$

13. $18x^4 + 27x^3 - 9x^2$ 14. $12x^2y + 27xy^3$ 15. $20a^4b^2 + 22ab^6$ 16. $27p^5q^3 + 3p^4q^6 - 6p^6q$

17. $6s^3t - 5s^3t^2 + s^2t^2$ 18. $10x^2y^3z^3 - 25xy^4z^3 + 40xy^3z^4$ 19. $21a^5b^2c^3 - 7a^3b^5c^4 - 35a^5b^2c^8$

20. $8t^7 + 12st^5 + 20s^2t^4$ 21. $36x^2y^7 + 27xy^6 - 18y^8$

In Exercises 22-31, factor out a negative coefficient from each polynomial.

22. $-2x + 4$ 23. $-3x + 6$ 24. $-5y - 30$ 25. $-4t - 36$

26. $-2x^2 + 6x - 10$ 27. $-16y^2 - 32y + 80$ 28. $-9m^3 + 18m^2 - 81$

29. $-5n^4 - 15n^3 - 55$ 30. $-24k^2 - 24k - 96$ 31. $-16t^2 + 32t + 64$

In Exercises 32-53, factor the differences of two squares.

32. $x^2 - 1$ 33. $y^2 - 9$ 34. $m^2 - 16$ 35. $n^2 - 36$

36. $a^2 - 49$ 37. $b^2 - 25$ 38. $81 - y^2$ 39. $49 - x^2$

40. $64a^2 - 1$ 41. $81t^2 - 64$ 42. $36p^2 - 25$ 43. $121a^2 - 4$

44. $x^2 - 100y^2$ 45. $p^2 - 144q^2$ 46. $169m^2 - 4n^2$ 47. $36u^2 - 49v^2$

48. $x^2 - \dfrac{1}{25}$ 49. $y^2 - \dfrac{1}{4}$ 50. $25t^2 - \dfrac{64}{121}$ 51. $\dfrac{49}{81} - 100d^2$

52. $\dfrac{100}{9}a^2 - 49b^2$ 53. $\dfrac{16}{121}x^2 - 144y^2$

In Exercises 54-72, factor the sums or differences of two cubes.

54. $x^3 + 1$ 55. $y^3 + 27$ 56. $k^3 + 64$ 57. $m^3 + 8$

58. $64 - x^3$ 59. $125 - y^3$ 60. $t^3 - 1,000$ 61. $q^3 - 216$

62. $27a^3 + 1$ 63. $8b^3 + 1$ 64. $27p^3 - q^3$ 65. $64x^3 - y^3$

66. $125a^3 + b^3$ 67. $27m^3 + 1,000$ 68. $8n^3 + 27$ 69. $343x^3 + 8y^3$

70. $27x^3 - 8y^3$ 71. $64a^3 - 125b^3$ 72. $216p^3 + 125q^3$

In Exercises 73-88, factor the binomials completely.

73. $7y^2 - 63$ 74. $5x^2 - 20$ 75. $2n^4 - 72n^2$ 76. $3m^5 - 48m^3$

77. $9b^2 - 9$ 78. $4a^2 - 16$ 79. $64x^2 - 16y^2$ 80. $4x^2 - 64y^2$

81. $5m^3 + 40$ 82. $4n^3 + 4$ 83. $12u^3 - 12$ 84. $9v^3 - 72$

85. $250t^7 - 2t^4$ 86. $7x^5 + 56x^2$ 87. $x^4y^2 - 1,000xy^2$ 88. $mn^4 + 216mn$

In Exercises 89-146, factor the quadratic trinomials. If any trinomial isn't factorable, state that it is prime.

89. $x^2 + 4x + 3$ 90. $x^2 + 10x + 24$ 91. $y^2 + 13y + 40$ 92. $y^2 + 12y + 35$

93. $x^2 + 7x - 18$ 94. $x^2 + 7x - 30$ 95. $y^2 + 8y - 20$ 96. $y^2 + 8y - 48$

97. $a^2 - 12a + 27$ 98. $a^2 - 10a + 16$ 99. $b^2 - 15b + 36$ 100. $b^2 - 13b + 36$

101. $x^2 - 4x - 21$ 102. $x^2 + 16x + 55$ 103. $q^2 + 21q + 38$ 104. $q^2 - 15q + 54$

105. $x^2 + 4x + 4$ 106. $y^2 + 8y + 16$ 107. $m^2 - 18m + 81$ 108. $k^2 - 24k + 144$

109. $t^2 + 22t + 121$ 110. $s^2 - 20s + 100$ 111. $x^2 - 10x + 25$ 112. $y^2 - 6y + 9$

113. $x^2 + 4x + 8$ 114. $x^2 + 5x + 14$ 115. $y^2 + 9y + 10$ 116. $a^2 + 8a + 13$

117. $2x^2 + 3x + 1$ 118. $2x^2 + 5x + 2$ 119. $2y^2 + y - 3$ 120. $3y^2 + y - 2$

121. $5x^2 + 19x - 4$ 122. $5y^2 - y - 4$ 123. $14m^2 + 11m + 2$ 124. $14n^2 + 13n + 3$

125. $4s^2 - 20s + 21$ 126. $4t^2 - 12t + 5$ 127. $4p^2 - 23p + 15$ 128. $4q^2 - 15p + 14$

129. $6a^2 + 31a + 35$ 130. $6b^2 + 17b + 12$ 131. $8x^2 - 38x + 45$ 132. $8x^2 - 42x + 27$

133. $30y^2 + y - 3$ 134. $12y^2 - 32y - 35$ 135. $9u^2 + 24u + 16$ 136. $25y^2 + 10y + 1$

137. $121m^2 + 132m + 36$ 138. $16x^2 + 56x + 49$ 139. $16p^2 - 40p + 25$ 140. $81q^2 - 36q + 4$

141. $3x^2 + 5x + 4$ 142. $3y^2 + 7y + 8$ 143. $7a^2 - 2a + 11$ 144. $7a^2 - 7a - 2$

145. $4x^2 - x + 12$ 146. $10u^2 - u + 8$

In Exercises 147-168, factor the polynomials by grouping.

147. $x^3 + x^2 + 4x + 4$ 148. $x^3 + x^2 + 2x + 2$ 149. $y^3 - 7y^2 + 2y - 14$

150. $y^3 - 6y^2 + 4y - 24$ 151. $3a^3 + 15a^2 + 2a + 10$ 152. $2b^3 + 8b^2 + 3b + 12$

153. $16m^3 - 40m^2 - 6m + 15$ 154. $21n^3 - 14n^2 - 12n + 8$ 155. $x^5 + x^3 + 12x^2 + 12$

156. $2y^4 + 7y^3 + 12y + 42$ 157. $8b^5 - 48b^3 + 3b^2 - 18$ 158. $10a^5 + 90a^3 - 5a^2 - 45$

159. $2p^3 + p + 6p^2q + 3q$ 160. $27m^3 + 36m^2 + 3mn + 4n$ 161. $80m^4 - 50m^2 - 24m^2n + 15n$

162. $36a^3 + 84a^2 - 33ab^2 - 77b^2$ 163. $x^2 + 8x + 16 - y^2$ 164. $x^2 - 6x + 9 - y^2$

165. $a^2 - 14a + 49 - 9b^2$ 166. $a^2 + 16a + 64 - 25b^2$ 167. $x^2 + 18x + 81 - 144y^2$

168. $u^2 - 4u + 4 - 121v^2$

In Exercises 169-216, factor the polynomials completely.

169. $6x^2 + 18x + 12$ 170. $6x^2 + 30x + 36$ 171. $4a^4 - 8a^3 - 60a^2$

172. $7a^5 + 21a^4 - 28a^3$ 173. $5u^7 - 55u^6 + 150u^5$ 174. $8v^7 - 40v^6 + 48v^5$

175. $2x^3y^3 - 6x^3y^2 - 56x^3y$ 176. $4m^3n - 12m^2n - 40mn$ 177. $27x^2y + 63xy + 18y$

178. $20st^2 + 32st + 12s$ 179. $56y^2 + 14y - 21$ 180. $24y^2 - 24y - 18$

181. $48u^5 - 58u^4 + 14u^3$ 182. $42v^4 - 75v^3 + 18v^2$ 183. $8s^3t^2 - 48s^2t^2 + 72st^2$

184. $6p^3q + 48p^2q + 96pq$ 185. $9a^4 + 6a^3 + a^2$ 186. $80x^4 - 120x^3 + 45x^2$

187. $20 + x - x^2$ 188. $35 + 2x - x^2$ 189. $-20 + 9t - t^2$

190. $-21 + 10s - s^2$ 191. $72 + 30x - 12x^2$ 192. $20 + 2x - 6x^2$

193. $x^4 + 10x^2 + 25$ 194. $x^4 - 4x^2 + 4$ 195. $y^6 + 18y^3 + 81$

196. $y^6 - 20y^3 + 100$ 197. $u^4 - 2u^2 + 1$ 198. $v^4 - 8v^2 + 16$

199. $16x^4 - 81$ 200. $16x^4 - 16$ 201. $x^6 + 2x^3 + 1$

202. $y^6 - 16y^3 + 64$ 203. $m^4 - 13m^2 - 48$ 204. $n^4 - 13n^2 - 36$

205. $a^6 - 10a^3 + 16$ 206. $b^6 + 29b^3 + 54$ 207. $1 - p^6$

208. $p^6 - 1$ 209. $1 - 64x^6$ 210. $y^6 - 64$

211. $28a^2 + 25ab + 3b^2$ 212. $3a^2 - 13ab - 10b^2$ 213. $9m^2 - 42mn + 49n^2$

214. $25p^2 - 40pq + 16q^2$ 215. $8x^4y + 42x^3y^2 + 54x^2y^3$ 216. $60x^3y^4 + 25x^2y^5 - 15xy^6$

END OF CHAPTER 3   QUIZ

1. The coefficient of the monomial $5x^2y^6$ is
  a) 5   b) 2   c) 6   d) 8   e) 12

2. The degree of the polynomial $-\frac{1}{2}x^3 + 5x^2 - x + 3$ is
  a) $-\frac{1}{2}$ b) 6   c) 3   d) $-\frac{1}{2}x^3$ e) 4

3. $\left(4a^2 + 3a - 7\right) + \left(-2a^2 + a - 15\right) =$
  a) $2a^2 + 3a + 8$ b) $2a^2 + 4a + 22$ c) $-2a^2 + 4a - 22$ d) $2a^2 + 4a - 8$ e) $2a^2 + 4a - 22$

4. $(-6a + 9b) - (7a - 12b) =$
   a) $a + 21b$ b) $-13a + 21b$ c) $-13a - 3b$ d) $13a - 21b$ e) $8ab$

5. $(6x^2 - 4y^2) - (3x^2 - xy + y^2) =$
   a) $3x^2 + xy - 5y^2$ b) $3x^2 - xy - 5y^2$ c) $3x^2 + xy - 3y^2$ d) $3x^2 + x^2y^2 + y^2$ e) $3x^2 - xy - 4y^2$

6. $(2m + 3n) + (5n - 7m) - (3m + 9n) =$
   a) $8m - n$ b) $-8m + n$ c) $-8m - n$ d) $5m - 13n$ e) $-9mn$

7. $5xy^2 (3x^2 + 2xy - 4y^2) =$
   a) $15x^2y^2 + 10x^2y^3 - 20xy^4$ b) $15x^3y^3 + 5x^2y^3 - 4xy^4$ c) $15x^3y^2 + 10x^2y^3 - 20x^3y$
   d) $15x^3y^2 + 10x^2y^3 - 20xy^4$ e) $15x^3y^2 + 10x^2y^3 - 20x^2y^2$

8. $(8a + 3b)(7a - 2b) =$
   a) $56a^2 - 5ab - 6b^2$ b) $56a^2 + 5ab + 6b^2$ c) $56a^2 + 37ab - 6b^2$
   d) $56a^2 + 5ab - 6b^2$ e) $56a^2 - 16ab + 21b - 6b^2$

9. $(4x - 3)^2 =$
   a) $16x^2 + 9$ b) $16x^2 - 24x + 9$ c) $16x^2 - 24x - 9$ d) $16x^2 - 9$ e) $4x^2 - 9$

10. $(2x - 7)(x^2 + 3x - 5) =$
    a) $2x^3 + x^2 - 31x + 35$ b) $2x^3 - x^2 - 31x - 35$ c) $2x^3 - x^2 + 31x + 35$
    d) $2x^3 - 13x^2 - 31x + 35$ e) $2x^3 - x^2 - 31x + 35$

11. $(42x^8y^{11}) \div (-7x^6y^3) =$
    a) $-6x^2y^8$ b) $6x^2y^8$ c) $-6x^{14}y^{14}$ d) $6x^{14}y^{14}$ e) $-6xy^8$

12. $\dfrac{-18a^2b^5 + 8a^9b^7}{-2a^2b^3} =$
    a) $9b^2 + 8a^9b^7$ b) $9b^2 + 4a^7b^4$ c) $9b^2 - 4a^7b^4$ d) $9ab^2 - 4a^7b^4$ e) $9b^2 - 8a^9b^7$

13. $(3x^2 - 4x - 5) \div (x + 7) =$
    a) $3x - 25$ R -180 b) $3x - 25$ R 170 c) $3x - 4$ R 25 d) $3x - \dfrac{7}{4}$ R 7 e) $3x + 17$ R -124

14. Factor completely: $12x^8 - 8x^5 + 14x^3$
    a) $2(6x^8 - 4x^5 + 7x^3)$ b) $2x^3(6x^5 + 4x^2 + 7)$ c) $2x^2(6x^6 - 4x^3 + 7x)$
    d) $x^3(12x^5 - 8x^2 + 14)$ e) $2x^3(6x^5 - 4x^2 + 7)$

15. Factor completely: $64a^2 - 16b^2$
    a) $(8a - 4b)^2$ b) $16(4a^2 - b^2)$ c) $16(2a - b)^2$ d) $16(2a + b)(2a - b)$ e) $16(2a + b)^2$

16. Factor completely: $u^3 - 125$
    a) $(u - 5)(u^2 + 5u - 25)$ b) $(u - 5)^3$ c) $(u - 5)(u^2 + 5u + 25)$ d) $(u - 5)(u^2 + 5u + 10)$
    e) $(u + 5)(u^2 - 5u + 25)$

17. Factor completely: $x^2 + 3x - 54$
    a) $(x - 9)(x - 6)$ b) $(x + 9)(x - 6)$ c) $(x + 9)(x + 6)$ d) $(x - 9)(x + 6)$ e) it is prime

18. Factor completely: $12a^2 + 8a - 15$
   a) $(6a - 5)(2a + 3)$ b) $(6a + 5)(2a - 3)$ c) $(6a - 3)(2a + 5)$ d) $(12a - 5)(a + 3)$
   e) it is prime

19. Factor completely: $3p^2 - 3p - 60$
   a) $3(p^2 - p - 20)$ b) $3(p + 5)(p - 4)$ c) $(3p + 12)(p - 5)$ d) $(p - 5)(p + 4)$ e) $3(p - 5)(p + 4)$

20. Factor completely: $x^2(x + 3) - 25(x + 3)$
   a) $(x^2 - 25)(x + 3)$ b) $(x + 3)(x + 5)(x - 5)$ c) $x + 3(x^2 - 25)$ d) $(x + 3)^2(x + 5)(x - 5)$
   e) $x + 3(x + 5)(x - 5)$

ANSWERS FOR QUIZ 3   1. a   2. c   3. e   4. b   5. a
                       6. c   7. d   8. d   9. b   10. e
                       11. a   12. c   13. b   14. e   15. d
                       16. c   17. b   18. a   19. e   20. b

Chapter 4:   Rational Expressions

In this chapter, we will study algebraic objects known as rational expressions. A **rational expression** is a fraction whose numerator and denominator consists of polynomials. As with rational numbers, we would like to know how to simplify, multiply, divide, add, and subtract rational expressions. In Section 4.1, we will learn some definitions which will be used throughout the section, as well as the method for simplifying a rational expression into lowest terms. As we will see, factoring plays a major role in simplifying a rational expression. Section 4.2 will be devoted to multiplication and division of rational expressions. Addition and subtraction of rational expressions will be studied in Section 4.3. We will learn how to find the LCM of polynomials as well. The chapter concludes with the study of simplifying a mixed quotient. Roughly speaking, a mixed quotient is a fraction whose numerator and/or denominator contains rational expressions. In Section 4.4, we will study two methods for simplifying such an algebraic expression.

Section 4.1   Definitions and Simplifying Rational Expressions

Definition: A **rational expression** is an expression of the form $\frac{p}{q}$, where both p and q are polynomials and $q \neq 0$.

Examples of rational expressions are $\frac{4}{7}$, $\frac{x-2}{3x+4}$, $\frac{8x^2 - x + 12}{-x^3 + 9x + 3}$, and $\frac{x^2 + 5xy - 3y^2}{10y^2 - 2yz + 3z^2}$.

Observe that any rational number is a rational expression since both the numerator and denominator contain constant monomials, namely integers. Moreover, any polynomial, P, may be considered as a rational expression by simply writing $P = \frac{P}{1}$.

There are many rational expressions which may all be 'the same' in the sense that they simplify to the same expression. For example, observe that the fractions $\frac{3}{9}$, $\frac{6}{18}$, and $\frac{-12}{-36}$ all simplify to $\frac{1}{3}$. In fact, if x represents **any** real number other than 0, then the fraction $\frac{x}{3x}$ will simplify to $\frac{1}{3}$.

Definition: Two or more rational expressions are called **equivalent** if they simplify to the same rational expression.

When we talk about rational expressions, we must always keep in mind that each of the variables in the expression has a domain (recall that the domain of a variable is the set of real numbers which can replace the variable to give a well-defined answer). When two rational expressions are equivalent, remember that they are equivalent provided that they are well-defined. We will see this in Examples 3 and 4 below.

Examples.

1) $\frac{4}{8}$ is equivalent to $\frac{10}{20}$ since $\frac{4}{8} = \frac{1}{2}$ and $\frac{10}{20} = \frac{1}{2}$.

2) $\frac{12}{16}$ is equivalent to $\frac{-6}{-8}$ since $\frac{12}{16} = \frac{3}{4}$ and $\frac{-6}{-8} = \frac{3}{4}$.

3) $\frac{5}{y}$ is equivalent to $\frac{5(y+4)}{y(y+4)}$, provided that $y \neq 0, -4$.

100

Notice that the numerator and denominator of $\dfrac{5(y+4)}{y(y+4)}$ are factored and there is an equal factor of $y+4$ in both. If you cancel these factors out, you'll get exactly the expression which is equivalent to it, $\dfrac{5}{y}$. In other words,

$$\frac{5(y+4)}{y(y+4)} = \frac{5}{y} \cdot \frac{\overset{1}{\cancel{y+4}}}{\underset{1}{\cancel{y+4}}} = \frac{5}{y}.$$

4) $\dfrac{5t+2}{-4t+20}$ is equivalent to $\dfrac{-t(5t+2)}{-t(-4t+20)}$, provided that $t \neq 0, 5$.

Once again, the numerator and denominator of $\dfrac{-t(5t+2)}{-t(-4t+20)}$ are factored and there is an equal factor of $-t$ in both. If you cancel out the $-t$, you'll get $\dfrac{5t+2}{-4t+20}$. In other words,

$$\frac{-t(5t+2)}{-t(-4t+20)} = \frac{\overset{1}{\cancel{-t}}}{\underset{1}{\cancel{-t}}} \cdot \frac{5t+2}{-4t+20} = \frac{5t+2}{-4t+20}.$$

This technique of cancelling out equal factors can always be performed.

Property of Simplifying a Rational Expression

If A, B, and C are polynomials and both $B, C \neq 0$, then

$$\frac{A\overset{1}{\cancel{C}}}{B\underset{1}{\cancel{C}}} = \frac{A}{B}.$$

In particular, we have $\dfrac{A\overset{1}{\cancel{C}}}{\underset{1}{\cancel{C}}} = \dfrac{A}{1} = A$ and $\dfrac{\overset{1}{\cancel{C}}}{B\underset{1}{\cancel{C}}} = \dfrac{1}{B}$.

We see that in order to simplify a rational expression, we first need to factor the numerator and denominator. Afterwards, we see if any common factors can be cancelled out.

There is a similar property when division occurs in the numerator and denominator, namely:

$$\frac{A \div \overset{1}{\cancel{C}}}{B \div \underset{1}{\cancel{C}}} = \frac{A}{B}, \text{ provided that } B, C \neq 0.$$

There are some very common mistakes which are often made with the simplifying property.

$$
\boxed{
\begin{array}{lll}
\textbf{BEWARE} \quad : & 1. & \dfrac{A \pm \cancel{C}}{B \pm \cancel{C}} \neq \dfrac{A}{B} \\[2ex]
 & 2. & \dfrac{A\cancel{C}}{B \pm \cancel{C}} \neq \dfrac{A}{B} \\[2ex]
 & 3. & \dfrac{A \pm \cancel{C}}{B\cancel{C}} \neq \dfrac{A}{B}
\end{array}
}
$$

Examples. Simplify.

1) $\dfrac{12}{32} = \dfrac{3 \times \overset{1}{\cancel{4}}}{8 \times \underset{1}{\cancel{4}}} = \dfrac{3}{8}$

Alternatively, we have $\dfrac{12}{32} = \dfrac{12 \div \overset{1}{\cancel{4}}}{32 \div \underset{1}{\cancel{4}}} = \dfrac{3}{8}$. This method of dividing is easy when we have numbers, but not easy when we have polynomials.

2) $\dfrac{\overset{1}{\cancel{4}}x^7 y^{12}}{\underset{4}{\cancel{16}}x^9 y^4} = \dfrac{1y^8}{4x^2} = \dfrac{y^8}{4x^2}$, $\ x \neq 0$ and $y \neq 0$

Notice that I cancelled out 7 x's and 4 y's from both the numerator and denominator.

3) $\dfrac{4x - 8}{5x - 10} = \dfrac{4(\overset{1}{\cancel{x - 2}})}{5(\underset{1}{\cancel{x - 2}})} = \dfrac{4}{5}$, $\ x \neq 2$

4) $\dfrac{3a - 18}{3a + 18} = \dfrac{\overset{1}{\cancel{3}}(a - 6)}{\underset{1}{\cancel{3}}(a + 6)} = \dfrac{a - 6}{a + 6}$, $\ a \neq -6$

5) $\dfrac{7y - 4}{8 - 14y} = \underbrace{\dfrac{1(7y - 4)}{2(4 - 7y)} = \dfrac{1(\overset{1}{\cancel{7y - 4}})}{-2(\underset{1}{\cancel{-4 + 7y}})}}_{\text{$7y-4$ and $4-7y$ are additive inverses.}} = -\dfrac{1}{2}$, $\ y \neq \dfrac{4}{7}$

6) $\dfrac{x^2 - 16}{x^2 - 8x + 16} = \dfrac{(x + 4)(\overset{1}{\cancel{x - 4}})}{(x - 4)(\underset{1}{\cancel{x - 4}})} = \dfrac{x + 4}{x - 4}$, $\ x \neq 4$

7) $\dfrac{t^3 - 7t^2 + 6t}{t^4 - t} = \underbrace{\dfrac{t(t^2 - 7t + 6)}{t(t^3 - 1)} = \dfrac{\overset{1}{\cancel{t}}(t - 6)(\overset{1}{\cancel{t - 1}})}{\underset{1}{\cancel{t}}(\underset{1}{\cancel{t - 1}})(t^2 + t + 1)}}_{\text{Factor the polynomials completely.}} = \dfrac{t - 6}{t^2 + t + 1}$, $\ t \neq 0, 1$

102

8) $\dfrac{4x^4 - 10x^3 - 24x^2}{6x^5 - 24x^4} = \dfrac{2x^2(2x^2 - 5x - 12)}{6x^4(x - 4)} = \dfrac{\overset{1}{\cancel{2x^2}}(2x + 3)(\overset{1}{\cancel{x - 4}})}{\underset{3x^2}{\cancel{6x^4}}(\underset{1}{\cancel{x - 4}})} = \dfrac{2x + 3}{3x^2}, \quad x \neq 0, 4$

9) $\dfrac{14x^2 + 3x - 5}{9x^2 - 4} = \dfrac{(7x + 5)(2x - 1)}{(3x + 2)(3x - 2)}, \quad x \neq -\dfrac{2}{3}, \dfrac{2}{3}$

Notice that nothing cancelled out since there are no common factors in the numerator and denominator. Therefore, this expression is already simplified.

Exercise 4.1. Simplify.

1. $\dfrac{4x^2}{7x}$

2. $\dfrac{2y^3}{9y}$

3. $\dfrac{5x^2}{10x^6}$

4. $\dfrac{4y^3}{12y^8}$

5. $\dfrac{32}{12x^7}$

6. $\dfrac{16}{18y^4}$

7. $\dfrac{8x^3}{x^{10}}$

8. $\dfrac{12y^9}{y^{18}}$

9. $\dfrac{x^{11}y^2}{x^6y^5}$

10. $\dfrac{x^{13}y^{12}}{x^3y^{15}}$

11. $\dfrac{10a^5b^6}{-16ab^4}$

12. $\dfrac{-6a^9b^{10}}{8a^2b}$

13. $\dfrac{6a^2b^3}{21a^7b^{10}}$

14. $\dfrac{22m^2n}{12m^{12}n^7}$

15. $\dfrac{8r^2s^8t^6}{20r^4st^9}$

16. $\dfrac{14a^5b^4c^7}{21a^2b^6c^2}$

17. $\dfrac{-18m^{16}n^8p^7}{-8m^4p^7}$

18. $\dfrac{-42m^3n^{16}p^2}{-22m^3n^{20}}$

19. $\dfrac{-56ac^7}{7a^8b^6}$

20. $\dfrac{-48x^{13}y}{8x^6z^5}$

21. $\dfrac{3x + 6}{7x + 14}$

22. $\dfrac{15x + 30}{2x + 4}$

23. $\dfrac{9y - 36}{3y - 12}$

24. $\dfrac{8y - 24}{6y - 18}$

25. $\dfrac{8t - 20}{8t + 20}$

26. $\dfrac{14n + 6}{14n - 6}$

27. $\dfrac{3x - 1}{3 - 9x}$

28. $\dfrac{14 - 10x}{5x - 7}$

29. $\dfrac{12 - 6x^2}{3x^2 - 6}$

30. $\dfrac{7y^2 - 21}{3 - y^2}$

31. $\dfrac{8x^2 + 16}{-30 - 15x^2}$

32. $\dfrac{-12x - 20}{50 + 30x}$

33. $\dfrac{7p^2 + p}{8p^2 - 3p}$

34. $\dfrac{2q^2 - 5q}{3q^2 + q}$

35. $\dfrac{10x^2 + 10x}{10x^2 + 15x}$

36. $\dfrac{24y^2 - 32y}{32y^2 - 16y}$

37. $\dfrac{2x^3y^3 - 2x^2y^4}{12x^5y + 12x^4y^2}$

38. $\dfrac{2t^3 + 6t^2}{-5t^4 - 15t^3}$

39. $\dfrac{4x^2 - 8x}{6x - 3x^2}$

40. $\dfrac{14y^4 + 7y^3}{-18y^5 - 9y^4}$

41. $\dfrac{x^2 + 4x + 4}{6x + 12}$

42. $\dfrac{x^2 + 8x + 15}{2x + 10}$

43. $\dfrac{7x^2 - 63}{2x^2 - 6x}$

44. $\dfrac{2x^2 - 8x}{3x^3 - 48x}$

45. $\dfrac{x^3 - 1}{x^2 - 1}$

46. $\dfrac{x^2 - 9}{x^3 + 27}$

47. $\dfrac{9t^2 - 30t + 25}{6t^2 - 7t - 5}$

48. $\dfrac{4t^2 - 8t - 21}{4t^2 + 12t + 9}$

49. $\dfrac{16x^3 - 8x^2}{4x^2 - 1}$

50. $\dfrac{64s^2t^3 + 4t^3}{4s^3 - s}$

51. $\dfrac{5x^2 + 22x + 21}{x^4 - 9x^2}$

52. $\dfrac{2x^4 - 8x^3 - 42x^2}{5x^6 - 45x^4}$

Section 4.2   Multiplication and Division of Rational Expressions

In this section, we will learn how to multiply and divide rational expressions. Let us recall how to multiply and divide rational numbers (see Section 1.2).

Suppose A, B, C, and D are integers and both B, $D \neq 0$. Then $\dfrac{A}{B} \cdot \dfrac{C}{D} = \dfrac{AC}{BD}$. Moreover, if $C \neq 0$ as well, then $\dfrac{A}{B} \div \dfrac{C}{D} = \dfrac{A}{B} \cdot \dfrac{D}{C} = \dfrac{AD}{BC}$. When we multiply (or divide) two fractions, we can sometimes simplify the problem by cancelling out common factors and then multiply them together. For example,

$$\frac{2}{3} \times \frac{9}{8} = \frac{\overset{1}{\cancel{2}}}{\underset{1}{\cancel{3}}} \times \frac{\overset{3}{\cancel{9}}}{\underset{4}{\cancel{8}}} = \frac{3}{4}$$

and

$$\frac{15}{16} \div (-10) = \frac{15}{16} \div \left(\frac{-10}{1}\right) = \frac{\overset{3}{\cancel{15}}}{16} \times \left(\frac{1}{\underset{2}{\cancel{-10}}}\right) = -\frac{3}{32}.$$

As we have seen in the previous section, before we cancel out any common factors, we must factor the numerator and denominator in order to see what these common factors are. The same method applies to rational expressions whose numerator and denominator contains polynomials.

In the Examples below, we will not be concerned with the domain of each variable.

Examples. Multiply and simplify.

1) $\dfrac{x^3}{4} \cdot \dfrac{xy^5}{3} = \dfrac{\left(x^3\right)\left(xy^5\right)}{(4)(3)} = \dfrac{x^4 y^5}{12}$

2) $\dfrac{18a^3}{b^2} \cdot \dfrac{a^6 b^8}{9} = \dfrac{\left(\overset{2}{\cancel{18}}a^3\right)\left(a^6 b^8\right)}{(b^2)\left(\underset{1}{\cancel{9}}\right)} = \dfrac{2a^9 b^8}{b^2} = \dfrac{2a^9 b^6}{1} = 2a^9 b^6$

3) $\dfrac{2y^2}{5x^3} \cdot \dfrac{11x^2 y^4}{7xy} = \dfrac{\left(2y^2\right)\left(11x^2 y^4\right)}{\left(5x^3\right)(7xy)} = \dfrac{22x^2 y^6}{35x^4 y} = \dfrac{22y^5}{35x^2}$

4) $\dfrac{14a^2 b}{3ab^4} \cdot \dfrac{a^8 b^5}{16b^3} = \dfrac{\left(\overset{7}{\cancel{14}}a^2 b\right)\left(a^8 b^5\right)}{\left(3ab^4\right)\left(\underset{8}{\cancel{16}}b^3\right)} = \dfrac{7a^{10} b^6}{24ab^7} = \dfrac{7a^9}{24b}$

5) $\dfrac{x}{2x+4} \cdot \dfrac{6}{5x} = \dfrac{\overset{1}{\cancel{x}}}{\underset{1}{\cancel{2}}(x+2)} \cdot \dfrac{\overset{3}{\cancel{6}}}{5\underset{1}{\cancel{x}}} = \dfrac{3}{5(x+2)}$

Notice that I factored $2x + 4$ and then cancelled out the common factors. We can leave our answers with the numerator and denominator in factored form.

6) $\dfrac{8a^4}{9a^2 - 1} \cdot \dfrac{3a+1}{16a} = \dfrac{\overset{1}{\cancel{8}}a^4}{\underset{1}{(\cancel{3a+1})}(3a-1)} \cdot \dfrac{\overset{1}{(\cancel{3a+1})}}{\underset{2}{\cancel{16}}a} = \dfrac{a^4}{2a(3a-1)} = \dfrac{a^3}{2(3a-1)}$

7) $\dfrac{5y+15}{y^3+27} \cdot \dfrac{y^4-2y}{5y^3} = \dfrac{\overset{1}{\cancel{5}}\overset{1}{(\cancel{y+3})}}{(\cancel{y+3})(y^2-3y+9)} \cdot \dfrac{y(y^3-2)}{\cancel{5}y^3} = \dfrac{y(y^3-2)}{y^3(y^2-3y+9)} = \dfrac{y^3-2}{y^2(y^2-3y+9)}$

8) $\dfrac{t^3-t^2-6t}{8t^2-24t} \cdot \dfrac{12t-12}{2t^3-2t} = \dfrac{\overset{1}{\cancel{t}}\overset{1}{(\cancel{t-3})}(t+2)}{8\cancel{t}(\cancel{t-3})} \cdot \dfrac{12\overset{1}{\cancel{(t-1)}}}{2t(t+1)\cancel{(t-1)}} = \dfrac{3(t+2)}{4t(t+1)}$

9) $\dfrac{x^2+14x+49}{2x^2+17x+21} \cdot \dfrac{4x-9}{18-8x} = \dfrac{(x+7)\overset{1}{\cancel{(x+7)}}}{(2x+3)\cancel{(x+7)}} \cdot \dfrac{1\overset{1}{\cancel{(4x-9)}}}{-2\cancel{(4x-9)}} = \dfrac{x+7}{-2(2x+3)}$ or $-\dfrac{x+7}{2(2x+3)}$

Examples. Divide and simplify.

1) $\dfrac{x^7}{2} \div \dfrac{x^2}{5} = \dfrac{x^7}{2} \cdot \dfrac{5}{x^2} = \dfrac{5x^5}{2}$

2) $\dfrac{20a^3b}{9ab^6} \div \left(-\dfrac{10b^7}{3a^2}\right) = \dfrac{\overset{2}{\cancel{20}}a^3b}{\underset{3}{\cancel{9}}ab^6} \cdot \left(-\dfrac{\overset{1}{\cancel{3}}a^2}{\underset{1}{\cancel{10}}b^7}\right) = -\dfrac{2a^5b}{3ab^{13}} = -\dfrac{2a^4}{3b^{12}}$

3) $\dfrac{9}{4x-28} \div \dfrac{18x^2-126x}{x^2-49} = \dfrac{9}{4x-28} \cdot \dfrac{x^2-49}{18x^2-126x} = \dfrac{\overset{1}{\cancel{9}}}{4(x-7)} \cdot \dfrac{(x+7)\overset{1}{\cancel{(x-7)}}}{\underset{2}{\cancel{18}}x\underset{1}{\cancel{(x-7)}}} = \dfrac{x+7}{8x(x-7)}$

4) $\dfrac{2a^2-3a-20}{a^3-8a^2+16a} \div \dfrac{10a^2+25a}{2a^2+5} = \dfrac{2a^2-3a-20}{a^3-8a^2+16a} \cdot \dfrac{2a^2+5}{10a^2+25a}$

$\qquad = \dfrac{(2a+5)\overset{1}{\cancel{(a-4)}}}{a(a-4)\underset{1}{\cancel{(a-4)}}} \cdot \dfrac{2a^2+5}{5a\cancel{(2a+5)}} = \dfrac{2a^2+5}{5a^2(a-4)}$

5) $\dfrac{x^3-64}{x^3+64} \div \dfrac{x^2-4x}{x^2+4x} = \dfrac{x^3-64}{x^3+64} \cdot \dfrac{x^2+4x}{x^2-4x} = \dfrac{\overset{1}{\cancel{(x-4)}}(x^2+4x+16)}{\underset{1}{\cancel{(x+4)}}(x^2-4x+16)} \cdot \dfrac{\overset{1}{\cancel{x}}\overset{1}{\cancel{(x+4)}}}{\underset{1}{\cancel{x}}\underset{1}{\cancel{(x-4)}}} = \dfrac{x^2+4x+16}{x^2-4x+16}$

6) $\dfrac{64-4x^2}{2x^2-32} \div \dfrac{24}{x^2+1} = \dfrac{64-4x^2}{2x^2-32} \cdot \dfrac{x^2+1}{24} = \dfrac{\overset{1}{\cancel{4}}\overset{1}{(\cancel{4+x})}\overset{-1}{(\cancel{4-x})}}{2\underset{1}{\cancel{(x+4)}}\underset{1}{\cancel{(x-4)}}} \cdot \dfrac{x^2+1}{\underset{6}{\cancel{24}}} = \dfrac{-1(x^2+1)}{12}$ or $-\dfrac{x^2+1}{12}$

As you can clearly see, division is just multiplication 'with a flip'. The name of the game for multiplication and division is factoring.

Exercise 4.2

In Exercises 1-16, multiply and simplify.

1. $\dfrac{8x^7y}{3x^2y^6} \cdot \dfrac{9x^4y^4}{7xy^{12}}$

2. $\dfrac{4x^2y^5}{12x^3y^2} \cdot \dfrac{6x^8y^2}{5xy^7}$

3. $\left(-\dfrac{10a^2}{b^6c^4}\right) \cdot \dfrac{2ab^3c^4}{5}$

4. $\dfrac{24m^5}{n^2p^4} \cdot \left(-\dfrac{7mn^{12}p}{8}\right)$

5. $\dfrac{4x+12}{8x-16} \cdot \dfrac{9x-18}{5x+15}$

6. $\dfrac{4x-16}{3x+3} \cdot \dfrac{12x+12}{8x-32}$

7. $\dfrac{12y^2+6y}{4y+4} \cdot \dfrac{5y-10}{3y^3-6y^2}$

8. $\dfrac{3t^3+18t^2}{9t^2-18t} \cdot \dfrac{t+1}{4t+24}$

9. $\dfrac{2a^2-2a-12}{2a^2+10a+12} \cdot \dfrac{3a-9}{a+1}$

10. $\dfrac{3b^2+24b+48}{3b^2+6b-24} \cdot \dfrac{2}{b+4}$

11. $\dfrac{8y^3-64}{4y+2} \cdot \dfrac{12y^2+12y+3}{y^2+2y+4}$

12. $\dfrac{7s^2-28s+28}{14s+28} \cdot \dfrac{27s+36}{6s^2-4s-16}$

13. $\dfrac{x^2-25}{x^2-64} \cdot \dfrac{x^2-10x+16}{x^2+9x+20}$

14. $\dfrac{3y^2+2y-1}{9y^2-1} \cdot \dfrac{y^2-4}{y^2-1}$

15. $\dfrac{-4u^2-5u+6}{8u-6} \cdot \dfrac{8u}{u+2}$

16. $\dfrac{9b^2+34b-8}{9b-2} \cdot \dfrac{b-4}{16-b^2}$

In Exercises 17-38, divide and simplify.

17. $\dfrac{x}{4} \div \dfrac{x^3}{20}$

18. $\dfrac{y^2}{12} \div \dfrac{y^7}{2}$

19. $\left(\dfrac{-25}{6y^8}\right) \div \left(\dfrac{10}{-9y^4}\right)$

20. $\left(-\dfrac{16}{y^2}\right) \div \left(\dfrac{34}{3y^{10}}\right)$

21. $\left(\dfrac{a}{-15}\right) \div \dfrac{b^2}{12}$

22. $\dfrac{m^2}{24} \div \left(-\dfrac{n^4}{18}\right)$

23. $\dfrac{3x^9y^3}{5x^4y} \div \dfrac{10xy}{15x^4y^3}$

24. $\dfrac{11s^4t^5}{7st^9} \div \dfrac{11s^5t^2}{14st^8}$

25. $\left(\dfrac{-10u^5v}{8uv^5}\right) \div \left(\dfrac{15u^3v}{-16u^4v}\right)$

26. $\left(\dfrac{24u^6v^2}{-10u^3v^4}\right) \div \left(\dfrac{18uv}{-8u^5v^3}\right)$

27. $\dfrac{7x}{6} \div \dfrac{x^2+x}{4x+4}$

28. $\dfrac{2y}{5} \div \dfrac{18y-36}{y^2-2y}$

29. $\dfrac{2t-14}{3t+18} \div \dfrac{2t+14}{6t+36}$

30. $\dfrac{4t+12}{5t+15} \div \dfrac{9t-54}{10t-60}$

31. $\dfrac{x^2+3x-4}{6x-6} \div \dfrac{x^2-6x+8}{x-2}$

32. $\dfrac{x^2+x-6}{2x+6} \div \dfrac{x^2-7x+12}{7x+28}$

33. $\dfrac{2y^3-16}{4y^2-5y-6} \div \dfrac{3y^2+6y+12}{8y^2-22y-21}$

34. $\dfrac{9p^2+15p-10}{3p^2-2p} \div \dfrac{9p^2-25}{14p^3+56p^2}$

35. $\dfrac{7t^3+2t^2-21t-6}{35t+10} \div \dfrac{14t^3+4t^2+7t+2}{6t^3+3t}$

36. $\dfrac{12y^3+18y^2+10y+15}{6y^2+7y-3} \div \dfrac{18y^3-6y^2+15y-5}{9y^2-6y+1}$

37. $\dfrac{9x^2+38xy+8y^2}{3x^2y^3+12xy^4} \div \dfrac{x^2-2xy+y^2}{27x^3y+6x^2y^2}$

38. $\dfrac{a^2+3ab-18b^2}{a^2-9b^2} \div \dfrac{12a^2b+72ab^2}{a^2+4ab+3b^2}$

Section 4.3   Addition and Subtraction of Rational Expressions

We will learn how to add and subtract rational expressions. As for real numbers, in order to add or subtract two rational expressions, the denominators of the rationals must be the same (as usual, we say that they are **common denominators**). Algebraically, we write

$$\dfrac{A}{C} \pm \dfrac{B}{C} = \dfrac{A \pm B}{C},\ C \neq 0.$$

106

We will begin by doing some examples in which the rationals already have common denominators. If the rationals have denominators which are additive inverses of each other, it is easy to obtain the common denominator. Examples like these will be given as well. Following this, we will learn how to add and subtract rational expressions whose denominators are neither common nor additive inverses of each other. In this case, we'll need to find the least common denominator (LCD) of the expressions. The key to doing these involves factoring the denominators. Finding the least common denominator is the same as finding the LCM of the denominators. We will learn how to find the LCM of polynomials, starting with the case in which the polynomials are integers. After we master this, we will be able to combine any two rational expressions.

Examples. Add or subtract and simplify.

1) $\dfrac{2}{x} + \dfrac{6}{x} = \dfrac{2+6}{x} = \dfrac{8}{x}$

Note that this makes sense as long as $x \neq 0$. For the rest of these examples, we won't worry about the domain of the variables.

2) $\dfrac{9}{y^2} - \dfrac{12}{y^2} = \dfrac{9-12}{y^2} = \dfrac{-3}{y^2} = -\dfrac{3}{y^2}$

3) $\dfrac{8x}{x+3} + \dfrac{2x}{x+3} = \dfrac{8x+2x}{x+3} = \dfrac{10x}{x+3}$

4) $\dfrac{6t}{4t+1} - \dfrac{2t}{4t+1} = \dfrac{6t-2t}{4t+1} = \dfrac{4t}{4t+1}$

Notice that the $4t$ in the numerator and denominator do not cancel since the denominator is **not** factored. Remember that the only time we can cancel out terms is when both the numerator and denominator are **factored**.

5) $\dfrac{5x+2}{4x-9} + \dfrac{3x-8}{4x-9} = \dfrac{(5x+2)+(3x-8)}{4x-9} = \dfrac{5x+2+3x-8}{4x-9} = \dfrac{8x-6}{4x-9} = \dfrac{2(4x-3)}{4x-9}$

The parentheses can be removed since the Associative Property holds for addition. Observe that I've factored the numerator in attempt to simplify my answer. No common factors appeared, so I left my answer alone.

6) $\dfrac{6x^2-9}{x+2} - \dfrac{5x^2-5}{x+2} = \dfrac{(6x^2-9)-(5x^2-5)}{x+2} = \dfrac{6x^2-9-5x^2+5}{x+2}$

$$= \dfrac{x^2-4}{x+2} = \dfrac{\overset{1}{\cancel{(x+2)}}(x-2)}{\underset{1}{\cancel{x+2}}} = \dfrac{x-2}{1} = x-2$$

This time, we cannot just throw away the parentheses since the Associative Property doesn't hold for subtraction. Instead, we need to distribute the negative sign (which is really just -1) into the second parenthesis. This changes the signs of each of the terms in it. Notice that our answer **did** simplify this time.

7) $\dfrac{2x^2+8x-5}{x^2+4x-32} + \dfrac{-x^2+3x+29}{x^2+4x-32} = \dfrac{(2x^2+8x-5)+(-x^2+3x+29)}{x^2+4x-32} = \dfrac{x^2+11x+24}{x^2+4x-32}$

$$= \dfrac{(x+3)\overset{1}{\cancel{(x+8)}}}{(x-4)\underset{1}{\cancel{(x+8)}}} = \dfrac{x+3}{x-4}$$

107

8) $\dfrac{4y+3}{5y-6} - \dfrac{14y-9}{5y-6} = \dfrac{(4y+3)-(14y-9)}{5y-6} = \underbrace{\dfrac{4y+3-14y+9}{5y-6}}$

Distributing the negative changes the signs.

$$= \dfrac{-10y+12}{5y-6} = \underbrace{\dfrac{2(\overset{-1}{\cancel{-5y+6}})}{\underset{1}{(\cancel{5y-6})}}} = \dfrac{-2}{1} \qquad = -2$$

$-5y+6$ and $5y-6$ are additive inverses.

9) $\dfrac{12}{x-11} + \dfrac{7}{11-x}$

The denominators are additive inverses of each other. To obtain common denominators, we will just multiply the numerator and denominator of either fraction by -1. I usually do this to the second fraction. We'll obtain

$$\dfrac{12}{x-11} + \left(\dfrac{7}{11-x}\right)\left(\dfrac{-1}{-1}\right) = \underbrace{\dfrac{12}{x-11} + \dfrac{-7}{-11+x}} \; \dfrac{12-7}{x-11} = \dfrac{5}{x-11}.$$

$x-11=-11+x$ by the Commutative Property.

There is short cut to do this example. All that you have to do is turn the second denominator into the first denominator, and change the operation to the opposite of what it is. In other words, we have

$$\dfrac{12}{x-11} + \dfrac{7}{11-x} = \underbrace{\dfrac{12}{x-11} - \dfrac{7}{x-11}} \; \dfrac{12-7}{x-11} = \dfrac{5}{x-11}.$$

Change addition to subtraction and $11-x$ to $x-11$.

This short cut will always work whenever the denominators are additive inverses of each other.

10) $\qquad \dfrac{5b}{1-10b} - \dfrac{8b}{10b-1} = \underbrace{\dfrac{5b}{1-10b} + \dfrac{8b}{1-10b}} = \dfrac{5b+8b}{1-10b} = \dfrac{13b}{1-10b}$

The denominators are additive inverses, so use the short cut.

11) $\qquad \dfrac{11y-16}{9y+5} - \dfrac{8-3y}{-9y-5} = \underbrace{\dfrac{11y-16}{9y+5} + \dfrac{8-3y}{9y+5}} = \dfrac{(11y-16)+(8-3y)}{9y+5} = \dfrac{8y-8}{9y+5} = \dfrac{8(y-1)}{9y+5}$

The denominators are additive inverses, so use the short cut.

12) $\dfrac{7t^2+4t-1}{t-3} + \dfrac{6t^2+5t+5}{3-t} = \underbrace{\dfrac{7t^2+4t-1}{t-3} - \dfrac{6t^2+5t+5}{t-3}} = \dfrac{(7t^2+4t-1)-(6t^2+5t+5)}{t-3}$

The denominators are additive inverses, so use the short cut.

$$= \dfrac{7t^2+4t-1-6t^2-5t-5}{t-3} = \dfrac{t^2-t-6}{t-3} = \dfrac{(t+2)\overset{1}{\cancel{(t-3)}}}{\underset{1}{\cancel{t-3}}} = \dfrac{t+2}{1} = t+2$$

Try These (Set 1): Add or subtract and simplify.

1) $\dfrac{7x}{2x+3} + \dfrac{x-4}{2x+3}$

2) $\dfrac{4y-10}{9y+1} - \dfrac{3y-5}{9y+1}$

3) $\dfrac{3x-3}{x^2+10x+16} + \dfrac{19-x}{x^2+10x+16}$

4) $\dfrac{14-2x}{3x^2-19x-14} - \dfrac{21-3x}{3x^2-19x-14}$

5) $\dfrac{5}{7x-12} - \dfrac{8}{12-7x}$

6) $\dfrac{7y+2}{y^2-36} + \dfrac{8y-4}{36-y^2}$

108

The previous set of examples dealt with combining rational expressions whose denominators were either common or additive inverses of each other. Before moving on, we need to understand how to find the LCM of 2 or more polynomials.

Definition: The **least common multiple** (abbreviated as **LCM**) of 2 or more polynomials (with integer coefficients) is the 'smallest' polynomial (with integer coefficients) in which the original polynomials divide into without remainder.

By the 'smallest' polynomial, I mean the polynomial of smallest possible degree. For example, let's find the LCM of the monomials $6x^3$ and $8x^5$. We want the 'smallest' monomial for which $6x^3$ and $8x^5$ divide into without a remainder. First, notice that the LCM of 6 and 8 is 24, since both 6 and 8 divide into 24 without a remainder and 24 is the smallest natural number for which this happens (we will recall how to find the LCM of two natural numbers shortly). Now, the LCM of x^3 and x^5 is x^5, since $x^5 \div x^3 = x^2$ and $x^5 \div x^5 = 1$, neither giving a remainder. Notice that x^5 is **the** 'smallest' monomial for which this happens (for example, if it was x^4 instead, then $x^4 \div x^5 = \dfrac{x^4}{x^5} = \dfrac{1}{x^1}$ which is a remainder term). Hence, the LCM is $24x^5$ and degree 5 is the smallest possible degree.

Let's practice finding the LCM of polynomials. To find the LCM, you must first factor the given polynomials. The factors of the polynomials are the 'building blocks' of the LCM and you 'build' the LCM by multiplying these factors together. However, if a common prime factor occurs in more than one of the polynomials, we only put it into the LCM with the largest of the exponents. This will become clearer as we do some examples.

Examples. Find the LCM.

1) The LCM of 5 and 3 is $5 \times 3 = 15$.

Notice that both 5 and 3 are prime. In general, whenever the given numbers (or polynomials) are prime and different from each other, the LCM is just their product.

2) The LCM of 2 and 13 is $2 \times 13 = 26$ since both numbers are prime.

3) The LCM of 7 and 9 is $7 \times 9 = 63$.

Notice that 9 factors into $3 \times 3 = 3^2$ and so the only prime factor of 9 is 3. The only prime factor of 7 is 7 itself (since 7 is prime). Now, note that there are no common prime factors of 7 (namely 7) and 9 (namely 3). Therefore, the LCM is their product. In general, whenever the given numbers (or polynomials) have no common **prime** factors, the LCM is just their product. Examples 1 and 2 are special cases of this.

4) The LCM of 8 and 15 is $8 \times 15 = 120$.

Observe that $8 = 2 \times 2 \times 2 = 2^3$, $15 = 5 \times 3$, and none of the prime factors of 8 (which is just 2) equal any of the prime factors of 15 (which are 5 and 3). Therefore, the LCM is the product of 8 and 15.

5) The LCM of 12 and 14 is 84.

Observe that $12 = 2 \times 2 \times 3 = 2^2 \times 3$ and $14 = 2 \times 7$. Notice that 12 and 14 have a common prime factor of 2. When there is a common prime factor, the LCM is **not** the product of the numbers (in this case, of 12 and 14). To find the LCM, you take all of the prime factors (with their **largest exponent**) of the numbers and build the LCM by multiplying these factors (with their largest exponent). Hence, our LCM must have as factors 2^2, 3, 2, and 7. However, notice that the prime factor of 2 appears twice in our list, in 2^2 and in $2 = 2^1$. **Only 2^2 will be used in building the LCM**, since the exponent of 2^2 (which is 2) is larger than the exponent of 2^1 (which is 1). By multiplying these factors together, we obtain $2^2 \times 3 \times 7 = 84$.

6) The LCM of 100 and 48 is $1,200$.

To begin with, notice that $100 = 5 \times 5 \times 2 \times 2 = 5^2 \times 2^2$ and $48 = 2 \times 2 \times 2 \times 2 \times 3 = 2^4 \times 3$. The LCM is built up from 5^2, 2^2, 2^4, and 3. Since the prime factor of 2 appears twice (in 2^2 and in 2^4), we only put 2^4 into the LCM since it has a larger exponent than 2^2. Therefore, the LCM is $5^2 \times 2^4 \times 3 = 1,200$.

7) The LCM of 336 and 72 is $1,008$.

Observe that $336 = 7 \times 2 \times 2 \times 2 \times 2 \times 3 = 7 \times 2^4 \times 3$ and $72 = 3 \times 3 \times 2 \times 2 \times 2 = 3^2 \times 2^3$. The LCM is built up from 7, 2^4, 3, 3^2, and 2^3. We will use **only** 7, 2^4, and 3^2 to build the LCM since 2^4 has a larger exponent than 2^3 and 3^2 has a larger exponent than $3 = 3^1$. The LCM is $7 \times 2^4 \times 3^2 = 1,008$.

8) The LCM of 50 and 75 is 150.

Notice that $50 = 5 \times 5 \times 2 = 5^2 \times 2$ and $75 = 5 \times 5 \times 3 = 5^2 \times 3$. The LCM is built up from 5^2, 2, 5^2, and 3. We will use only 5^2, 2, and 3 to build it since the exponents of 5^2 and 5^2 are the same (whenever the exponents are equal, just use one of those terms as your 'building block'). The LCM, therefore, is $5^2 \times 2 \times 3 = 150$.

9) The LCM of $2^4 \times 5^2 \times 11^3$ and $2^4 \times 3^1 \times 11^1$ is $2^4 \times 5^2 \times 3^1 \times 11^3$.

10) The LCM of $3^5 \times 7^4 \times 13^2$ and $3^3 \times 7^2 \times 11^2$ is $3^5 \times 7^4 \times 13^2 \times 11^2$.

11) The LCM of $7x^3$ and $5x^6$ is $35x^6$.

Note that monomials are already in factored form. To find the LCM of two or more monomials, first find the LCM of their coefficients. Then multiply it by the product of the variables in the monomials with their corresponding exponents, choosing the largest one if the variable repeats itself. In this example, the LCM of 7 and 5 is $7 \times 5 = 35$. As for the variables, we will use x^6 since it has a larger exponent than x^3. Therefore, the LCM is $35x^6$.

12) The LCM of $9x^2y^3$ and $15xy^5$ is $45x^2y^5$.

The LCM of 9 and 15 is 45. For the variable x, we use x^2 since it has a larger exponent than $x = x^1$. For the variable y, we use y^5 since it has a larger exponent than y^3. Therefore, the LCM is $45x^2y^5$.

13) The LCM of $2ab^8$ and $2a^3b^4$ is $2a^3b^8$.

The LCM of 2 and 2 is just 2. For the variable a, we use a^3 since it has a larger exponent than $a = a^1$. For the variable b, we use b^8 since it has a larger exponent than b^4. Therefore, the LCM is $2a^3b^8$.

14) The LCM of xy^3 and $9z^2$ is $9xy^3z^2$.

15) The LCM of $8x^5$ and $4y^3$ is $8x^5y^3$.

16) The LCM of $3x + 6$ and $2x + 4$ is $6(x + 2)$.

To obtain this LCM, first factor the polynomials. You proceed exactly as before (build the LCM by using the factors as the building blocks), keeping in mind that if a prime factor appears in more than one polynomial, then use the largest exponent. Well, observe that $3x + 6 = 3(x + 2)$ and $2x + 4 = 2(x + 2)$. The LCM will contain 3, $x + 2$, 2, and $x + 2$. Since $x + 2 = (x + 2)^1$ has exponent 1 in both occurences, it will only appear once in the LCM. Hence, the LCM is $3(2)(x + 2) = 6(x + 2)$. Notice that 6 is just the LCM of 2 and 3.

17) The LCM of $6x^2 - 6$ and $4x^2 + 8x + 4$ is $12(x + 1)^2(x - 1)$.

Notice that $6x^2 - 6 = 6\left(x^2 - 1\right) = 6\left(x + 1\right)\left(x - 1\right)$ and $4x^2 + 8x + 4 = 4\left(x^2 + 2x + 1\right) = 4\left(x + 1\right)\left(x + 1\right) = 4\left(x + 1\right)^2$. The LCM of 6 and 4 is 12. We will use $\left(x + 1\right)^2$ in the LCM since it has a larger exponent than the factor $x + 1 = \left(x + 1\right)^1$ of the first polynomial. The LCM will also contain the factor $x - 1$. After multiplying these, we see that the LCM is $12\left(x + 1\right)^2\left(x - 1\right)$.

18) The LCM of x and $x - 7$ is $x\left(x - 7\right)$ since both polynomials are prime.

19) The LCM of $x - 3$ and $2x + 5$ is $\left(x - 3\right)\left(2x + 5\right)$ since both polynomials are prime.

20) The LCM of $20x^3\left(x - 4\right)^2\left(3x + 5\right)^3$ and $10x^5\left(x + 2\right)\left(x - 4\right)^3\left(3x + 5\right)^2$ is $20x^5\left(x + 2\right)\left(x - 4\right)^3\left(3x + 5\right)^3$.

Observe that the LCM of 20 and 10 is 20, the factor x^5 has a larger exponent than the factor x^3, the factor $\left(x - 4\right)^3$ has a larger exponent than the factor $\left(x - 4\right)^2$, and the factor $\left(3x + 5\right)^3$ has a larger exponent than the factor $\left(3x + 5\right)^2$. Since the factor $x + 2 = \left(x + 2\right)^1$ only occurs in the second polynomial, it will only appear with exponent 1 in the LCM.

21) The LCM of $x^2\left(2x - 1\right)^3\left(2x + 3\right)^5$ and $x^4\left(2x + 1\right)^2\left(2x + 3\right)^6$ is $x^4\left(2x - 1\right)^3\left(2x + 1\right)^2\left(2x + 3\right)^6$.

Try These (Set 2): Find the LCM.

1) 60 and 24
2) 28 and 49   3) $15x^4y^3$ and $25x^5y$ 4) $10x^2 - 5x$ and $8x^3 - 2x^2$
5) $x^2 - 8x + 15$ and $x^2 - 9$ 6) $24x^4\left(x + 1\right)\left(x - 3\right)^3$ and $5x\left(x + 1\right)^3\left(x - 2\right)\left(x - 3\right)^2$

Now that we've practiced finding LCM's, let's go back to combining rational expressions. The name of the game is to find the LCM of the denominators (the least common denominator) and change the denominators of the fractions into this LCM. Let's give it a try.

Examples. Add or subtract and simplify.

1) $\underbrace{\dfrac{5}{x} + \dfrac{6}{y} = \left(\dfrac{y}{y}\right)\dfrac{5}{x} + \left(\dfrac{x}{x}\right)\dfrac{6}{y}}_{\text{The LCM of } x \text{ and } y \text{ is } xy.} = \dfrac{5y + 6x}{xy}$

2) $\underbrace{\dfrac{2x}{x + 3} + \dfrac{5x}{x - 1} = \left(\dfrac{x - 1}{x - 1}\right)\dfrac{2x}{x + 3} + \left(\dfrac{x + 3}{x + 3}\right)\dfrac{5x}{x - 1}}_{\text{The LCM of } x+3 \text{ and } x-1 \text{ is } (x+3)(x-1).} = \dfrac{2x\left(x - 1\right) + 5x\left(x + 3\right)}{\left(x - 1\right)\left(x + 3\right)}$

$= \dfrac{2x^2 - 2x + 5x^2 + 15x}{\left(x + 3\right)\left(x - 1\right)} = \dfrac{7x^2 + 13x}{\left(x + 3\right)\left(x - 1\right)} = \dfrac{x\left(7x + 13\right)}{\left(x + 3\right)\left(x - 1\right)}$

3) $\underbrace{\dfrac{7}{2x} + \dfrac{4}{5y} = \left(\dfrac{5y}{5y}\right)\dfrac{7}{2x} + \left(\dfrac{2x}{2x}\right)\dfrac{4}{5y}}_{\text{The LCM of } 2x \text{ and } 5y \text{ is } 10xy.} = \dfrac{35y}{10xy} + \dfrac{8x}{10xy} = \dfrac{35y + 8x}{10xy}$

4) $\underbrace{\dfrac{9}{8x^2y} - \dfrac{1}{6xy^2} = \left(\dfrac{3y}{3y}\right)\dfrac{9}{8x^2y} - \left(\dfrac{4x}{4x}\right)\dfrac{1}{6xy^2}}_{\text{The LCM of } 8x^2y \text{ and } 6xy^2 \text{ is } 24x^2y^2.} = \dfrac{27y}{24x^2y^2} - \dfrac{4x}{24x^2y^2} = \dfrac{27y - 4x}{24x^2y^2}$

111

5) $\underbrace{\dfrac{6t}{t^2 - 9} + \dfrac{3t}{t^2 + 6t + 9} = \left(\dfrac{t+3}{t+3}\right)\dfrac{6t}{(t+3)(t-3)} + \left(\dfrac{t-3}{t-3}\right)\dfrac{3t}{(t+3)^2}}_{\text{The LCM of } (t+3)(t-3) \text{ and } (t+3)^2 \text{ is } (t+3)^2(t-3).} = \dfrac{6t(t+3) + 3t(t-3)}{(t+3)^2(t-3)}$

$$= \dfrac{6t^2 + 18t + 3t^2 - 9t}{(t+3)^2(t-3)} = \dfrac{9t^2 + 9t}{(t+3)^2(t-3)} = \dfrac{9t(t+1)}{(t+3)^2(t-3)}$$

6) $\underbrace{\dfrac{x-3}{4x^2 + 8x} - \dfrac{x+4}{x^2 + 9x + 14} = \left(\dfrac{x+7}{x+7}\right)\dfrac{x-3}{4x(x+2)} - \left(\dfrac{4x}{4x}\right)\dfrac{x+4}{(x+7)(x+2)}}_{\text{The LCM of } 4x(x+2) \text{ and } (x+7)(x+2) \text{ is } 4x(x+7)(x+2).} = \dfrac{(x+7)(x-3) - 4x(x+4)}{4x(x+2)(x+7)}$

$$= \dfrac{x^2 + 4x - 21 - 4x^2 - 16x}{4x(x+2)(x+7)} = \dfrac{-3x^2 - 12x - 21}{4x(x+2)(x+7)} = \dfrac{-3\left(x^2 + 4x + 7\right)}{4x(x+2)(x+7)}$$

7) $\underbrace{\dfrac{3a}{a+4} + \dfrac{2a+5}{a^3 + 64} = \left(\dfrac{a^2 - 4a + 16}{a^2 - 4a + 16}\right)\dfrac{3a}{a+4} + \dfrac{2a+5}{(a+4)(a^2 - 4a + 16)}}_{\text{The LCM of } a+4 \text{ and } (a+4)(a^2-4a+16) \text{ is } (a+4)(a^2-4a+16).} = \dfrac{3a\left(a^2 - 4a + 16\right) + (2a+5)}{(a^2 - 4a + 16)(a+4)}$

$$= \dfrac{3a^3 - 12a^2 + 48a + 2a + 5}{(a^2 - 4a + 16)(a+4)} = \dfrac{3a^3 - 12a^2 + 50a + 5}{(a^2 - 4a + 16)(a+4)}$$

If we try to factor $2a^3 - 8a^2 + 33a - 3$ by using the Grouping Method (see Section 3.5), we'll see that it doesn't work. Therefore, we will leave our answer as it is.

8) $\underbrace{\dfrac{1}{x^2 + x} + \dfrac{1}{x^2 + 3x + 2} = \left(\dfrac{x+2}{x+2}\right)\dfrac{1}{x(x+1)} + \left(\dfrac{x}{x}\right)\dfrac{1}{(x+2)(x+1)}}_{\text{The LCM of } x(x+1) \text{ and } (x+2)(x+1) \text{ is } x(x+2)(x+1).} = \dfrac{x+2+x}{x(x+2)(x+1)}$

$$= \dfrac{2x+2}{x(x+2)(x+1)} = \dfrac{2(\overset{1}{\cancel{x+1}})}{x(x+2)(\underset{1}{\cancel{x+1}})} = \dfrac{2}{x(x+2)}$$

9) $\underbrace{\dfrac{5}{x-2} + \dfrac{3}{x^2} - \dfrac{1}{x+3} = \left(\dfrac{x^2(x+3)}{x^2(x+3)}\right)\dfrac{5}{x-2} + \left(\dfrac{(x-2)(x+3)}{(x-2)(x+3)}\right)\dfrac{3}{x^2} - \left(\dfrac{x^2(x-2)}{x^2(x-2)}\right)\dfrac{1}{x+3}}_{\text{The LCM of } x-2, \ x^2, \text{ and } x+3 \text{ is } x^2(x-2)(x+3).}$

$$= \dfrac{5x^2(x+3) + 3(x-2)(x+3) - x^2(x-2)}{x^2(x-2)(x+3)} = \dfrac{5x^3 + 15x^2 + 3\overbrace{\left(x^2 + x - 6\right)}^{(x-2)(x+3)} - x^3 + 2x^2}{x^2(x-2)(x+3)}$$

$$= \dfrac{5x^3 + 15x^2 + 3x^2 + 3x - 18 - x^3 + 2x^2}{x^2(x-2)(x+3)} = \dfrac{4x^3 + 20x^2 + 3x - 18}{x^2(x-2)(x+3)}$$

Once again, the Grouping Method does not help us when we try to factor $4x^3 - x^2 - 6x + 8$. Therefore, we will leave our answer as it is.

10) $\underbrace{\dfrac{2y-7}{5y+1} + 3 = \dfrac{2y-7}{5y+1} + \dfrac{3}{1} = \dfrac{2y-7}{5y+1} + \left(\dfrac{5y+1}{5y+1}\right)\dfrac{3}{1}}_{\text{The LCM of } 5y+1 \text{ and } 1 \text{ is } 5y+1.} = \dfrac{2y-7+3(5y+1)}{5y+1}$

$$= \dfrac{2y-7+15y+3}{5y+1} = \dfrac{17y-4}{5y+1}$$

Try These (Set 3): Add or subtract and simplify.

1) $\dfrac{5}{7} + \dfrac{3}{2y}$ 2) $\dfrac{5}{6t} - \dfrac{7}{12t}$ 3) $\dfrac{1}{x+2} + \dfrac{1}{x-9}$ 4) $\dfrac{2}{a^2-3a} - \dfrac{3}{a^2+5a}$

5) $\dfrac{3y-1}{y^2-16} - \dfrac{y-3}{y^2-4y}$ 6) $\dfrac{4}{x^2+16x+64} + \dfrac{5x}{x^2+10x+16}$ 7) $4u + \dfrac{u^2+9}{u+7}$

Exercise 4.3

In Exercises 1-28, perform the indicated operation and simplify.

1. $\dfrac{5}{x} + \dfrac{1}{x}$ 2. $\dfrac{3}{a} + \dfrac{2}{a}$ 3. $\dfrac{10}{7b} + \dfrac{2}{7b}$ 4. $\dfrac{19}{11t} + \dfrac{4}{11t}$

5. $\dfrac{10}{3y} - \dfrac{4}{3y}$ 6. $\dfrac{9}{4p} - \dfrac{7}{4p}$ 7. $\dfrac{3}{x+5} + \dfrac{x+3}{x+5}$ 8. $\dfrac{x+3}{x+4} + \dfrac{6}{x+4}$

9. $\dfrac{2t-8}{7t-1} + \dfrac{5t}{7t-1}$ 10. $\dfrac{3s}{3s-13} + \dfrac{5s+1}{3s-13}$ 11. $\dfrac{m-7}{8m+5} + \dfrac{3m-9}{8m+5}$ 12. $\dfrac{3a+5}{2a-6} + \dfrac{2a-9}{2a-6}$

13. $\dfrac{4x+1}{x^2-25} - \dfrac{3x-4}{x^2-25}$ 14. $\dfrac{7y-5}{y^2-49} - \dfrac{6y+2}{y^2-49}$ 15. $\dfrac{5t-7}{7t-8} - \dfrac{3t+7}{7t-8}$ 16. $\dfrac{6b+11}{5b+3} - \dfrac{7b+2}{5b+3}$

17. $\dfrac{9u^2-10}{5u+2} - \dfrac{4u^2+13u-4}{5u+2}$ 18. $\dfrac{18t^2-8}{4t+1} - \dfrac{2t^2-7}{4t+1}$ 19. $\dfrac{-2y^2+8y-7}{3y^2+y+10} + \dfrac{4y^2-11y-2}{3y^2+y+10}$

20. $\dfrac{10x^2-x-2}{2x^2+4x-5} + \dfrac{-3x^2-3x+7}{2x^2+4x-5}$ 21. $\dfrac{3x}{x-3} + \dfrac{5}{3-x}$ 22. $\dfrac{6}{y-7} + \dfrac{10y}{7-y}$

23. $\dfrac{2u+3}{2u-9} - \dfrac{7u}{9-2u}$ 24. $\dfrac{4v-8}{3v-7} - \dfrac{9}{7-3v}$ 25. $\dfrac{5x-4}{6-8x} + \dfrac{4x-9}{8x-6}$

26. $\dfrac{12y-1}{8-3y} + \dfrac{y-6}{3y-8}$ 27. $\dfrac{7a+12}{3a-13} - \dfrac{7-5a}{13-3a}$ 28. $\dfrac{9t+6}{t-6} - \dfrac{5t-3}{6-t}$.

In Exercises 29-74, find the LCM of the given polynomials.

29. 5 and 3   30. 13 and 3   31. 40 and 6   32. 20 and 30

33. 16 and 10   34. 6 and 9   35. 90 and 75   36. 44 and 8

37. $2x^5$ and $7x^2$ 38. $17y^2$ and $3y^6$ 39. $12a^3b^5$ and $20ab^7$ 40. $28ab^3$ and $49a^4b$

41. $9x^2y^6$ and $9x^5y^6$ 42. $4a^6b$ and $4a^3b$ 43. $2a$ and $19b$ 44. $7x$ and $5y$

45. $4x^2$ and $18y$ 46. $10a^4$ and $12b$ 47. 14 and mn^2 48. 42 and m^2n^3

49. x and $x-7$ 50. t and $t+6$ 51. x and $x+h$ 52. y and $y-10$

53. $3x$ and $5x+1$ 54. $8y^2$ and $2y-9$ 55. $x+4$ and $x-4$ 56. $y-14$ and $y-3$

57. $3y-5$ and $y+2$ 58. $11-2y$ and $3y+16$ 59. $3t-9$ and $4t-12$ 60. $4x+8$ and $7x+14$

61. x^2-8x and x^2+2x 62. y^2+y and y^2-3y 63. y^3+7y^2 and y^2-49

64. $x^3 - 10x$ and $x^2 - 100$ 65. $x^2 - 5x + 4$ and $x^2 + 3x - 28$ 66. $x^2 + 6x - 7$ and $x^2 - 2x + 1$

67. $3x^4 - 3x^3 - 18x^2$ and $6x^3 + 30x^2 + 36x$ 68. $5y^5 - 20y^4 + 15y^3$ and $4y^3 - 28y^2 - 32y$

69. $10x^3 (x-2)^2 (x+1)$ and $25x^3 (x-2) (x+1)^3$ 70. $12y (y+2) (y+3)^3$ and $8y^2 (y+2)^2 (y+3)$

71. $18a^4 (3a+4) (a-6)^2$ and $a^5 (3a-4)^2 (a-6)^2$ 72. $13b (b-7)^5 (b-1)$ and $13b (b-7)^2 (b+1)$

73. $2 (x-3)^2 (x^2+4)^2$ and $2 (x-3)^2 (x^2-3)$ 74. $11 (8-y)^3 (2y^2+3)^2$ and $11 (8+y) (2y^2+3)^2$

In Exercises 75-120, perform the indicated operation and simplify.

75. $\dfrac{3x}{5} + \dfrac{4}{3}$

76. $\dfrac{6}{5} + \dfrac{9x}{2}$

77. $\dfrac{5y}{9} - \dfrac{7}{12}$

78. $\dfrac{14}{15} - \dfrac{7t}{25}$

79. $\dfrac{11}{4x} + \dfrac{1}{6}$

80. $\dfrac{12}{7y} + \dfrac{1}{21}$

81. $\dfrac{2}{x+8} + \dfrac{5}{x-1}$

82. $\dfrac{5}{y-4} + \dfrac{6}{y-3}$

83. $\dfrac{3a}{3a+1} - \dfrac{2}{5a-2}$

84. $\dfrac{7}{2b+1} - \dfrac{b}{3b-1}$

85. $\dfrac{t+4}{t-2} + \dfrac{t+2}{t-4}$

86. $\dfrac{s+4}{s+1} + \dfrac{s-2}{s+2}$

87. $\dfrac{1}{5+h} - \dfrac{1}{5}$

88. $\dfrac{1}{2+h} - \dfrac{1}{2}$

89. $\dfrac{1}{(4+h)^2} - \dfrac{1}{16}$

90. $\dfrac{1}{(x+h)^2} - \dfrac{1}{x^2}$

91. $\dfrac{2m-1}{3m+2} - \dfrac{m+2}{m-4}$

92. $\dfrac{2n+5}{3n-2} - \dfrac{3n-4}{6n+1}$

93. $\dfrac{5}{12xy} + \dfrac{1}{9x^2}$

94. $\dfrac{3}{20y^2} + \dfrac{7}{8x^3}$

95. $\dfrac{6}{11a^2b} - \dfrac{10}{3ab^2}$

96. $\dfrac{4}{15ab^2} - \dfrac{2}{25ab^2}$

97. $\dfrac{11x}{18y^2} - \dfrac{7y}{6x^3}$

98. $\dfrac{3x}{7y^2} + \dfrac{2y}{21x^2}$

99. $\dfrac{1}{x+6} + \dfrac{12}{x^2-36}$

100. $\dfrac{1}{y+3} + \dfrac{1}{y^2+5y+6}$

101. $\dfrac{6}{a^2-a} - \dfrac{9}{a^2-1}$

102. $\dfrac{10}{b^2+4b} - \dfrac{2}{b^2+3b-4}$

103. $\dfrac{a+3}{a^2-4a-5} - \dfrac{a}{a^2-8a+15}$

104. $\dfrac{b-2}{b^2-4b-12} + \dfrac{b}{b^2-10b+24}$

105. $\dfrac{3x-10}{2x^2-11x+5} - \dfrac{7x+8}{2x^2-7x-15}$

106. $\dfrac{5y+12}{3y^2-5y-8} - \dfrac{6y-11}{12y^2-17y-40}$

107. $\dfrac{4m-1}{m^2+2m+1} + \dfrac{2}{m-3}$

108. $\dfrac{2n-5}{n^2-6n+5} + \dfrac{1}{n-4}$

109. $\dfrac{1}{x} - \dfrac{3x+2}{x+1} + \dfrac{2}{x-2}$

110. $\dfrac{3}{t} + \dfrac{4}{t+3} - \dfrac{6t+1}{t-2}$

111. $\dfrac{7}{a^2-6a} + \dfrac{4}{a^2+5a} + \dfrac{3}{a+1}$

112. $\dfrac{2}{b^2+4b} + \dfrac{3}{b^2-5b} + \dfrac{1}{b+3}$

113. $3 + \dfrac{x-7}{4x+3}$

114. $5 + \dfrac{a}{2a-7}$

115. $4b - \dfrac{1}{2b+1}$

116. $9p - \dfrac{5}{p-2}$

117. $x^2 + 4x + \dfrac{10}{x}$

118. $t^2 - 3t + \dfrac{11}{t}$

119. $3u - 4 - \dfrac{14}{u-1}$

120. $-v + 2 - \dfrac{5v}{4v+1}$

114

Section 4.4   Mixed Quotients (Complex Fractions)

In this section, we'll learn how to simplify a mixed quotient. Roughly speaking, a mixed quotient is a fraction whose numerator and denominator contain fractions in them. There are two methods for simplifying a mixed quotient. One of them requires the usage of LCM's, while the other deals with converting the 'big' fraction into the quotient of two fractions. I prefer using the LCM method and will use it throughout, although the other method will be demonstrated as well.

Definition: A mixed quotient (or **complex fraction**) is a fraction whose numerator and denominator contain rational expressions.

The expressions $\dfrac{\frac{2}{5}+\frac{1}{2}}{3}$, $\dfrac{1-\frac{6}{5x^2}}{\frac{3x}{10}-x}$, $\dfrac{2x+\frac{x}{y}-\frac{y}{x}}{5x+y}$, and $\dfrac{a^2+3a+\frac{1}{a^2-4}}{a^2-7a+\frac{8}{a^2-4}}$ are examples of mixed quotients. Our goal is to simplify such an expression into a reduced, rational expression. In order to explain the LCM method, I will give names for the expressions in a mixed quotient. In the expression $\dfrac{\frac{2}{5}+\frac{1}{2}}{3}$, for example, there are two fractions in the numerator ($\frac{2}{5}$ and $\frac{1}{2}$) and one fraction in the denominator ($3=\frac{3}{1}$). I will refer to these as the 'little fractions' and the expression $\dfrac{\frac{2}{5}+\frac{1}{2}}{3}$ as the 'big fraction'. In the mixed quotient $\dfrac{2x+\frac{x}{y}-\frac{y}{x}}{5x+y}$, the 'big fraction' is $\dfrac{2x+\frac{x}{y}-\frac{y}{x}}{5x+y}$ itself and the 'little fractions' contained in it are $2x=\frac{2x}{1}$, $\frac{x}{y}$, $\frac{y}{x}$, $5x=\frac{5x}{1}$, and $y=\frac{y}{1}$. As we will see, the 'little fractions' which we are concerned with are those which have a denominator different from 1. Hence, $2x$, $5x$, and y will not play a role in the LCM method (see Step I below).

We are now ready to simplify some mixed quotients. In the first example, I will explain the LCM method step by step. Afterwards, I will demonstrate the other method. You may use either one.

Examples. Simplify.

1) $\dfrac{\frac{1}{6}+\frac{2}{3}}{\frac{3}{4}-2}$

The LCM method goes as follows:

Step I.   Find the LCM of the denominators of the 'little fractions'.

The denominators of our 'little fractions' are 6, 3, 4, and 1 (if we write $2=\frac{2}{1}$). The LCM of these is 12. Notice that the denominator of 1 doesn't contribute any new factors to the LCM. In other words, the LCM of 6, 3, 4, and 1 is the same as the LCM of 6, 3, and 4. The number 1 isn't needed in 'building' the LCM and can be left out of its construction. That is why I've mentioned before that any 'little fractions' whose denominator is 1 can be ignored.

Step II.   Multiply the 'big fraction' by $\dfrac{\text{LCM}}{\text{LCM}}$.

We have

$$\frac{\frac{1}{6}+\frac{2}{3}}{\frac{3}{4}-2}=\left(\frac{\frac{1}{6}+\frac{2}{3}}{\frac{3}{4}-2}\right)\left(\frac{12}{12}\right)=\left(\frac{\frac{1}{6}+\frac{2}{3}}{\frac{3}{4}-2}\right)\left(\frac{\frac{12}{1}}{\frac{12}{1}}\right)$$

$$=\frac{\frac{1}{6}\left(\frac{\overset{2}{\cancel{12}}}{1}\right)+\frac{2}{3}\left(\frac{\overset{4}{\cancel{12}}}{1}\right)}{\frac{3}{4}\left(\frac{\overset{3}{\cancel{12}}}{1}\right)-2\left(\frac{12}{1}\right)}=\frac{2+2(4)}{3(3)-2(12)}$$

115

Notice that after writing 12 as $\frac{12}{1}$ and distributing it in the numerator and denominator of the 'big fraction', all I really did was to multiply every expression in the 'big fraction' by $\frac{12}{1}$. Furthermore, observe that Step II allows us to kill off all of the denominators of the 'little fractions'. This is exactly what we wanted.

Step III. Simplify our answer.

$$\frac{2+2(4)}{3(3)-2(12)} = \frac{2+8}{9-24} = \frac{10}{-15} = -\frac{2}{3}$$

And we now have a rational expression in simplified form.

Before doing more examples using this method, let me show you the other approach. We'll begin by combining the 'little fractions' in the numerator and denominator of the 'big fraction'. We will then use the fact that

$$\frac{\frac{a}{b}}{\frac{c}{d}} = \frac{a}{b} \div \frac{c}{d} \quad \text{where } b, c, d \neq 0.$$

Following this method, we obtain

$$\frac{\frac{1}{6}+\frac{2}{3}}{\frac{3}{4}-\frac{2}{1}} = \frac{\frac{1}{6}+\frac{4}{6}}{\frac{3}{4}-\frac{8}{4}} = \frac{\frac{5}{6}}{\frac{-5}{4}} = \frac{5}{6} \div \left(\frac{-5}{4}\right) = \frac{\overset{1}{\cancel{5}}}{\underset{3}{\cancel{6}}}\left(-\frac{\overset{2}{\cancel{4}}}{\underset{1}{\cancel{5}}}\right) = -\frac{2}{3}$$

as before. If you like this method better than the LCM method, use it. It's a matter of preference. I prefer to use the LCM method.

2) $\underbrace{\frac{\frac{1}{5x}-\frac{3}{2x}}{\frac{7}{10x}+\frac{1}{2}} = \left(\frac{\frac{1}{5x}-\frac{3}{2x}}{\frac{7}{10x}+\frac{1}{2}}\right)\left(\frac{\frac{10x}{1}}{\frac{10x}{1}}\right) =}_{\text{The LCM of } 5x, 2x, 10x, \text{ and } 2 \text{ is } 10x.} \underbrace{\frac{\frac{1}{5x}\left(\frac{\overset{2}{\cancel{10x}}}{1}\right)-\frac{3}{2x}\left(\frac{\overset{5}{\cancel{10x}}}{1}\right)}{\frac{7}{10x}\left(\frac{\cancel{10x}}{1}\right)+\frac{1}{2}\left(\frac{\overset{5}{\cancel{10x}}}{1}\right)} = \frac{2-3(5)}{7(1)+5x}}_{\text{Cancel out the denominators of the 'little fractions'.}}$

$$= \frac{2-15}{7+5x} = \frac{-13}{7+5x} = -\frac{13}{7+5x}$$

If we use the other method, we have:

$$\frac{\frac{1}{5x}-\frac{3}{2x}}{\frac{7}{10x}+\frac{1}{2}} = \frac{\frac{1}{5x}\left(\frac{2}{2}\right)-\frac{3}{2x}\left(\frac{5}{5}\right)}{\frac{7}{10x}+\frac{1}{2}\left(\frac{5x}{5x}\right)} = \frac{\frac{2}{10x}-\frac{15}{10x}}{\frac{7}{10x}+\frac{5x}{10x}} = \frac{-\frac{13}{10x}}{\frac{7+5x}{10x}}$$

$$= \left(-\frac{13}{10x}\right) \div \left(\frac{7+5x}{10x}\right) = \left(-\frac{13}{\cancel{10x}}\right)\left(\frac{\overset{1}{\cancel{10x}}}{7+5x}\right) = -\frac{13}{7+5x}$$

3) $\underbrace{\frac{\frac{9y}{2x}+3}{4x-\frac{3}{7xy}} = \left(\frac{\frac{9y}{2x}+3}{4x-\frac{3}{7xy}}\right)\left(\frac{\frac{14xy}{1}}{\frac{14xy}{1}}\right) =}_{\text{The LCM of } 2x \text{ and } 7xy \text{ is } 14xy.} \underbrace{\frac{\frac{9y}{2x}\left(\frac{\overset{7}{\cancel{14xy}}}{1}\right)+3\left(\frac{14xy}{1}\right)}{4x\left(\frac{14xy}{1}\right)-\frac{3}{7xy}\left(\frac{\overset{2}{\cancel{14xy}}}{1}\right)} = \frac{9y(7y)+42xy}{56x^2y-3(2)}}_{\text{Cancel out the denominators of the 'little fractions'.}}$

$$= \frac{63y^2+42xy}{56x^2y-6} = \frac{21y(3y+2x)}{2(28x^2y-3)}$$

116

4) $\dfrac{\frac{a}{2b} - \frac{b}{2a}}{\frac{a-b}{4ab}} = \left(\dfrac{\frac{a}{2b} - \frac{b}{2a}}{\frac{a-b}{4ab}} \right) \left(\dfrac{\frac{4ab}{1}}{\frac{4ab}{1}} \right) = \dfrac{\frac{a}{2b}\left(\frac{\overset{2a}{\cancel{4ab}}}{1}\right) - \frac{b}{2a}\left(\frac{\overset{2b}{\cancel{4ab}}}{1}\right)}{\frac{a-b}{4ab}\left(\frac{\overset{1}{\cancel{4ab}}}{1}\right)} = \dfrac{a\,(2a) - b\,(2b)}{a - b}$

$\underbrace{\phantom{\dfrac{\frac{a}{2b} - \frac{b}{2a}}{\frac{a-b}{4ab}}}}_{\text{The LCM of } 2b,\, 2a,\, \text{and } 4ab \text{ is } 4ab.}$ $\underbrace{\phantom{\dfrac{\frac{a}{2b}\left(\frac{4ab}{1}\right) - \frac{b}{2a}\left(\frac{4ab}{1}\right)}{\frac{a-b}{4ab}\left(\frac{4ab}{1}\right)}}}_{\text{Cancel out the denominators of the 'little fractions'.}}$

$$= \dfrac{2a^2 - 2b^2}{a - b} = \dfrac{2\,(a+b)\,(\overset{1}{\cancel{a-b}})}{\underset{1}{\cancel{a-b}}} = \dfrac{2\,(a+b)}{1} = 2\,(a+b)$$

$$\underbrace{\phantom{\dfrac{2\,(a+b)\,(a-b)}{a-b}}}_{\text{Factor the numerator completely.}}$$

5) $\dfrac{\frac{4}{x-6} + \frac{x}{x+3}}{1 + \frac{2}{x^2-3x-18}} = \left(\dfrac{\frac{4}{x-6} + \frac{x}{x+3}}{1 + \frac{2}{x^2-3x-18}} \right)\left(\dfrac{\frac{(x-6)(x+3)}{1}}{\frac{(x-6)(x+3)}{1}} \right) = \dfrac{\frac{4}{\cancel{x-6}}\left(\frac{(\cancel{x-6})(x+3)}{1}\right) + \frac{x}{x+3}\left(\frac{(x-6)(\overset{1}{\cancel{x+3}})}{1}\right)}{1\left(\frac{(x-6)(x+3)}{1}\right) + \frac{2}{(\cancel{x-6})(\cancel{x+3})}\left(\frac{(\cancel{x-6})(\overset{1}{\cancel{x+3}})}{1}\right)}$

$\underbrace{}_{\text{The LCM of } x-6,\, x+3,\, \text{and } x^2-3x-18=(x-6)(x+3) \text{ is } (x-6)(x+3).}$

$$= \underbrace{\dfrac{4\,(x+3) + x\,(x-6)}{(x-6)\,(x+3) + 2}}_{\text{after cancelling out the denominators}} = \dfrac{4x + 12 + x^2 - 6x}{x^2 - 3x - 18 + 2} = \dfrac{x^2 - 2x + 12}{x^2 - 3x - 16}$$

6) $\dfrac{\frac{1}{9+h} - \frac{1}{9}}{h} = \left(\dfrac{\frac{1}{9+h} - \frac{1}{9}}{h} \right)\left(\dfrac{\frac{9(9+h)}{1}}{\frac{9(9+h)}{1}} \right) = \dfrac{\frac{1}{\cancel{9+h}}\left(\frac{9(\overset{1}{\cancel{9+h}})}{1}\right) - \frac{1}{\cancel{9}}\left(\frac{\overset{1}{\cancel{9}}(9+h)}{1}\right)}{h\left(\frac{9(9+h)}{1}\right)} = \dfrac{9 - (9+h)}{9h(9+h)}$

$\underbrace{}_{\text{The LCM of } 9 \text{ and } 9+h \text{ is } 9(9+h).}$ $\underbrace{}_{\text{Cancel out the denominators of the 'little fractions'.}}$

$$= \dfrac{9 - 9 - h}{9h(9+h)} = \dfrac{\overset{1}{-\cancel{h}}}{9\underset{1}{\cancel{h}}(9+h)} = \dfrac{-1}{9(9+h)} \ \text{ or } -\dfrac{1}{9(9+h)}$$

In Chapter 2, we've learned how to work with negative exponents by using a 'flipping technique'. Let's see why this technique works. Suppose we want to write $\left(\dfrac{a}{b}\right)^{-4}$ without negative exponents, where a and b are non-zero real numbers. Recall from Section 2.1 (Property IV) that if a is any non-zero real number and n is any whole number, then

$$a^{-n} = \dfrac{1}{a^n}.$$

By Property IV, we can write $\left(\dfrac{a}{b}\right)^{-4} = \dfrac{1}{\left(\frac{a}{b}\right)^4}$. Now,

$$\dfrac{1}{\left(\frac{a}{b}\right)^4} = \dfrac{1}{\frac{a^4}{b^4}} = \left(\dfrac{1}{\frac{a^4}{b^4}}\right)\left(\dfrac{\frac{b^4}{1}}{\frac{b^4}{1}}\right) = \dfrac{1\left(\frac{b^4}{1}\right)}{\left(\frac{a^4}{\cancel{b^4}}\right)\left(\frac{\cancel{b^4}}{1}\right)} = \dfrac{b^4}{a^4},$$

which is the same answer that we would get by using the 'flipping technique' (Property VIII of Section 2.1).

Let's try another one. Recall that $\dfrac{a^{-2}}{b^3} = \dfrac{1}{a^2 b^3}$ by the 'flipping technique'. Well, this works because

$$\underbrace{\dfrac{a^{-2}}{b^3} = \dfrac{\frac{1}{a^2}}{b^3}}_{\text{by Property IV}} = \dfrac{\frac{1}{a^2}}{b^3}\left(\dfrac{\frac{a^2}{1}}{\frac{a^2}{1}}\right) = \dfrac{\frac{1}{\cancel{a^2}}\left(\frac{\overset{1}{\cancel{a^2}}}{1}\right)}{b^3\left(\frac{a^2}{1}\right)} = \dfrac{1}{b^3 a^2} = \dfrac{1}{a^2 b^3}.$$

On your own, try to verify that $\dfrac{a^4}{b^{-5}} = \dfrac{a^4 b^5}{1} = a^4 b^5$ by using Property IV.

Exercises 4.4

In Exercises 1-26, simplify.

1. $\dfrac{\frac{1}{8} - \frac{3}{4}}{\frac{1}{16}}$

2. $\dfrac{\frac{3}{8} + \frac{1}{4}}{\frac{7}{2}}$

3. $\dfrac{1 + \frac{2}{5}}{3 - \frac{1}{10}}$

4. $\dfrac{2 - \frac{1}{6}}{1 + \frac{3}{10}}$

5. $\dfrac{4 - \frac{5}{7}}{4}$

6. $\dfrac{\frac{1}{9} + 5}{6}$

7. $\dfrac{5}{2 + \frac{2}{3}}$

8. $\dfrac{2}{1 - \frac{7}{12}}$

9. $\dfrac{\frac{1}{18} + \frac{5}{6}}{\frac{7}{12} - \frac{1}{36}}$

10. $\dfrac{\frac{7}{6} + \frac{1}{2}}{-\frac{5}{12} + \frac{3}{4}}$

11. $\dfrac{\frac{1}{3x} - 4}{\frac{2}{9x} + 3}$

12. $\dfrac{6 + \frac{1}{2a}}{\frac{7}{4a} - 8}$

13. $\dfrac{\frac{1}{y-2} - \frac{4}{y+5}}{\frac{3}{y^2+3y-10}}$

14. $\dfrac{\frac{2}{x-3} + \frac{4}{x-2}}{\frac{11}{x^2-5x+6}}$

15. $\dfrac{\frac{1}{12x^2} - \frac{5}{4x}}{\frac{2}{3x^2}}$

16. $\dfrac{\frac{2}{9t} - \frac{1}{6t^2}}{\frac{1}{4t}}$

17. $\dfrac{\frac{2a}{a^2-6a} + \frac{3}{a^2-36}}{\frac{4}{a^2+6a}}$

18. $\dfrac{\frac{5}{t^2-6t} - \frac{1}{t^2+4t}}{\frac{4}{t^2-2t-24}}$

19. $\dfrac{-x + 2 + \frac{1}{x-5}}{x + 3}$

20. $\dfrac{\frac{4}{3x+2} - x + 5}{x - 6}$

21. $\dfrac{\frac{5}{2} + \frac{3}{x-2}}{4x - 9}$

22. $\dfrac{\frac{2}{5} + \frac{6}{x+10}}{2x + 5}$

23. $\dfrac{\frac{1}{3+h} - \frac{1}{3}}{h}$

24. $\dfrac{\frac{1}{x+h} - \frac{1}{x}}{h}$

25. $\dfrac{\frac{1}{(8+h)^2} - \frac{1}{64}}{h}$

26. $\dfrac{\frac{1}{(a+h)^2} - \frac{1}{a^2}}{h}$

In Exercises 27-42, perform the indicated operation and simplify.

27. $1 + \dfrac{1}{1 + \frac{1}{2}}$

28. $1 + \dfrac{3}{1 + \frac{1}{4}}$

29. $x - \dfrac{x}{1 + \frac{x+1}{2}}$

30. $t + \dfrac{3t}{1 - \frac{t}{4}}$

31. $\dfrac{a}{2 + \frac{1}{1+\frac{a}{4}}}$

32. $\dfrac{y}{\frac{4}{1+\frac{y}{3}} - 1}$

33. $1 - \dfrac{1}{1 - \frac{1}{x+3}}$

34. $1 + \dfrac{1}{1 + \frac{1}{x+1}}$

35. $\dfrac{6^{-1} + 12^{-1}}{6^{-1}}$

36. $\dfrac{2^{-1} + 4^{-1}}{2^{-1}}$

37. $\dfrac{2 + 4^{-2}}{1 + 8^{-1}}$

38. $\dfrac{5 + 6^{-1}}{2 - 3^{-2}}$

39. $\dfrac{x^{-2} + x^{-3}}{x^3}$

40. $\dfrac{y^{-2} - y^2}{y^{-1}}$

41. $\dfrac{1 - 3a^{-1} + a^{-2}}{1 + 3a^{-1} + a^{-2}}$

42. $\dfrac{7 - 3a - a^{-1}}{7 + 3a + a^{-1}}$

END OF CHAPTER 4   QUIZ

1. Simplify: $\dfrac{7x^2 - 14x}{x^3 - 4x}$

    a) $\dfrac{7x}{x+2}$ b) $\dfrac{7x}{x-2}$ c) $\dfrac{7}{x+2}$ d) $\dfrac{7}{x} + 5$ e) $\dfrac{7(x-2)}{x^2 - 4}$

2. Simplify: $\dfrac{a^3 - 10a^2 + 25a}{2a^3 - 9a^2 - 5a}$

    a) $\dfrac{a^2 - 5}{2a + 1}$ b) $\dfrac{a^2 - 10a + 25}{2a^2 - 9a - 5}$ c) $6\tfrac{11}{18}$ d) $\dfrac{a - 5}{2a + 1}$ e) $\dfrac{a + 5}{2a - 1}$

3. Simplify: $\dfrac{27 - y^3}{y^2 - 7y + 12}$

    a) $\dfrac{y^2 + 3y + 9}{y - 4}$ b) $-\dfrac{y^2 + 3y + 9}{y - 4}$ c) $\dfrac{(3 - y)^2}{y - 4}$ d) $\dfrac{-(3 - y)^2}{y - 4}$ e) $\dfrac{27 - y}{-7y + 12}$

4. $\dfrac{2t^2}{t + 6} \cdot \dfrac{t^2 - 36}{10t^2} =$

    a) $\dfrac{t - 6}{5t^2}$ b) $\dfrac{1}{5(t - 6)}$ c) $5(t - 6)$ d) $\dfrac{t - 6}{5}$ e) $\dfrac{t - 36}{5}$

5. $\dfrac{4a^2 - 12ab}{6a^2b - 18ab^2} \cdot \dfrac{3a + 9b}{a + b} =$

    a) $\dfrac{2(a + 3b)}{ab(a + b)}$ b) $\dfrac{a + 3b}{a + b}$ c) $\dfrac{8}{b}$ d) $\dfrac{a + 3b}{b(a + b)}$ e) $\dfrac{2(a + 3b)}{b(a + b)}$

6. $\dfrac{2t^2 - t - 28}{4t^2 + 12t - 7} \cdot \dfrac{t^3 + 3t^2}{t^3 - 4t^2} =$

    a) $\dfrac{(t - 4)(t + 3)}{2t - 1}$ b) $\dfrac{t + 3}{t^2(2t - 1)}$ c) $\dfrac{t + 3}{2t - 1}$ d) $\dfrac{t + 3}{2t + 1}$ e) $\dfrac{(2t - 7)(t + 3)}{2t - 1}$

7. $\dfrac{4b^8}{9a^2b^3} \div \dfrac{8a^2}{5a^5b^9} =$

    a) $\dfrac{5b^{14}}{18a}$ b) $\dfrac{32}{45a^5b^4}$ c) $\dfrac{5ab^{14}}{18}$ d) $\dfrac{18}{5ab^{14}}$ e) $\dfrac{5ab^4}{18}$

8. $\dfrac{16x^2}{x^2 - 1} \div \dfrac{8x + 8}{1 - x} =$

    a) $-\dfrac{2x^2}{(x + 1)^2}$ b) $\dfrac{2x^2}{(x + 1)^2}$ c) $\dfrac{128x}{(x - 1)(1 - x)}$ d) $-\dfrac{2}{2x + 1}$ e) $-\dfrac{16x^2}{(x + 1)^2}$

9. $\dfrac{y^2 + 4y + 16}{y^2 - 16} \div \dfrac{y^3 - 64}{y + 4} =$

a) $\dfrac{y - 4}{y + 4}$ b) $(y - 4)^2$ c) $\dfrac{y + 4}{y^2 + 4y + 16}$ d) $\dfrac{1}{(y - 4)^2}$ e) $\dfrac{1}{y^2 - 4}$

10. $\dfrac{7x + 3}{4x - 5} + \dfrac{8x - 12}{4x - 5} =$

a) $\dfrac{101}{20}$ b) $\dfrac{3(5x - 3)}{4x - 5}$ c) $\dfrac{3(5x - 3)}{2(4x - 5)}$ d) $\dfrac{15(x - 1)}{4x - 5}$ e) $\dfrac{6x}{4x - 5}$

11. $\dfrac{5a - 9}{a^2 - 81} - \dfrac{4a - 18}{a^2 - 81} =$

a) $\dfrac{a - 27}{(a + 9)(a - 9)}$ b) $\dfrac{a^2 + 9}{(a + 9)(a - 9)}$ c) $\dfrac{a}{a - 9}$ d) $\dfrac{a - 27}{a - 9}$ e) $\dfrac{1}{a - 9}$

12. $\dfrac{4b}{7b - 2} - \dfrac{3b}{2 - 7b} =$

a) $\dfrac{b}{7b - 2}$ b) $\dfrac{b}{2(7b - 2)}$ c) $\dfrac{7b}{2 - 7b}$ d) $\dfrac{7b}{7b - 2}$ e) $\dfrac{1}{-2}$

13. $\dfrac{12}{x - 8} - \dfrac{3}{x + 1} =$

a) $\dfrac{9(x + 4)}{(x - 8)(x + 1)}$ b) $\dfrac{9x - 12}{(x - 8)(x + 1)}$ c) -1 d) $\dfrac{9}{(x - 8)(x + 1)}$ e) $\dfrac{9(x + 36)}{(x - 8)(x + 1)}$

14. $\dfrac{x + 5}{x^2 - 2x} + \dfrac{4x - 1}{x^2 + x} =$

a) $\dfrac{5x + 4}{2x^2 - x}$ b) $\dfrac{6x + 5}{(x - 2)(x + 1)}$ c) $\dfrac{5x^2 - 3x + 7}{x(x - 2)(x + 1)}$ d) $\dfrac{5x^2 - 3x + 7}{x^2(x - 2)(x + 1)}$ e) $\dfrac{5x + 4}{x}$

15. $y^2 - 3y + \dfrac{y - 1}{y + 6} =$

a) $\dfrac{y^2 - 2y - 1}{y + 6}$ b) $\dfrac{y^3 + 3y^2 + 17y + 1}{y + 6}$ c) $\dfrac{y^3 - 3y^2 - 17y - 1}{y + 6}$ d) $y^3 + 3y^2 - 17y - 1$

e) $\dfrac{y^3 + 3y^2 - 17y - 1}{y + 6}$

16. $\dfrac{5}{8x^4 y^6} - \dfrac{3}{20x^5 y^2} =$

a) $\dfrac{19}{40x^4 y^2}$ b) $\dfrac{25x - 6y^4}{40x^5 y^6}$ c) $\dfrac{-1}{6x^{-1} y^4}$ d) $\dfrac{15xy^4}{4x^5 y^6}$ e) $\dfrac{25x^2 - 6y^3}{40x^5 y^6}$

17. The LCM of $16a^3b^2$ and $10ab^5$ is:

   a) $80a^3b^5$ b) $80ab^2$ c) $160a^4b^7$ d) $2a^3b^5$ e) $80a^4b^7$

18. The LCM of $5x^3(x+2)^2(x-3)^4$ and $6x^5(x+2)(x-3)^5$ is:

   a) $30x^8(x+2)^3(x-3)^9$ b) $30x^5(x+2)^2(x-3)^5$ c) $x^3(x+2)(x-3)^4$
   d) $30x^3(x+2)^2(x-3)^5$ e) $30x^5(x+2)(x-3)^4$

19. $\dfrac{\dfrac{4}{x}-\dfrac{3}{5x}}{1+\dfrac{3}{5x}} =$

   a) $\dfrac{17}{8x}$ b) $\dfrac{17}{5x+3}$ c) $\dfrac{34}{5x+3}$ d) $\dfrac{23}{5x+3}$ e) $\dfrac{17}{5x+6}$

20. $\dfrac{\dfrac{1}{7+h}-\dfrac{1}{7}}{h} =$

   a) $-\dfrac{1}{7(7+h)}$ b) $\dfrac{1}{7(7+h)}$ c) 0 d) $\dfrac{h^2}{7(7+h)}$ e) $\dfrac{-h^2}{7(7+h)}$

ANSWERS FOR QUIZ 4   1. c   2. d   3. b   4. d   5. e

6. c   7. c   8. a   9. d   10. b

11. e   12. d   13. a   14. c   15. e

16. b   17. a   18. b   19. b   20. a

Chapter 5:   Radical Expressions

In this chapter, we will study algebraic expressions known as **radicals**. We will primarily focus our attention on a specific type of radical called a **square root**. In our studies, we will learn how to do the usual arithmetic and algebraic operations such as simplifying, multiplying, dividing, and combining (that is, adding or subtracting). One important thing which we will observe is that such operations are related to those which were done for polynomials. For example, the Distributive Property, the FOIL method, combining like terms, and factoring for square roots works the same way as for polynomials Another operation, called rationalizing, will be introduced as well. After we get a strong grasp on square roots, we will look at radical expressions in general.

Section 5.1 Square Roots

Section 5.1.1 Introduction to Square Roots

We'll begin by defining the square root of a real number.

Definition: Let a and b be two real numbers. If $b^2 = a$, then b is called a **square root** of a.

For example, since $3^2 = 9$, the definition tells us that 3 is a square root of 9. Notice that $(-3)^2 = 9$ as well, so the definition tells us that -3 is also a square root of 9.

The example above shows us that 9 has two square roots, -3 and 3. In fact, **every** positive number has two square roots (one positive and one negative). We would like to consider only one of these two answer. From this point on, we will recognize the **positive** square root as **the** square root of a whenever a is a positive number. We call this the **principal square root** of a and denote it by $\sqrt{a}$. For example, $\sqrt{64} = 8$ ONLY and $\sqrt{25} = 5$ ONLY. Observe that $\sqrt{0} = 0$ ONLY since $0^2 = 0$. The expression 'a' underneath the **square root symbol** is referred to as the **radicand** of $\sqrt{a}$.

Question: What is $\sqrt{-1}$? Well, suppose that $b = \sqrt{-1}$ for some real number, b. By the definition, we would have $b^2 = -1$. Let's think about the possible numbers for which b could equal. If b is a positive number, then b^2 is also positive since $(+)^2 = +$. If b is a negative number, then b^2 is a positive number since $(-)^2 = +$. If $b = 0$, then $b^2 = 0$. In all three possible situations, observe that b^2 is either positive, or zero. Therefore, b^2 cannot equal -1. This means that there is no real number which $\sqrt{-1}$ can equal. In fact, $\sqrt{a}$ will never equal a real number when a is a negative number.

To summarize the above,

$$\boxed{\sqrt{+} = + \text{ (the principal square root)}, \ \sqrt{0} = 0, \text{ and } \sqrt{-} \text{ is not a real number.}}$$

Before discussing the algebra of square roots, it is important to establish a list of square roots which appear often.

List of Commonly Used Square Roots

$\sqrt{1} = 1$	$\sqrt{49} = 7$
$\sqrt{4} = 2$	$\sqrt{64} = 8$
$\sqrt{9} = 3$	$\sqrt{81} = 9$
$\sqrt{16} = 4$	$\sqrt{100} = 10$
$\sqrt{25} = 5$	$\sqrt{121} = 11$
$\sqrt{36} = 6$	$\sqrt{144} = 12$

You should notice that the list I've given contains the square roots of the integers which are perfect squares (recall that a **perfect square** is a natural number which is the square of another natural number). As I've mentioned before, **every** positive number has a square root. For example, there are numbers like $\sqrt{3}$, $\sqrt{19}$, $\sqrt{203.61}$, and $\sqrt{\pi}$. However, the numbers which they equal are very strange looking. As a demonstration, let's look at $\sqrt{2}$. If we write $n = \sqrt{2}$, then we'll obtain $n^2 = 2$. It turns out that n is approximately equal to 1.414. In order to figure out this value, you would need to use a calculator or computer. In fact, the actual value of $\sqrt{2}$ can be expressed as a decimal which is non-terminating and non-repeating (recall that such a number is called an **irrational number**). By writing $\sqrt{2}$ as 1.414, we are rounding off the actual answer to the nearest thousandth. There are many real numbers which have square roots that are irrational numbers. An enormous set of such numbers is described in the following:

Theorem. If n is a natural number which is *not* a perfect square, then $\sqrt{n}$ is an irrational number. If $a > 0$, $b > 0$ (neither are perfect squares), and $\dfrac{a}{b}$ is in reduced form, then $\sqrt{\dfrac{a}{b}}$ is an irrational number.

So, now we have an idea of which numbers can and cannot be 'square rooted'. We also have a grasp on which positive numbers have 'nice looking' decimal forms and which have 'ugly looking' decimal forms. Let's begin doing some algebra. We'll start by listing some properties which square roots satisfy.

PROPERTIES OF SQUARE ROOTS

> **PROPERTY I.** If a is any real number, then
> $$\sqrt{a^2} = |a|.$$

For example, if $a = 4$, then $\sqrt{4^2} = |4| = 4$. If $a = -4$, then $\sqrt{(-4)^2} = |-4| = 4$.

Note: Over the years, I've noticed that this property caused confusion for students because of the presence of the absolute value. After doing some examples using this property, we will make things easier and assume that all variables represent either **positive numbers** or **nonnegative numbers** (a **nonnegative number** is a real number which is either positive or zero). By doing so, Property I will simply become $\sqrt{a^2} = a$. Think of the square root and the square as cancelling each other out when a is a nonnegative number.

> **PROPERTY II.** Suppose that a and b are nonnegative numbers. Then
> $$\sqrt{a} \cdot \sqrt{b} = \sqrt{a \cdot b}.$$

Examples.

1) $\sqrt{(4)(81)} = \sqrt{4} \cdot \sqrt{81} = 2 \cdot 9 = 18$ 2) $\sqrt{16x^2} = \sqrt{16} \cdot \sqrt{x^2} = 4\,|x|$

3) $\sqrt{100x^4} = \sqrt{100} \cdot \sqrt{x^4} = \sqrt{100} \cdot \sqrt{\left(x^2\right)^2} = 10\,\left|x^2\right| = 10x^2$ since $x^2 \geq 0$ for any real number x.

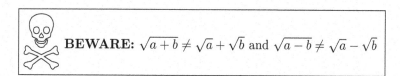
BEWARE: $\sqrt{a + b} \neq \sqrt{a} + \sqrt{b}$ and $\sqrt{a - b} \neq \sqrt{a} - \sqrt{b}$

123

For example, $\sqrt{1} + \sqrt{1} \neq \sqrt{2}$ and $\sqrt{49} - \sqrt{9} \neq \sqrt{40}$.

PROPERTY III. Suppose that a is a nonnegative number and b is a positive number. Then
$$\sqrt{\frac{a}{b}} = \frac{\sqrt{a}}{\sqrt{b}}.$$

Examples.

1) $\sqrt{\dfrac{16}{25}} = \dfrac{\sqrt{16}}{\sqrt{25}} = \dfrac{4}{5}$.

2) $\sqrt{\dfrac{y^2}{4}} = \dfrac{\sqrt{y^2}}{\sqrt{4}} = \dfrac{|y|}{2}$.

3) $\sqrt{\dfrac{a^4}{49}} = \dfrac{\sqrt{a^4}}{\sqrt{49}} = \dfrac{\sqrt{(a^2)^2}}{\sqrt{49}} = \dfrac{|a^2|}{7} = \dfrac{a^2}{7}$ since $a^2 \geq 0$ for any real number a.

Exercise 5.1.1

In Exercises 1-30, evaluate (if possible).

1. $\sqrt{1}$ 2. $-\sqrt{1}$ 3. $\sqrt{0}$ 4. $\sqrt{4}$ 5. $-\sqrt{4}$

6. $\sqrt{-4}$ 7. $\sqrt{5^2}$ 8. $\sqrt{(-5)^2}$ 9. $\sqrt{(-12)^2}$ 10. $\sqrt{12^2}$

11. $-\sqrt{13^2}$ 12. $-\sqrt{(-13)^2}$ 13. $-\sqrt{-13^2}$ 14. $\sqrt{(25)(64)}$ 15. $\sqrt{(81)(81)}$

16. $\sqrt{(121)(100)}$ 17. $\sqrt{(144)(4)}$ 18. $\sqrt{(9)(-64)}$ 19. $\sqrt{-100}\sqrt{9}$

20. $\sqrt{-1}\sqrt{-49}$ 21. $\sqrt{\dfrac{1}{16}}$ 22. $\sqrt{\dfrac{81}{49}}$ 23. $\sqrt{\dfrac{25}{36}}$

24. $\sqrt{\dfrac{9}{16}}$ 25. $\sqrt{\dfrac{169}{4}}$ 26. $-\sqrt{\dfrac{1}{16}}$ 27. $-\sqrt{\dfrac{144}{49}}$

28. $\sqrt{-\dfrac{144}{49}}$ 29. $-\sqrt{\left(\dfrac{36}{25}\right)\left(\dfrac{144}{121}\right)}$ 30. $\sqrt{(16)\left(\dfrac{4}{81}\right)}$

In Exercises 31-48, simplify. Assume that all variables represent positive numbers.

31. $\sqrt{x^2}$ 32. $\sqrt{36y^2}$ 33. $\sqrt{64a^2}$ 34. $\sqrt{(5x)^2}$ 35. $\sqrt{(-5x)^2}$

36. $\sqrt{(-2y)^2}$ 37. $-\sqrt{(2y)^2}$ 38. $\sqrt{(2y)^2}$ 39. $\sqrt{(15ab^2)^2}$ 40. $\sqrt{(-12x^3)^2}$

41. $\sqrt{\dfrac{y^2}{16}}$ 42. $\sqrt{\dfrac{4}{x^2}}$ 43. $\sqrt{\dfrac{121}{t^2}}$ 44. $\sqrt{\dfrac{144}{x^2}}$ 45. $\sqrt{\dfrac{(7x)^2}{100}}$

46. $\sqrt{\dfrac{9x^2}{(4y)^2}}$ 47. $\sqrt{\left(\dfrac{17}{10x^4}\right)^2}$ 48. $\sqrt{\dfrac{(13a)^2}{(20b^2)^2}}$

In Exercises 49-61, determine whether or not the number is rational or irrational.

49. $\sqrt{1}$

50. $\sqrt{16}$

51. $\sqrt{17}$

52. $\sqrt{29}$

53. $\sqrt{\dfrac{9}{100}}$

54. $-\sqrt{\dfrac{2}{3}}$

55. $-\sqrt{\dfrac{5}{6}}$

56. $\sqrt{\dfrac{9}{4}}$

57. $\sqrt{0.16}$

58. $\sqrt{0.15}$

59. $\sqrt{0.2}$

60. $\sqrt{1.21}$

61. $\sqrt{1.69}$

Section 5.1.2 Simplifying Square Roots

Next we will learn how to simplify a square root. Let's begin by simplifying square roots of natural numbers. Suppose we want to simplify $\sqrt{8}$. The first thing we need to do is to factor the number 8 so that one of the factors is a perfect square. Notice that $8 = 4 \times 2$ and 4 is a perfect square. Next, we apply Property II of Section 5.1.1 and factor the given square root into a product of square roots. Once this is done, we simplify $\sqrt{4}$. In other words, we have

$$\sqrt{8} = \sqrt{4 \times 2} = \underbrace{\sqrt{4} \times \sqrt{2}}_{\text{by Property II}} = 2 \times \sqrt{2}, \text{ or just } 2\sqrt{2}.$$ Note that the '$\times$' symbol is omitted in the final answer.

Examples. Simplify.

1) $\sqrt{12} = \sqrt{4 \times 3} = \sqrt{4} \times \sqrt{3} = 2 \times \sqrt{3} = 2\sqrt{3}$

2) $\sqrt{18} = \sqrt{9 \times 2} = \sqrt{9} \times \sqrt{2} = 3 \times \sqrt{2} = 3\sqrt{2}$

3) $\sqrt{75} = \sqrt{25 \times 3} = \sqrt{25} \times \sqrt{3} = 5 \times \sqrt{3} = 5\sqrt{3}$

4) $\sqrt{40} = \sqrt{4 \times 10} = \sqrt{4} \times \sqrt{10} = 2 \times \sqrt{10} = 2\sqrt{10}$

5) $-\sqrt{162} = -\sqrt{81 \times 2} = -\sqrt{81} \times \sqrt{2} = -9 \times \sqrt{2} = -9\sqrt{2}$

6) $\sqrt{32} = \sqrt{16 \times 2} = \sqrt{16} \times \sqrt{2} = 4 \times \sqrt{2} = 4\sqrt{2}$

Notice that I used $32 = 16 \times 2$, not $32 = 4 \times 8$. If I had used $32 = 4 \times 8$ instead, then

$$\sqrt{32} = \sqrt{4 \times 8} = \sqrt{4} \times \sqrt{8} = 2\sqrt{8}.$$

However, $\sqrt{8}$ could be further simplified to become $2\sqrt{2}$ by an earlier example. Therefore, $\sqrt{32} = 2\sqrt{8} = 2(2\sqrt{2}) = 4\sqrt{2}$, the same answer as before obtained by doing twice the amount of work. The moral of the story is:

> When you have different possible ways of factoring your number, choose as one of your factors the largest possible perfect square in the factorization.

Another thing to notice is that not all square roots will simplify (in other words, they are already expressed in simplified form). For example, $\sqrt{35}$ doesn't simplify since $35 = 7 \times 5$ and neither 7 nor 5 are perfect squares. Similarly, $\sqrt{23}$ doesn't simplify since $23 = 23 \times 1$ and 23 is not a perfect square. Observe that $\sqrt{23} = \sqrt{23} \times \sqrt{1} = \sqrt{23} \times 1 = \sqrt{23}$ and we don't get anything new. In fact, if n is **any** prime number, then $\sqrt{n}$ doesn't simplify (which is the same as saying that it is already simplified).

Try These (Set 1): Simplify (if possible).

1) $\sqrt{24}$

2) $\sqrt{45}$

3) $\sqrt{110}$

4) $\sqrt{98}$

5) $\sqrt{29}$

Now let's simplify square roots whose radicand contains variables. Let's assume that the variables represent any real number for which the square root is well-defined. Suppose we want to simplify $\sqrt{x^9}$. We want to apply a method similar to before and somehow incorporate some of our properties into the problem. First of all, notice that x must represent a nonnegative number for this to make sense (if x were allowed to be a negative number, then x^9 would also be negative and this would not have a square root). Now, the trick is to divide $9 \div 2 = 4\ R\ 1$. This means that we can write $9 = 4(2) + 1$ (remember that this is how you check a division problem). We can rewrite our example as follows:

$$\sqrt{x^9} = \underbrace{\sqrt{x^{4(2)+1}} = \sqrt{(x^4)^2 \cdot x^1}}_{\text{by Properties I and V of exponents}} = \underbrace{\sqrt{(x^4)^2} \cdot \sqrt{x^1} = x^4\sqrt{x}}_{\text{by Properties I and II of square roots}}$$

And now it is simplified.

There is a much simpler way of handling this example, but let's do one more example using this technique before we do it the easier way. Suppose we want to simplify $\sqrt{x^{14}}$. Notice that x may be **any** real number since x^{14} will be either positive or zero and we can always take the square root of such a number. As before, we divide $14 \div 2 = 7\ R\ 0$. This means that we can write $14 = 7(2)$. Our example now simplifies to

$$\sqrt{x^{14}} = \underbrace{\sqrt{x^{7(2)}} = \sqrt{(x^7)^2}}_{\text{Property V of exponents}} = \left|x^7\right|.$$

Notice, however, that by using our properties of absolute value (see Section 1.7), we obtain

$$\left|x^7\right| = \left|x^6 \cdot x^1\right| = \underbrace{\left|x^6\right| \cdot |x| = x^6\,|x|}_{\text{Since } x^6 \geq 0,\ |x^6| = x^6}.$$

And so $\sqrt{x^{14}} = x^6\,|x|$ is in simplified form. This is all tedious stuff, especially the part with the absolute value. To make our lives a bit easier, we will assume that **all variables represent either positive or nonnegative numbers only.** By doing so, the absolute value becomes unnecessary and the examples that we've just done become much simpler. For example, to simplify $\sqrt{x^7}$, all that we have to do is to divide (as before) $9 \div 2 = 4\ R\ 1$. The quotient, 4, tells us 'how many x's come out of the square root'. The remainder, 1, tells us 'how many x's remain inside of the square root'. Therefore, $\sqrt{x^9} = \underbrace{x^4\sqrt{x^1}}_{\text{4 out, 1 in}} = x^4\sqrt{x}$. Similarly, to

simplify $\sqrt{x^{14}}$, just divide $14 \div 2 = 7\ R\ 0$. We get $\sqrt{x^{14}} = \underbrace{x^7}_{\text{7 out, 0 in}}$. Let's try some more examples using

this easier technique.

Examples. Simplify. Assume that all variables represent nonnegative numbers.

1) $\sqrt{a^5} = \underbrace{a^2\sqrt{a^1}}_{5 \div 2\ =\ 2\ R\ 1} = a^2\sqrt{a}$ 2) $\sqrt{x^{11}} = \underbrace{x^5\sqrt{x^1}}_{11 \div 2\ =\ 5\ R\ 1} = x^5\sqrt{x}$

3) $\sqrt{y^{10}} = \underbrace{y^5}_{10 \div 2\ =\ 5\ R\ 0}$ 4) $\sqrt{t^{16}} = \underbrace{t^8}_{16 \div 2\ =\ 8\ R\ 0}$

5) $\sqrt{b^2} = \underbrace{b^1}_{2 \div 2\ =\ 1\ R\ 0} = b$ 6) $\sqrt{y} = \underbrace{\sqrt{y}}_{1 \div 2\ =\ 0\ R\ 1}$ ($\sqrt{y}$ is **already simplified.**)

Try These (Set 2): Simplify. Assume that all variables represent nonnegative numbers.

1) $\sqrt{x^4}$ 2) $\sqrt{y^{13}}$ 3) $\sqrt{t^3}$ 4) $\sqrt{x^{28}}$ 5) $\sqrt{p^{21}}$

By using what we've learned, we could actually simplify the square root of **any** monomial. To do so, we'll simplify each 'piece' of the monomial seperately and then 'put it all together'.

126

Examples. Simplify. Assume that all variables represent nonnegative numbers.

1) $\sqrt{4x^2} = 2x$ since $\sqrt{4} = 2$ and $\underbrace{\sqrt{x^2} = x^1 = x}_{2 \div 2 \,=\, 1 \; R \; 0}$.

2) $\sqrt{48y^3} = 4y\sqrt{3y}$ since $\sqrt{48} = \sqrt{16}\sqrt{3} = 4\sqrt{3}$ and $\underbrace{\sqrt{y^3} = y^1\sqrt{y^1} = y\sqrt{y}}_{3 \div 2 \,=\, 1 \; R \; 1}$.

3) $\sqrt{9a^2b^3} = 3ab\sqrt{b}$ since $\sqrt{9} = 3$, $\underbrace{\sqrt{a^2} = a^1 = a}_{2 \div 2 \,=\, 1 \; R \; 0}$ and $\underbrace{\sqrt{b^3} = b^1\sqrt{b^1} = b\sqrt{b}}_{3 \div 2 \,=\, 1 \; R \; 1}$.

4) $\sqrt{20x^{13}y^4} = 2x^6y^2\sqrt{5x}$ since $\sqrt{20} = \sqrt{4}\sqrt{5} = 2\sqrt{5}$, $\underbrace{\sqrt{x^{13}} = x^6\sqrt{x^1} = x^6\sqrt{x}}_{13 \div 2 \,=\, 6 \; R \; 1}$, and $\underbrace{\sqrt{y^4} = y^2}_{4 \div 2 \,=\, 2 \; R \; 0}$.

5) $\sqrt{500s^6t} = 10s^3\sqrt{5t}$ since $\sqrt{500} = \sqrt{100}\sqrt{5} = 10\sqrt{5}$, $\underbrace{\sqrt{s^6} = s^3}_{6 \div 2 \,=\, 3 \; R \; 0}$, and $\underbrace{\sqrt{t} = \sqrt{t}}_{1 \div 2 \,=\, 0 \; R \; 1}$.

Try These (Set 3): Simplify. Assume that all variables represent nonnegative numbers.

1) $\sqrt{12x^5y^2}$ 2) $\sqrt{54x^4y^7}$ 3) $\sqrt{100p^6q^9}$ 4) $-\sqrt{98a^4bc^{11}}$ 5) $\sqrt{15xy^{12}}$

Exercise 5.1.2

Simplify each square root. Assume that all variables represent nonnegative numbers.

1. $\sqrt{12}$ 2. $\sqrt{8}$ 3. $\sqrt{27}$ 4. $\sqrt{24}$ 5. $\sqrt{44}$

6. $\sqrt{50}$ 7. $-\sqrt{125}$ 8. $\sqrt{99}$ 9. $\sqrt{32}$ 10. $-\sqrt{72}$

11. $\sqrt{60}$ 12. $\sqrt{300}$ 13. $-\sqrt{48}$ 14. $\sqrt{150}$ 15. $-\sqrt{54}$

16. $\sqrt{x^3}$ 17. $\sqrt{y^2}$ 18. $\sqrt{t^9}$ 19. $\sqrt{y^4}$ 20. $\sqrt{a^{17}}$

21. $\sqrt{b^{19}}$ 22. $\sqrt{9x}$ 23. $\sqrt{64y}$ 24. $\sqrt{36a^2}$ 25. $\sqrt{81b^4}$

26. $\sqrt{8xy^6}$ 27. $\sqrt{32a^7b^4}$ 28. $\sqrt{20x^{13}y}$ 29. $\sqrt{33mn^3}$

30. $-\sqrt{90x^7y}$ 31. $-\sqrt{80xy^5}$ 32. $\sqrt{68x^{14}y^{11}z}$ 33. $\sqrt{56a^6b^{15}c}$

Section 5.1.3 Multiplying and Dividing Square Roots

We will apply the properties learned in Section 5.1.1 to divide and multiply square roots. From this point on, we will **assume that all variables represent positive numbers.**

Recall Properties I and II from Section 5.1.1:

$$\sqrt{a} \cdot \sqrt{b} = \sqrt{a \cdot b} \quad \text{and} \quad \sqrt{\frac{a}{b}} = \frac{\sqrt{a}}{\sqrt{b}}, \; b \neq 0.$$

(provided that these square roots are well-defined).

Examples. Multiply or divide. Simplify your answers.

1) $\sqrt{7} \cdot \sqrt{7} = \sqrt{7 \cdot 7} = \sqrt{49} = 7$

2) $\sqrt{6} \cdot \sqrt{5} = \sqrt{6 \cdot 5} = \sqrt{30}$ (in simplified form)

3) $\sqrt{6x^2} \cdot \sqrt{2x^4} = \sqrt{6x^2 \cdot 2x^4} = \underbrace{\sqrt{12x^6} = 2x^3\sqrt{3}}_{\sqrt{12}=2\sqrt{3} \text{ and } \sqrt{x^6}=x^3.}$

4) $\sqrt{2xy^3} \cdot \sqrt{8x^6y^3} = \sqrt{2xy^3 \cdot 8x^6y^3} = \underbrace{\sqrt{16x^7y^6} = 4x^3y^3\sqrt{x}}_{\sqrt{16}=4, \ \sqrt{x^7}=x^3\sqrt{x}, \text{ and } \sqrt{y^6}=y^3.}$

5) $\underbrace{\sqrt{3a^2b}\left(\sqrt{5b^3}\right)\left(\sqrt{6a^2b^7}\right) = \sqrt{3a^2b\,(5b^3)\,(6a^2b^7)}}_{\text{Multiply the radicands together.}} = \underbrace{\sqrt{90a^4b^{11}} = 3a^2b^5\sqrt{10b}}_{\sqrt{90}=3\sqrt{10}, \ \sqrt{a^4}=a^2, \text{ and } \sqrt{b^{11}}=b^5\sqrt{b}.}$

6) $\dfrac{\sqrt{48x^{14}}}{\sqrt{3x^9}} = \sqrt{\dfrac{48x^{14}}{3x^9}} = \underbrace{\sqrt{16x^5} = 4x^2\sqrt{x}}_{\sqrt{16}=4 \text{ and } \sqrt{x^5}=x^2\sqrt{x}.}$

7) $\dfrac{\sqrt{155a^{16}b^4}}{\sqrt{5a^9b^5}} = \sqrt{\dfrac{155a^{16}b^4}{5a^9b^5}} = \underbrace{\sqrt{\dfrac{31a^7}{b}} = \dfrac{a^3\sqrt{31a}}{\sqrt{b}}}_{\sqrt{31} \text{ and } \sqrt{b} \text{ are simplified, and } \sqrt{a^7}=a^3\sqrt{a}.} = \dfrac{a^3\sqrt{31a}}{1\sqrt{b}} = \dfrac{a^3}{1}\left(\dfrac{\sqrt{31a}}{\sqrt{b}}\right) = a^3\sqrt{\dfrac{31a}{b}}$

Try These (Set 4): Multiply or divide. Simplify your answers.

1) $\sqrt{11x^2y^5} \cdot \sqrt{11xy}$

2) $\dfrac{\sqrt{56x^{10}}}{\sqrt{7x^8}}$

3) $\dfrac{\left(\sqrt{15a^{14}}\right)\left(\sqrt{12a^6}\right)}{\sqrt{5a^7}}$

Exercise 5.1.3

In Exercises 1-23, multiply and simplify the square roots. Assume that all variables represent nonnegative numbers.

1. $\sqrt{7} \cdot \sqrt{2}$ | 2. $\sqrt{3} \cdot \sqrt{5}$ | 3. $\sqrt{10} \cdot \sqrt{3}$ | 4. $\sqrt{11} \cdot \sqrt{2}$ | 5. $\sqrt{5} \cdot \sqrt{10}$

6. $\sqrt{2} \cdot \sqrt{9}$ | 7. $\sqrt{6} \cdot \sqrt{6}$ | 8. $\sqrt{2} \cdot \sqrt{2}$ | 9. $\sqrt{14} \cdot \sqrt{6}$ | 10. $\sqrt{10} \cdot \sqrt{15}$

11. $\sqrt{12} \cdot \sqrt{3}$ | 12. $\sqrt{x^4} \cdot \sqrt{x^3}$ | 13. $\sqrt{y^4} \cdot \sqrt{y^7}$ | 14. $\sqrt{a} \cdot \sqrt{a}$ | 15. $\sqrt{xy^3} \cdot \sqrt{x^4y}$

16. $\sqrt{2x^6y^5} \cdot \sqrt{xy^3}$ | 17. $\sqrt{5a^5b} \cdot \sqrt{a^4b^3}$ | 18. $\sqrt{8x} \cdot \sqrt{8x^4}$ | 19. $\sqrt{8x^5y^4} \cdot \sqrt{5x^2y^2}$

20. $\sqrt{16x^5} \cdot \sqrt{3x^3y^7}$ | 21. $\sqrt{10a^4b^3} \cdot \sqrt{10a^4b}$ | 22. $\sqrt{12x^2y^5} \cdot \sqrt{6x^4y^4}$ | 23. $\sqrt{12m^3n} \cdot \sqrt{12m^2n}$

In Exercises 24-38, divide and simplify the square roots. Assume that all variables represent positive numbers.

24. $\dfrac{\sqrt{40}}{\sqrt{10}}$ | 25. $\dfrac{\sqrt{32}}{\sqrt{2}}$ | 26. $\dfrac{\sqrt{40}}{\sqrt{2}}$ | 27. $\dfrac{\sqrt{56}}{\sqrt{7}}$ | 28. $\dfrac{\sqrt{30x^2}}{\sqrt{2x}}$

29. $\dfrac{\sqrt{24x^5}}{\sqrt{2x^4}}$ 30. $\dfrac{\sqrt{24x^9}}{\sqrt{8x^3}}$ 31. $\dfrac{\sqrt{48y^{11}}}{\sqrt{8y^4}}$ 32. $\dfrac{\sqrt{75m^{10}n^9}}{\sqrt{3m^2n^6}}$ 33. $\dfrac{\sqrt{200x^{15}y^4}}{\sqrt{4x^8y^4}}$

34. $\dfrac{\sqrt{68a^9b^3}}{\sqrt{17a^4b^7}}$ 35. $\dfrac{\sqrt{5a^4b}}{\sqrt{45a^3b^5}}$ 36. $\dfrac{\sqrt{8a^5b^7c}}{\sqrt{24a^4b^{11}c^2}}$ 37. $\dfrac{\sqrt{23xy^5z^7}}{\sqrt{14x^2y^3}}$ 38. $\dfrac{\sqrt{21x^8yz^9}}{\sqrt{5x^8y^2z^7}}$

Section 5.1.4 Combining (Adding and Subtracting) Square Roots

Now we will learn how to combine square roots. It turns out that combining square roots is just like combining like terms when adding or subtracting monomials. How does it work? Suppose we want to combine $6\sqrt{3} + 4\sqrt{3}$. The first thing to notice is that both square roots have the same radicand, 3. If we think of $\sqrt{3}$ as 'x', then the problem could be thought of as $6x + 4x$. This we can handle. Since these are like terms, we'll combine them by adding their coefficients and keep the same variable part, x. As we know, the answer is $10x$. The same technique works for square roots. We have $6\sqrt{3} + 4\sqrt{3} = (6 + 4)\sqrt{3} = 10\sqrt{3}$. We can think of $6\sqrt{3}$ and $4\sqrt{3}$ as 'like roots' and the numbers 6 and 4 as the 'coefficients' of the terms. Let's see some examples.

Examples. Combine and simplify.

1) $3\sqrt{5} + 7\sqrt{5} = (3 + 7)\sqrt{5} = 10\sqrt{5}$

2) $9\sqrt{11} - 5\sqrt{11} = (9 - 5)\sqrt{11} = 4\sqrt{11}$

3) $13\sqrt{6} + 6\sqrt{6} - 20\sqrt{6} = (13 + 6 - 20)\sqrt{6} = -1\sqrt{6} = -\sqrt{6}$

4) $\underbrace{7\sqrt{2} + 2\sqrt{8}}_{\text{not like roots}} = 7\sqrt{2} + 2\underbrace{(2\sqrt{2})}_{\sqrt{8}=2\sqrt{2}} = \underbrace{7\sqrt{2} + 4\sqrt{2}}_{\text{like roots}} = 11\sqrt{2}$

5) $\underbrace{11\sqrt{5} - 8\sqrt{20} + \sqrt{125}}_{\text{no like roots}} = \underbrace{11\sqrt{5} - 8(2\sqrt{5}) + 5\sqrt{5}}_{\sqrt{20}=2\sqrt{5} \text{ and } \sqrt{125}=5\sqrt{5}.} = \underbrace{11\sqrt{5} - 16\sqrt{5} + 5\sqrt{5}}_{\text{like roots}} = 0\sqrt{5} = 0$

6) $\underbrace{9\sqrt{14} + 3\sqrt{18}}_{\text{not like roots}} = 9\sqrt{14} + 3\underbrace{\left(3\sqrt{2}\right)}_{\sqrt{18}=3\sqrt{2}} = \underbrace{9\sqrt{14} + 9\sqrt{2}}_{\text{still not like roots}}$ (These **DO NOT** combine.)

7) $\underbrace{\dfrac{\sqrt{12} + 5\sqrt{3}}{7}}_{\text{Simplify } \sqrt{12}.} = \dfrac{2\sqrt{3} + 5\sqrt{3}}{7} = \dfrac{\overset{1}{\cancel{7}}\sqrt{3}}{\underset{1}{\cancel{7}}} = \dfrac{\sqrt{3}}{1} = \sqrt{3}$

8) $\underbrace{\dfrac{2\sqrt{20} - 7\sqrt{45}}{34}}_{\text{Simplify } \sqrt{20} \text{ and } \sqrt{45}.} = \dfrac{2\left(2\sqrt{5}\right) - 7\left(3\sqrt{5}\right)}{34} = \dfrac{4\sqrt{5} - 21\sqrt{5}}{34} = \dfrac{\overset{1}{-\cancel{17}}\sqrt{5}}{\underset{2}{\cancel{34}}} = \dfrac{-\sqrt{5}}{2} \text{ or } -\dfrac{1}{2}\sqrt{5}$

9) $\underbrace{\dfrac{12 + 8\sqrt{40}}{16}}_{\text{Simplify } \sqrt{40}.} = \dfrac{12 + 8\left(2\sqrt{10}\right)}{16} = \underbrace{\dfrac{12 + 16\sqrt{10}}{16}}_{\text{Factor the numerator the same way as } 12+16x.} = \dfrac{\overset{1}{\cancel{4}}\left(3 + 4\sqrt{10}\right)}{\underset{4}{\cancel{16}}} = \dfrac{3 + 4\sqrt{10}}{4} \text{ or } \dfrac{1}{4}\left(3 + 4\sqrt{10}\right)$

129

10) $\dfrac{-5+\sqrt{200}}{-25} = \dfrac{-5+10\sqrt{2}}{-25} = \dfrac{\overset{1}{\cancel{5}}\left(-1+2\sqrt{2}\right)}{\underset{5}{-\cancel{25}}} = \dfrac{-1+2\sqrt{2}}{-5}$ or $-\dfrac{1}{5}\left(-1+2\sqrt{2}\right)$

$\underbrace{\qquad\qquad\qquad}_{\text{Simplify } \sqrt{200}.}$

Notice that we can eliminate the negative sign in the denominator as follows:

$$\frac{-1+2\sqrt{2}}{-5} = \frac{\cancel{-}1\left(1-2\sqrt{2}\right)}{\cancel{-}5} = \frac{1-2\sqrt{2}}{5}$$

As you can see, all that I've done was to change the signs of EACH of the terms in the fraction.

Try These (Set 5): Combine and simplify.

1) $2\sqrt{13}+9\sqrt{13}$

2) $\dfrac{\sqrt{3}+\sqrt{27}}{8}$

3) $9\sqrt{24}-5\sqrt{6}$

4) $\dfrac{36-\sqrt{18}}{3}$

5) $2\sqrt{52}-12\sqrt{13}+4\sqrt{4}$

6) $\dfrac{2\sqrt{3}+4\sqrt{75}}{10}$

Exercise 5.1.4

Combine and simplify the square roots (if possible).

1. $\sqrt{3}+4\sqrt{3}$

2. $5\sqrt{2}+\sqrt{2}$

3. $9\sqrt{10}-13\sqrt{10}$

4. $16\sqrt{11}-3\sqrt{11}$

5. $9\sqrt{5}+8\sqrt{5}-16\sqrt{5}$

6. $5\sqrt{2}-12\sqrt{2}-2\sqrt{2}$

7. $-9\sqrt{7}+4\sqrt{7}-\sqrt{7}$

8. $6\sqrt{15}-7\sqrt{15}-3\sqrt{15}$

9. $\sqrt{5}+\sqrt{20}$

10. $\sqrt{8}+2\sqrt{2}$

11. $4\sqrt{6}-5\sqrt{72}$

12. $-8\sqrt{12}+4\sqrt{3}$

13. $-7\sqrt{8}-2\sqrt{18}$

14. $4\sqrt{24}-3\sqrt{54}$

15. $8\sqrt{6}-3\sqrt{24}+\sqrt{54}$

16. $10\sqrt{5}+\sqrt{20}-18\sqrt{45}$

17. $3\sqrt{7}+\sqrt{3}$

18. $6\sqrt{40}-\sqrt{7}$

19. $-4\sqrt{3}+2\sqrt{40}+9\sqrt{243}$

20. $3\sqrt{8}+5\sqrt{20}-2\sqrt{500}$

21. $5\sqrt{16}-8\sqrt{7}-\sqrt{63}+\sqrt{144}$

22. $2\sqrt{49}+3\sqrt{121}+\sqrt{7}-5\sqrt{28}$

23. $\dfrac{3\sqrt{7}+9\sqrt{28}}{9}$

24. $\dfrac{3\sqrt{18}-2\sqrt{2}}{14}$

25. $\dfrac{-\sqrt{9}+4\sqrt{81}}{11}$

26. $\dfrac{8\sqrt{4}-2\sqrt{25}}{23}$

27. $\dfrac{10+\sqrt{32}}{2}$

28. $\dfrac{12-\sqrt{128}}{2}$

29. $\dfrac{9\sqrt{5}+12\sqrt{7}}{3}$

30. $\dfrac{8\sqrt{3}-12\sqrt{2}}{4}$

31. $\dfrac{2+\sqrt{24}}{2}$

32. $\dfrac{-4+\sqrt{60}}{2}$

33. $\dfrac{-18-\sqrt{18}}{-9}$

34. $\dfrac{10-\sqrt{200}}{-2}$

Section 5.1.5 Multiplying Square Roots (Revisited)

In Section 5.1.2, we've learned how to multiply and divide square roots which contain monomials as radicands. We will continue our study of multiplication of square roots in this subsection. Once again, we will see a huge resemblence between square roots and polynomials. **Whenever you get stuck with a square root problem, think of the square roots as monomials and use your knowledge of polynomials to help you solve the problem.** I will demonstrate how to do this as we continue.

Examples. Multiply and simplify.

1) $\underbrace{\left(5\sqrt{3}\right)\left(6\sqrt{3}\right) = 5(6)(\sqrt{3})(\sqrt{3})}_{\text{by the Associative and Commutative Properties}} \quad = 30\sqrt{9} = 30(3) = 90$

2) $\underbrace{\left(2\sqrt{5}\right)\left(-4\sqrt{10}\right) = -8\sqrt{50}}_{\text{Compute } 2(-4), \text{ then } \sqrt{5}(\sqrt{10}).} = -8(5\sqrt{2}) = -40\sqrt{2}$

3) $\underbrace{\left(2\sqrt{6}\right)\left(-4\sqrt{3}\right)\left(-\sqrt{6}\right) = 8\sqrt{108}}_{\text{Compute } 2(-4)(-1), \text{ then } \sqrt{6}(\sqrt{3})(\sqrt{6}).} = 8(6\sqrt{3}) = 48\sqrt{3}$

4) $4\sqrt{3}\underbrace{(5\sqrt{3} + \sqrt{2})}_{\text{Do not combine.}} = \underbrace{4\sqrt{3}(5\sqrt{3}) + 4\sqrt{3}(\sqrt{2})}_{\text{by the Distributive Property}} = 20\sqrt{9} + 4\sqrt{6} = 20(3) + 4\sqrt{6}$

$$= 60 + 4\sqrt{6}$$

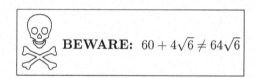

> ☠ **BEWARE:** $60 + 4\sqrt{6} \neq 64\sqrt{6}$

If you think of $60 + 4\sqrt{6}$ as $60 + 4x$, you would realize that this binomial can't be simplified into a monomial. The same is true for $60 + 4\sqrt{6}$.

Before moving on, I would like to mention a property which will be useful to us. It says that squares cancel out square roots.

> **PROPERTY:** If a is a nonnegative number, then $\left(\sqrt{a}\right)^2 = a$.

5) $\underbrace{\left(\sqrt{2} + 3\right)\left(\sqrt{2} - 2\right)}_{\text{binomial} \times \text{binomial}} = \underbrace{\overbrace{\left(\sqrt{2}\right)^2}^{2} - 2\left(\sqrt{2}\right) + 3\left(\sqrt{2}\right) + 3(-2)}_{\text{FOIL method}} = 2 - 2\sqrt{2} + 3\sqrt{2} - 6$

$$= -4 + 1\sqrt{3} = -4 + \sqrt{3}$$

6) $\underbrace{\left(4\sqrt{3}-5\right)\left(2\sqrt{5}-1\right)}_{\text{binomial}\,\times\,\text{binomial}} = \underbrace{4\sqrt{3}\left(2\sqrt{5}\right)+4\sqrt{3}\left(-1\right)-5\left(2\sqrt{5}\right)-5(-1)}_{\text{FOIL method}}$

$$= \underbrace{8\sqrt{15}-4\sqrt{3}-10\sqrt{5}+5}_{\text{Nothing combines.}}$$

7) $\left(\sqrt{7}+5\right)^2 = \left(\sqrt{7}+5\right)\left(\sqrt{7}+5\right) = \overset{7}{\overbrace{\left(\sqrt{7}\right)^2}}+5\sqrt{7}+5\sqrt{7}+(5)^2$

$$= 7 + \underbrace{5\sqrt{7}+5\sqrt{7}}_{\text{Combine these.}} + 25 = 32 + 10\sqrt{7}$$

Another way to do this is to use the '**Square of a Sum**' formula from Chapter 3,

$$(A+B)^2 = (A+B)(A+B) = A^2 + 2AB + B^2.$$

If we set $A=\sqrt{7}$ and $B=5$, we'll obtain:

$$\left(\sqrt{7}+5\right)^2 = \overset{7}{\overbrace{\left(\sqrt{7}\right)^2}}+2\left(\sqrt{7}\right)(5)+(5)^2$$
$$= 7 + 10\sqrt{7} + 25$$
$$= 32 + 10\sqrt{7}$$

A common mistake which is often made in the previous problem is:

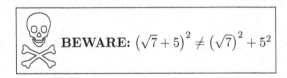

BEWARE: $\left(\sqrt{7}+5\right)^2 \neq \left(\sqrt{7}\right)^2 + 5^2$

Be careful!!!

8) Assume that y represents a nonnegative number. By the FOIL method,

$$(4\sqrt{y}+1)(3\sqrt{y}-7) = 12\overset{y}{\overbrace{(\sqrt{y})^2}}\underbrace{-28\sqrt{y}+3\sqrt{y}}_{\text{Combine.}}-7 = 12y - 25\sqrt{y} - 7$$

In the next example, we'll use the formula

$$(A+B)(A-B) = A^2 - B^2.$$

9) $\underbrace{\left(3\sqrt{6}+2\right)\left(3\sqrt{6}-2\right)}_{\text{Let A}=3\sqrt{6}\text{ and B}=2.} = \left(3\sqrt{6}\right)^2 - (2)^2 = \underset{9}{3^2}\underset{6}{\left(\sqrt{6}\right)^2} - 4 = 9(6) - 4 = 54 - 4 = 50$

Try These (Set 6): Multiply and simplify.

1) $\left(3\sqrt{5}\right)\left(2\sqrt{12}\right)$

2) $\left(4\sqrt{3}+6\sqrt{2}\right)\left(\sqrt{2}-5\sqrt{3}\right)$

3) $4\sqrt{3}\left(-2\sqrt{3}+4\sqrt{27}\right)$

4) $\left(2+y\sqrt{10}\right)^2$

132

Exercise 5.1.5

Multiply and simplify. Assume that all variables represent nonnegative numbers.

1. $\sqrt{2}\left(5\sqrt{2}\right)$

2. $\sqrt{3}\left(2\sqrt{3}\right)$

3. $\left(4\sqrt{6}\right)\left(3\sqrt{6}\right)$

4. $\left(2\sqrt{8}\right)\left(7\sqrt{8}\right)$

5. $\left(6\sqrt{5}\right)\left(-3\sqrt{5}\right)$

6. $\left(-9\sqrt{2}\right)\left(-4\sqrt{2}\right)$

7. $\left(8\sqrt{6}\right)\left(2\sqrt{2}\right)$

8. $\left(4\sqrt{8}\right)\left(3\sqrt{2}\right)$

9. $\left(6\sqrt{2}\right)\left(2\sqrt{12}\right)$

10. $\left(6\sqrt{5}\right)\left(2\sqrt{16}\right)$

11. $\left(-2\sqrt{49}\right)\left(3\sqrt{2}\right)$

12. $\left(2\sqrt{18}\right)\left(\sqrt{3}\right)$

13. $\left(\sqrt{7}\right)\left(4\sqrt{20}\right)$

14. $\left(3\sqrt{15}\right)\left(-2\sqrt{5}\right)$

15. $\left(-9\sqrt{7}\right)\left(-4\sqrt{8}\right)$

16. $\left(3\sqrt{2}\right)^2$

17. $\left(6\sqrt{3}\right)^2$

18. $\left(-9\sqrt{2}\right)^2$

19. $\left(-5\sqrt{5}\right)^2$

20. $2\sqrt{3}\left(7\sqrt{3}-5\right)$

21. $\sqrt{2}\left(3\sqrt{2}+4\right)$

22. $4\sqrt{5}\left(3\sqrt{5}-\sqrt{20}\right)$

23. $2\sqrt{3}\left(4\sqrt{27}+6\sqrt{3}\right)$

24. $6\sqrt{8}\left(2\sqrt{3}+\sqrt{5}\right)$

25. $-10\sqrt{6}\left(4\sqrt{3}+\sqrt{2}\right)$

26. $4\sqrt{2}\left(5-3\sqrt{6}+2\sqrt{12}\right)$

27. $6\sqrt{3}\left(3\sqrt{3}+\sqrt{6}-5\sqrt{10}\right)$

28. $\left(2\sqrt{3}+3\sqrt{2}\right)\left(\sqrt{3}+\sqrt{2}\right)$

29. $\left(\sqrt{3}-2\sqrt{7}\right)\left(\sqrt{3}-\sqrt{7}\right)$

30. $\left(5\sqrt{6}+2\sqrt{3}\right)\left(\sqrt{6}-3\sqrt{3}\right)$

31. $\left(5\sqrt{2}+2\sqrt{10}\right)\left(2\sqrt{2}-2\sqrt{10}\right)$

32. $\left(\sqrt{3}+\sqrt{5}\right)^2$

33. $\left(\sqrt{5}+\sqrt{7}\right)^2$

34. $\left(3\sqrt{6}-\sqrt{3}\right)^2$

35. $\left(\sqrt{11}-5\sqrt{2}\right)^2$

36. $\left(\sqrt{t}+4\right)^2$

37. $\left(\sqrt{y}-6\right)^2$

38. $\left(\sqrt{a}+9\right)\left(\sqrt{a}-7\right)$

39. $\left(12+\sqrt{y}\right)\left(5-\sqrt{y}\right)$

40. $\left(4-3\sqrt{t}\right)\left(5+\sqrt{t}\right)$

41. $\left(\sqrt{3}-\sqrt{13}\right)\left(\sqrt{3}+\sqrt{13}\right)$

42. $\left(\sqrt{15}+\sqrt{17}\right)\left(\sqrt{15}-\sqrt{17}\right)$

43. $\left(2\sqrt{3}+5\right)\left(2\sqrt{3}-5\right)$

44. $\left(8-3\sqrt{2}\right)\left(8+3\sqrt{2}\right)$

45. $\left(-6\sqrt{2}+9\right)\left(-6\sqrt{2}-9\right)$

46. $\left(\sqrt{a}+12\right)\left(\sqrt{a}-12\right)$

47. $\left(\sqrt{b}-14\right)\left(\sqrt{b}+14\right)$

Section 5.1.6 Rationalizing the Numerator or Denominator

Suppose we are given a fraction which contains a square root in the numerator (or denominator) and we wish to get rid of this square root. The process of rewriting the given fraction into an equivalent one which has a numerator (or denominator) **without** a square root is called **rationalizing the numerator (or the denominator)**.

Examples. Rationalize the denominator.

Note: Remember that the goal in these examples is to get rid of the square root in the denominator.

1) $\dfrac{1}{\sqrt{2}} = \dfrac{1}{\sqrt{2}}\left(\dfrac{\sqrt{2}}{\sqrt{2}}\right) = \dfrac{\sqrt{2}}{\left(\sqrt{2}\right)^2} = \dfrac{\sqrt{2}}{2}$ or $\dfrac{1}{2}\sqrt{2}$

2) $\dfrac{5}{\sqrt{5}} = \dfrac{5}{\sqrt{5}}\left(\dfrac{\sqrt{5}}{\sqrt{5}}\right) = \dfrac{5\sqrt{5}}{\left(\sqrt{5}\right)^2} = \dfrac{\overset{1}{\cancel{5}}\sqrt{5}}{\underset{1}{\cancel{5}}} = \sqrt{5}$

                                                 Simplify.

(Notice that $\dfrac{5\sqrt{5}}{5}$ is just like $\dfrac{5x}{5}$, and the 5's cancel out.)

3) $\dfrac{9}{2\sqrt{3}} = \underbrace{\dfrac{9}{2\sqrt{3}}\left(\dfrac{\sqrt{3}}{\sqrt{3}}\right)}_{\text{We only need the }\sqrt{3}.} = \dfrac{9\sqrt{3}}{2\left(\sqrt{3}\right)^2} = \dfrac{9\sqrt{3}}{2(3)} = \dfrac{\overset{3}{\cancel{9}}\sqrt{3}}{\underset{2}{\cancel{6}}} = \dfrac{3\sqrt{3}}{2} \text{ or } \dfrac{3}{2}\sqrt{3}$

4) $\dfrac{4}{\sqrt{20}} = \dfrac{4}{\sqrt{20}}\left(\dfrac{\sqrt{20}}{\sqrt{20}}\right) = \dfrac{4\sqrt{20}}{\left(\sqrt{20}\right)^2} = \underbrace{\dfrac{4\sqrt{20}}{20}}_{\text{Simplify the square root.}} = \dfrac{4\left(2\sqrt{5}\right)}{20} = \dfrac{\overset{2}{\cancel{8}}\sqrt{5}}{\underset{5}{\cancel{20}}} = \dfrac{2\sqrt{5}}{5} \text{ or } \dfrac{2}{5}\sqrt{5}$

Observe that in the above example, $\sqrt{20}$ could've been simplified in the very beginning. Let's do the problem again by simplifying first.

4) (again) $\underbrace{\dfrac{4}{\sqrt{20}} = \dfrac{\overset{2}{\cancel{4}}}{\underset{1}{\cancel{2}}\sqrt{5}} = \dfrac{2}{1\sqrt{5}}}_{\text{Simplify the square root.}} = \underbrace{\dfrac{2}{\sqrt{5}}\left(\dfrac{\sqrt{5}}{\sqrt{5}}\right)}_{\text{Rationalize the denominator.}} = \dfrac{2\sqrt{5}}{\left(\sqrt{5}\right)^2} = \dfrac{2\sqrt{5}}{5}$

In my opinion, it is easier to simplify the problem BEFORE doing the rationalizing. I will use the second method from now on.

5) $\underbrace{\dfrac{8\sqrt{3}}{\sqrt{24}} = \dfrac{\overset{4}{\cancel{8}}\sqrt{3}}{\underset{1}{\cancel{2}}\sqrt{6}} = \dfrac{4\sqrt{3}}{1\sqrt{6}} = \dfrac{4\sqrt{3}}{\sqrt{6}}}_{\text{Simplify things first.}}\left(\dfrac{\sqrt{6}}{\sqrt{6}}\right) = \dfrac{4\sqrt{18}}{\left(\sqrt{6}\right)^2} = \dfrac{4\left(3\sqrt{2}\right)}{6} = \dfrac{\overset{2}{\cancel{12}}\sqrt{6}}{\underset{1}{\cancel{6}}} = \dfrac{2\sqrt{6}}{1} = 2\sqrt{6}$

6) $\sqrt{\dfrac{7}{24}} = \underbrace{\dfrac{\sqrt{7}}{\sqrt{24}} = \dfrac{\sqrt{7}}{2\sqrt{6}}}_{\text{Simplify things first.}} = \left(\dfrac{\sqrt{7}}{2\sqrt{6}}\right)\left(\dfrac{\sqrt{6}}{\sqrt{6}}\right) = \dfrac{\sqrt{42}}{2\left(\sqrt{6}\right)^2} = \dfrac{\sqrt{42}}{2(6)} = \dfrac{\sqrt{42}}{12} \text{ or } \dfrac{1}{12}\sqrt{42}$

7) Assume that x represents a positive number. Then

$$\dfrac{3}{10\sqrt{x}} = \left(\dfrac{3}{10\sqrt{x}}\right)\left(\dfrac{\sqrt{x}}{\sqrt{x}}\right) = \dfrac{3\sqrt{x}}{10\left(\sqrt{x}\right)^2} = \dfrac{3\sqrt{x}}{10x} \text{ or } \dfrac{3}{10x}\sqrt{x}.$$

Let's do an example of rationalizing the numerator. It's the same as before, except for the numerator.

Example. Rationalize the numerator: $\dfrac{6\sqrt{5}}{\sqrt{3}} = \dfrac{6\sqrt{5}}{\sqrt{3}}\left(\dfrac{\sqrt{5}}{\sqrt{5}}\right) = \dfrac{6\left(\sqrt{5}\right)^2}{\sqrt{15}} = \dfrac{6(5)}{\sqrt{15}} = \dfrac{30}{\sqrt{15}}$

Let's move on to something slightly different. Suppose we want to rationalize the denominator of the expression $\dfrac{3}{2-\sqrt{2}}$. To begin with, notice that the denominator contains two terms which don't combine

134

into a single one. This reminds us of a binomial. The examples that we've looked at so far had only a single term in the denominator, which reminded us of a monomial. If we try to rationalize the denominator using the same method as before, let's see what will happen:

$$\frac{3}{2-\sqrt{2}} = \underbrace{\left(\frac{3}{2-\sqrt{2}}\right)\left(\frac{\sqrt{2}}{\sqrt{2}}\right) = \frac{3\sqrt{2}}{2\sqrt{2}-\left(\sqrt{2}\right)^2}}_{\text{Distribute in the denominator.}} = \frac{3\sqrt{2}}{2\sqrt{2}-2}$$

Notice that we did **NOT** rationalize the denominator since there is still a square root in it. This means that we need a different method from the one that we used before. To prepare for this new method, we need the following definition.

Definition: The **conjugate** of the binomial $A + B$ is $A - B$.

For example, the conjugate of $2 - \sqrt{2}$ is $2 + \sqrt{2}$ and the conjugate of $-12 + 9\sqrt{3}$ is $-12 - 9\sqrt{3}$. Observe that when we multiply the binomial $A + B$ by its conjugate, $A - B$, we'll obtain $A^2 - B^2$. This is useful for us since the squaring of the terms A and B would eliminate any square roots present in them. This is precisely what rationalizing is all about; **getting rid of the square roots.**

Examples. Rationalize the denominator.

1) $\dfrac{3}{2-\sqrt{2}} = \underbrace{\left(\dfrac{3}{2-\sqrt{2}}\right)\left(\dfrac{2+\sqrt{2}}{2+\sqrt{2}}\right) = \dfrac{3\left(2+\sqrt{2}\right)}{(2)^2-\left(\sqrt{2}\right)^2}}_{\text{Multiply the numerator and denominator by the conjugate.}} = \dfrac{3\left(2+\sqrt{2}\right)}{4-2} = \underbrace{\dfrac{3\left(2+\sqrt{2}\right)}{2}}_{\text{Nothing simplifies.}}$

Note that our answer could've been written in various ways:

$$\frac{3\left(2-\sqrt{2}\right)}{2} = \frac{3}{2}\left(2-\sqrt{2}\right) = \frac{6-3\sqrt{2}}{2} = \frac{-3\sqrt{2}+6}{2}$$

2) $\dfrac{8-\sqrt{6}}{8+\sqrt{6}} = \underbrace{\left(\dfrac{8-\sqrt{6}}{8+\sqrt{6}}\right)\left(\dfrac{8-\sqrt{6}}{8-\sqrt{6}}\right) = \dfrac{64-8\sqrt{6}-8\sqrt{6}+\left(\sqrt{6}\right)^2}{(8)^2-\left(\sqrt{6}\right)^2}}_{\text{Multiply the numerator and denominator by the conjugate and FOIL on top.}}$

$$= \frac{64-8\sqrt{6}-8\sqrt{6}+6}{64-6} = \frac{70-16\sqrt{6}}{58} = \frac{\overset{1}{\cancel{2}}\left(35-8\sqrt{6}\right)}{\underset{1}{\cancel{2}}(29)} = \frac{35-8\sqrt{6}}{29}$$

Note that the numerator could've been worked out by using the 'Square of a Sum' formula from Chapter 3. Give it a try.

3) Suppose that x represents a nonnegative number not equal to 3. Then:

$$\frac{\sqrt{x}-4\sqrt{3}}{\sqrt{x}-\sqrt{3}} = \left(\frac{\sqrt{x}-4\sqrt{3}}{\sqrt{x}-\sqrt{3}}\right)\left(\frac{\sqrt{x}+\sqrt{3}}{\sqrt{x}+\sqrt{3}}\right) = \frac{\overset{x}{\overbrace{\left(\sqrt{x}\right)^2}}+\sqrt{3x}-4\sqrt{3x}-\overset{4(3)}{\overbrace{4\left(\sqrt{3}\right)^2}}}{\underbrace{\left(\sqrt{x}\right)^2}_{x}-\underbrace{\left(\sqrt{3}\right)^2}_{3}}$$

$$= \frac{x+\overbrace{\sqrt{3x}-4\sqrt{3x}}^{\text{Combine.}}-12}{x-3} = \frac{x-3\sqrt{3x}-12}{x-3}$$

Examples. Rationalize the numerator.

1) $\dfrac{\sqrt{6}+5}{3} = \left(\dfrac{\sqrt{6}+5}{3}\right)\left(\dfrac{\sqrt{6}-5}{\sqrt{6}-5}\right) = \dfrac{\left(\sqrt{6}\right)^2 - (5)^2}{3\left(\sqrt{6}-5\right)} = \dfrac{6-25}{3\left(\sqrt{6}-5\right)}$

$\qquad = \dfrac{-19}{3\left(\sqrt{6}-5\right)} \left(\text{or } \dfrac{-19}{3\sqrt{6}-15} = \dfrac{19}{-3\sqrt{6}+15}\right)$

2) $\dfrac{\sqrt{7}-1}{2\sqrt{5}} = \left(\dfrac{\sqrt{7}-1}{2\sqrt{5}}\right)\left(\dfrac{\sqrt{7}+1}{\sqrt{7}+1}\right) = \dfrac{\left(\sqrt{7}\right)^2 - (1)^2}{2\sqrt{5}\left(\sqrt{7}+1\right)} = \dfrac{7-1}{2\sqrt{5}\left(\sqrt{7}+1\right)}$

$\qquad = \dfrac{\overset{3}{\cancel{6}}}{\underset{1}{\cancel{2}}\sqrt{5}\left(\sqrt{7}+1\right)} = \dfrac{3}{\sqrt{5}\left(\sqrt{7}+1\right)} \text{ or } \dfrac{3}{\sqrt{35}+\sqrt{5}}$

3) $\dfrac{\sqrt{5}+3\sqrt{3}}{\sqrt{5}-2\sqrt{2}} = \left(\dfrac{\sqrt{5}+3\sqrt{3}}{\sqrt{5}-2\sqrt{2}}\right)\left(\dfrac{\sqrt{5}-3\sqrt{3}}{\sqrt{5}-3\sqrt{3}}\right) = \dfrac{\left(\sqrt{5}\right)^2 - \left(3\sqrt{3}\right)^2}{\left(\sqrt{5}\right)^2 - 3\sqrt{15} - 2\sqrt{10} + 6\sqrt{6}}$

$\qquad = \dfrac{5-9(3)}{5-3\sqrt{15}-2\sqrt{10}+6\sqrt{6}} = \dfrac{-22}{5-3\sqrt{15}-2\sqrt{10}+6\sqrt{6}}$

$\qquad = -\dfrac{22}{5-3\sqrt{15}-2\sqrt{10}+6\sqrt{6}}$

Try These (Set 7): Rationalize the denominator.

1) $\dfrac{6}{7\sqrt{5}}$ 　　　2) $\dfrac{6\sqrt{3}}{\sqrt{18}}$ 　　　3) $\dfrac{7\sqrt{13}}{\sqrt{13}+\sqrt{6}}$ 　　　4) $\dfrac{2+\sqrt{6}}{4-\sqrt{6}}$

Try These (Set 8): Rationalize the numerator.

1) $\dfrac{2\sqrt{3}}{\sqrt{5}}$ 　　　2) $\dfrac{\sqrt{56}}{16}$ 　　　3) $\dfrac{\sqrt{34}-\sqrt{14}}{10}$ 　　　4) $\dfrac{2+\sqrt{6}}{4-\sqrt{6}}$

Exercise 5.1.6

In Exercises 1-38, rationalize the denominator. Assume that all variables represent positive numbers.

1. $\dfrac{1}{\sqrt{5}}$ 　　　2. $\dfrac{7}{\sqrt{2}}$ 　　　3. $\dfrac{5}{\sqrt{3}}$ 　　　4. $\dfrac{4}{\sqrt{7}}$ 　　　5. $\dfrac{11}{\sqrt{22}}$

6. $\dfrac{5}{\sqrt{15}}$ 　　　7. $\dfrac{16}{\sqrt{10}}$ 　　　8. $\dfrac{21}{\sqrt{7}}$ 　　　9. $\dfrac{10}{\sqrt{8}}$ 　　　10. $\dfrac{4}{\sqrt{12}}$

11. $\dfrac{21}{4\sqrt{18}}$ 　　12. $\dfrac{8}{3\sqrt{20}}$ 　　13. $\dfrac{-6}{7\sqrt{52}}$ 　　14. $\dfrac{-12}{5\sqrt{24}}$ 　　15. $\sqrt{\dfrac{1}{6}}$

16. $\sqrt{\dfrac{2}{3}}$ 　　17. $\sqrt{\dfrac{13}{7}}$ 　　18. $\sqrt{\dfrac{17}{5}}$ 　　19. $\sqrt{\dfrac{7}{12}}$ 　　20. $\sqrt{\dfrac{3}{8}}$

21. $\dfrac{5}{\sqrt{y}}$ 22. $\dfrac{7}{\sqrt{x}}$ 23. $\dfrac{4}{9\sqrt{2x}}$ 24. $\dfrac{20}{\sqrt{5y}}$ 25. $\dfrac{1}{\sqrt{2}-1}$

26. $\dfrac{1}{\sqrt{3}-2}$ 27. $\dfrac{1}{\sqrt{5}+2}$ 28. $\dfrac{1}{\sqrt{6}-2}$ 29. $\dfrac{2}{\sqrt{5}+3}$ 30. $\dfrac{4}{\sqrt{3}+5}$

31. $\dfrac{2-\sqrt{3}}{1+\sqrt{3}}$ 32. $\dfrac{1+\sqrt{2}}{2-\sqrt{2}}$ 33. $\dfrac{\sqrt{10}-\sqrt{2}}{\sqrt{10}+\sqrt{2}}$ 34. $\dfrac{\sqrt{5}+\sqrt{11}}{\sqrt{5}-\sqrt{11}}$ 35. $\dfrac{-2\sqrt{6}+3}{3\sqrt{2}+\sqrt{6}}$

36. $\dfrac{7+6\sqrt{3}}{-2\sqrt{3}+\sqrt{5}}$ 37. $\dfrac{3+\sqrt{x}}{8-\sqrt{x}},\ x\neq 64$ 38. $\dfrac{\sqrt{x}-2}{\sqrt{x}+4}$

In Exercises 39-60, rationalize the numerator. Assume that all variables represent positive numbers.

39. $\dfrac{\sqrt{3}}{2}$ 40. $\dfrac{\sqrt{5}}{3}$ 41. $\dfrac{\sqrt{12}}{4}$ 42. $\dfrac{\sqrt{40}}{2}$ 43. $\dfrac{\sqrt{7}}{2\sqrt{5}}$

44. $\dfrac{6\sqrt{10}}{\sqrt{3}}$ 45. $\dfrac{\sqrt{24}}{\sqrt{5}}$ 46. $\dfrac{\sqrt{8}}{\sqrt{7}}$ 47. $\sqrt{\dfrac{11}{9}}$ 48. $\sqrt{\dfrac{4}{16}}$

49. $\dfrac{\sqrt{x}}{6}$ 50. $\dfrac{\sqrt{2x}}{15}$ 51. $\dfrac{2-\sqrt{6}}{4}$ 52. $\dfrac{-4+\sqrt{6}}{3}$ 53. $\dfrac{\sqrt{2}+\sqrt{5}}{\sqrt{3}}$

54. $\dfrac{\sqrt{5}+\sqrt{3}}{\sqrt{7}}$ 55. $\dfrac{\sqrt{6}+4}{\sqrt{6}-4}$ 56. $\dfrac{\sqrt{7}-2}{\sqrt{7}+2}$ 57. $\dfrac{\sqrt{x}+3}{\sqrt{x}-9},\ x\neq 81$

58. $\dfrac{\sqrt{x}+6}{\sqrt{x}-5},\ x\neq 25$ 59. $\dfrac{\sqrt{6+h}-\sqrt{6}}{h}$ 60. $\dfrac{\sqrt{x+h}-\sqrt{x}}{h}$

Section 5.2   Cube Roots

In this section, we will learn about another type of radical called a **cube root**.

Definition: Let a and b be two real numbers. If $b^3 = a$, then b is called a **cube root** of a.

Examples.

1) Since $3^3 = 27$, the definition tells us that 3 is a cube root of 27. In fact, 3 is the **only** real number which is a cube root of 27. It turns out that **every** positive number has one cube root which is a real number and is positive.

2) Since $(-3)^3 = -27$, the definition tells us that -3 is a cube root of -27. As above, -3 is the **only** real number which is a cube root of -27. In fact, **every** negative number has one cube root which is a real number and is negative.

3) Since $0^3 = 0$, we have that 0 is the unique cube root of 0.

In general, every real number has a unique (real) cube root. This root is called the **principal cube root.** We denote the phrase 'b is the (principal) **cube root** of a' by $b = \sqrt[3]{a}$. As for square roots, we call the term 'a' under the **cube root symbol** the **radicand.** The '3' on the left of the symbol is there to tell us that this is a cube root.

Here is a list of cube roots of perfect cubes. Recall that a perfect cube is an integer which is the cube of another integer.

List of Commonly Used Cube Roots

$$\sqrt[3]{1} = 1 \qquad\qquad \sqrt[3]{-1} = -1$$
$$\sqrt[3]{8} = 2 \qquad\qquad \sqrt[3]{-8} = -2$$
$$\sqrt[3]{27} = 3 \qquad\qquad \sqrt[3]{-27} = -3$$
$$\sqrt[3]{64} = 4 \qquad\qquad \sqrt[3]{-64} = -4$$
$$\sqrt[3]{125} = 5 \qquad\qquad \sqrt[3]{-125} = -5$$
$$\sqrt[3]{216} = 6 \qquad\qquad \sqrt[3]{-216} = -6$$
$$\sqrt[3]{1,000} = 10 \qquad\qquad \sqrt[3]{-1,000} = -10$$

The numbers in the list above are cube roots of some perfect cubes. It turns out that **every** real number has a cube root. For example, there are numbers such as $\sqrt[3]{2}$, $\sqrt[3]{9.013}$, and $\sqrt[3]{\pi}$. However, we will not be concerned with the exact values of these (in decimal form). We only need to know that they exist. If we **did** want to know $\sqrt[3]{2}$, we would use a calculator to figure it out. If $n = \sqrt[3]{2}$, then $n^3 = 2$. You can imagine how strange the value of n must be when expressed in decimal form.

Properties of Cube Roots

PROPERTY I. Suppose that a is a real number. Then
$$\sqrt[3]{a^3} = a.$$

PROPERTY II. Suppose that a and b are real numbers. Then
$$\sqrt[3]{a} \cdot \sqrt[3]{b} = \sqrt[3]{a \cdot b}.$$

PROPERTY III. Suppose that a and b are real numbers and $b \neq 0$. Then
$$\frac{\sqrt[3]{a}}{\sqrt[3]{b}} = \sqrt[3]{\frac{a}{b}}.$$

PROPERTY IV. Suppose that a is a real number. Then
$$\sqrt[3]{-a} = -\sqrt[3]{a}.$$

Notice that in Property I, there is no need for absolute value (like for the square roots). Putting absolute value would, in fact, be incorrect. The reason for this is that we can get a negative answer when we take a cube root, but not when we take a square root. Furthermore, Property IV isn't true for square roots unless $a = 0$. Property IV can be easily obtained from Property II as follows:

$$\sqrt[3]{-a} = \sqrt[3]{(-1)(a)} = \left(\sqrt[3]{-1}\right)\left(\sqrt[3]{a}\right) = (-1)\left(\sqrt[3]{a}\right) = -\sqrt[3]{a}$$

Let's do a series of examples which are similar to those we did for square roots.

Examples. Simplify.

1) $\sqrt[3]{24} = \underbrace{\sqrt[3]{8 \times 3}}_{\text{8 is a perfect cube.}} = \sqrt[3]{8} \times \sqrt[3]{3} = 2 \times \sqrt[3]{3} = 2\sqrt[3]{3}$

2) $\sqrt[3]{54} = \underbrace{\sqrt[3]{27 \times 2}}_{\text{27 is a perfect cube.}} = \sqrt[3]{27} \times \sqrt[3]{2} = 3 \times \sqrt[3]{2} = 3\sqrt[3]{2}$

3) $\underbrace{\sqrt[3]{x^{14}} = x^4 \sqrt[3]{x^2}}_{14 \div 3 = 4\ R\ 2,\ \text{so 4 out and 2 in.}}$

Note that, for square roots, we divided the exponent by 2. For cube roots, we divide the exponent by 3.

4) $\underbrace{\sqrt[3]{y^{31}} = y^{10}\sqrt[3]{y^1} = y^{10}\sqrt[3]{y}}_{31 \div 3 = 10\ R\ 1,\ \text{so 10 out and 1 in.}}$

5) $\sqrt[3]{40m^2n^{14}} = 2n^4\sqrt[3]{5m^2n^2}$

Notice that $\sqrt[3]{40} = \sqrt[3]{8}\sqrt[3]{5} = 2\sqrt[3]{5}$, $\underbrace{\sqrt[3]{n^{14}} = n^4\sqrt[3]{n^2}}_{14 \div 3 = 4\ R\ 2}$, and $\sqrt[3]{m^2}$ is already simplified since $2 \div 3 = 0\ R\ 2$.

Examples. Perform the indicated operation and simplify.

1) $\sqrt[3]{3x^4} \cdot \sqrt[3]{16x^5} = \sqrt[3]{3x^4 \cdot 16x^5} = \underbrace{\sqrt[3]{48x^9} = 2x^3\sqrt[3]{6}}_{\sqrt[3]{48} = \sqrt[3]{8 \times 6} = 2\sqrt[3]{6}\ \text{and}\ 9 \div 3 = 3\ R\ 0.}$

2) $\dfrac{\sqrt[3]{65x^{16}}}{\sqrt[3]{13x^4}} = \sqrt[3]{\dfrac{65x^{16}}{13x^4}} = \sqrt[3]{5x^{12}} = \underbrace{x^4\sqrt[3]{5}}_{12 \div 3 = 4\ R\ 0}$

3) $\sqrt[3]{4} + 12\sqrt[3]{4} - 7\sqrt[3]{4} = (1 + 12 - 7)\sqrt[3]{4} = 6\sqrt[3]{4}$

4) $\underbrace{9\sqrt[3]{24}}_{\sqrt[3]{24} = \sqrt[3]{8}\,\sqrt[3]{3} = 2\sqrt[3]{3}} + \sqrt[3]{3} = 9\left(2\sqrt[3]{3}\right) + \sqrt[3]{3} = 18\sqrt[3]{3} + \sqrt[3]{3} = (18 + 1)\sqrt[3]{3} = 19\sqrt[3]{3}$

5) $\underbrace{7x\sqrt[3]{3x} - 2\sqrt[3]{81x^4} = 7x\sqrt[3]{3x} - 2\left(3x\sqrt[3]{3x}\right)}_{\sqrt[3]{81} = \sqrt[3]{27}\,\sqrt[3]{3} = 3\sqrt[3]{3}\ \text{and}\ \sqrt[3]{x^4} = x\sqrt[3]{x}.} = \underbrace{7x\sqrt[3]{3x} - 6x\sqrt[3]{3x} = (7x - 6x)\sqrt[3]{3x} = x\sqrt[3]{3x}}_{\text{These are like roots, so combine them.}}$

6) $\left(\sqrt[3]{12}\right)\left(-\sqrt[3]{9}\right) = -\sqrt[3]{(12)(9)} = -\underbrace{\sqrt[3]{108}}_{\sqrt[3]{27} \times \sqrt[3]{4}} = -3\sqrt[3]{4}$

7) $\sqrt[3]{5}\left(3\sqrt[3]{-2} + 6\sqrt[3]{25}\right) = \sqrt[3]{5}\left(3\sqrt[3]{-2}\right) + \sqrt[3]{5}\left(6\sqrt[3]{25}\right) = 3\sqrt[3]{-10} + 6\sqrt[3]{125}$

$= 3\sqrt[3]{-10} + 6(5) = \underbrace{3\sqrt[3]{-10} + 30 = -3\sqrt[3]{10} + 30}_{\text{by Property IV of cube roots}}$

8) $\left(\sqrt[3]{x^2} - 5\right)\left(\sqrt[3]{x^2} - 2\right) = \underbrace{\sqrt[3]{x^4} - 2\sqrt[3]{x^2} - 5\sqrt[3]{x^2} + 10}_{\text{by the FOIL method}} = x\sqrt[3]{x} - 7\sqrt[3]{x^2} + 10$

Try These (Set 9):

1) Simplify: $\sqrt[3]{56}$

2) Simplify: $\sqrt[3]{-128x^6y^{20}}$

3) Multiply and simplify: $\sqrt[3]{5}\left(2\sqrt[3]{25}+7\right)$

4) Multiply and simplify: $\left(\sqrt[3]{4}-1\right)^2$

Exercise 5.2

In Exercises 1-20, evaluate.

1. $\sqrt[3]{8}$

2. $\sqrt[3]{-8}$

3. $-\sqrt[3]{-8}$

4. $\sqrt[3]{27}$

5. $\sqrt[3]{-27}$

6. $-\sqrt[3]{-27}$

7. $\sqrt[3]{\dfrac{1}{64}}$

8. $-\sqrt[3]{-\dfrac{1}{64}}$

9. $\sqrt[3]{-\dfrac{1}{64}}$

10. $\sqrt[3]{\dfrac{125}{216}}$

11. $\sqrt[3]{-\dfrac{125}{8}}$

12. $\sqrt[3]{\dfrac{0}{1,000}}$

13. $\sqrt[3]{(27)(0)}$

14. $\sqrt[3]{(-8)(216)}$

15. $\left(\sqrt[3]{12}\right)^3$

16. $\left(\sqrt[3]{7}\right)^3$

17. $\left(\sqrt[3]{-21}\right)^3$

18. $\left(\sqrt[3]{-18}\right)^3$

19. $\sqrt[3]{(15)^3(8)}$

20. $\sqrt[3]{(15)^3(-27)}$

In Exercises 21-40, simplify.

21. $\sqrt[3]{32}$

22. $\sqrt[3]{24}$

23. $\sqrt[3]{-24}$

24. $\sqrt[3]{-32}$

25. $\sqrt[3]{54}$

26. $\sqrt[3]{250}$

27. $\sqrt[3]{-54}$

28. $\sqrt[3]{-250}$

29. $\sqrt[3]{2,000}$

30. $\sqrt[3]{-2,000}$

31. $\sqrt[3]{y^3}$

32. $\sqrt[3]{y^5}$

33. $\sqrt[3]{x^{13}}$

34. $\sqrt[3]{x^{15}}$

35. $\sqrt[3]{y^{23}}$

36. $\sqrt[3]{y^{25}}$

37. $\sqrt[3]{14x^6y^{11}}$

38. $\sqrt[3]{16xy^{22}}$

39. $\sqrt[3]{-40x^{10}y^2}$

40. $\sqrt[3]{-27xy^3}$

In Exercises 41-50, combine and simplify.

41. $2\sqrt[3]{2}+9\sqrt[3]{2}$

42. $5\sqrt[3]{4}+8\sqrt[3]{4}$

43. $12\sqrt[3]{9}-7\sqrt[3]{9}$

44. $-2\sqrt[3]{14}+18\sqrt[3]{14}$

45. $3\sqrt[3]{16}+\sqrt[3]{24}$

46. $6\sqrt[3]{54}-4\sqrt[3]{81}$

47. $12\sqrt[3]{2}+5\sqrt[3]{16}-7\sqrt[3]{54}$

48. $\sqrt[3]{2,000}-\sqrt[3]{3,000}-\sqrt[3]{4,000}$

49. $-3x\sqrt[3]{2x}-\sqrt[3]{250x^4}$

50. $-6x\sqrt[3]{5x}+\sqrt[3]{40x^4}$

In Exercises 51-72, multiply and simplify.

51. $\left(\sqrt[3]{4}\right)\left(\sqrt[3]{2}\right)$

52. $\left(\sqrt[3]{25}\right)\left(\sqrt[3]{5}\right)$

53. $\left(\sqrt[3]{3}\right)\left(-\sqrt[3]{9}\right)$

54. $\left(\sqrt[3]{10}\right)\left(-\sqrt[3]{100}\right)$

55. $\left(\sqrt[3]{-4}\right)\left(-\sqrt[3]{10}\right)$

56. $\left(-\sqrt[3]{-6}\right)\left(\sqrt[3]{4}\right)$

57. $\left(\sqrt[3]{27}\right)^2$

58. $\left(-\sqrt[3]{8}\right)^2$

59. $\left(\sqrt[3]{100}\right)^2$

60. $\left(\sqrt[3]{12}\right)^2$

61. $\sqrt[3]{3}\left(\sqrt[3]{9}+12\right)$

62. $\sqrt[3]{5}\left(\sqrt[3]{25}-1\right)$

63. $\sqrt[3]{16}\left(\sqrt[3]{2}+5\sqrt[3]{3}\right)$

64. $\sqrt[3]{12}\left(3\sqrt[3]{3}+5\sqrt[3]{6}\right)$

65. $\left(\sqrt[3]{2}-3\right)\left(\sqrt[3]{2}+1\right)$

66. $\left(\sqrt[3]{3}+2\right)\left(\sqrt[3]{3}-3\right)$

67. $\left(\sqrt[3]{4}+2\right)^2$ 68. $\left(\sqrt[3]{12}-3\right)^2$ 69. $\left(\sqrt[3]{x}+8\right)\left(\sqrt[3]{x}+5\right)$

70. $\left(\sqrt[3]{x}-6\right)\left(\sqrt[3]{x}-4\right)$ 71. $\left(\sqrt[3]{x^2}-12\right)\left(\sqrt[3]{x^5}-7\right)$ 72. $\left(\sqrt[3]{x^4}+11\right)\left(\sqrt[3]{x^2}-8\right)$

Section 5.3 Radicals

Up until this point, we have studied square roots and cube roots. In this section, we will examine radicals of any index. The square root and the cube root are special types of radicals. I will begin by defining a radical in general. Afterwards, we will look at some properties of radicals and examples which are analogous to those we've already studied.

Definition: Suppose that a and b are real numbers and let n be a natural number greater than 2 (in other words, n can equal 2, 3, ...). If $b^n = a$, then we say that b **is an** n^{th} **root of** a.

We have already seen that if $n = 2$, then we are dealing with a square root. Recall that 'a' must be a nonnegative number and $b = \sqrt{a}$ is the (principal) square root of 'a'. If $n = 3$, then we are dealing with a cube root. In this case, a can be any real number and $b = \sqrt[3]{a}$ has the same sign as 'a'. It is called the principal cube root of 'a'.

Definition: Suppose that a is a real number which has an nth root. Then the **principal** n^{th} **root of** a, written as $\sqrt[n]{a}$, is the nth root that has the same sign as a. The natural number n is called the **index** of the radical and the real number a is called the **radicand**. The symbol is called the **radical symbol**.

For example, if the index is 2, then we'd have a square root. Note that the 2 is not written in the radical symbol. If the index is 3, then we'd have a cube root.

Examples. Evaluate.

1) $\sqrt{4} = 2$ since $2^2 = 4$.

2) $\sqrt[3]{\dfrac{27}{125}} = \dfrac{3}{5}$ since $\left(\dfrac{3}{5}\right)^3 = \dfrac{3^3}{5^3} = \dfrac{27}{125}$.

3) $\sqrt[4]{256} = 4$ since $4^4 = 256$.

4) $\sqrt[4]{-256}$ is not a real number. To see this, suppose that $\sqrt[4]{-256} = b$ for some real number b.
Then $b^4 = -256$, which doesn't make sense since any real number raised to the fourth power must be either positive or zero. We have already seen something like this when we studied square roots.

5) $\sqrt[5]{32} = 2$ since $2^5 = 32$.

6) $\sqrt[5]{-32} = -2$ since $(-2)^5 = -32$.

Let's list some properties of radicals, keeping in mind what we've already learned about square roots and cube roots.

Properties of Radicals of Index n

PROPERTY I.   Suppose that a is any real number.
        If n is an even number, then $\sqrt[n]{a^n} = \lvert a \rvert$
        If n is an odd number, then $\sqrt[n]{a^n} = a$.

> **PROPERTY II.** $\sqrt[n]{a} \cdot \sqrt[n]{b} = \sqrt[n]{a \cdot b}$, provided that these radicals are real numbers.

> **PROPERTY III.** $\sqrt[n]{\dfrac{a}{b}} = \dfrac{\sqrt[n]{a}}{\sqrt[n]{b}}$, provided that these radicals are real numbers and $b \neq 0$.

Just as for square roots, if we assume that a is a nonnegative number, then $\sqrt[n]{a^n} = a$ for any $n = 2, 3, \ldots$.

Examples. Simplify. Assume that all variables represent nonnegative numbers.

1) $\sqrt[4]{243} = \sqrt[4]{81 \times 3} = \underbrace{\sqrt[4]{81} \times \sqrt[4]{3}}_{3^4 = 81} = 3 \times \sqrt[4]{3} = 3\sqrt[4]{3}$

2) $\sqrt[6]{128} = \sqrt[6]{64 \times 2} = \underbrace{\sqrt[6]{64} \times \sqrt[6]{2}}_{2^6 = 64} = 2 \times \sqrt[6]{2} = 2\sqrt[6]{2}$

3) $\sqrt[5]{-\dfrac{1}{160}} = \dfrac{\sqrt[5]{-1}}{\sqrt[5]{160}} = \dfrac{-1}{\sqrt[5]{32 \times 5}} = \underbrace{\dfrac{-1}{\sqrt[5]{32} \times \sqrt[5]{5}} = \dfrac{-1}{2 \times \sqrt[5]{5}}}_{2^5 = 32} = \dfrac{-1}{2\sqrt[5]{5}}$ or $-\dfrac{1}{2\sqrt[5]{5}}$

When we simplify a radical which contains variables (nonnegative valued), we will apply the 'division technique' discussed earlier in this chapter. When we worked with square roots, we divided 'exponent ÷ 2'. When we worked with cube roots, we divided 'exponent ÷ 3'. In general, we will divide 'exponent ÷ index'.

4) $\sqrt[4]{x^{29}} = \underbrace{x^7 \sqrt[4]{x^1}}_{29 \div 4 = 7 \ R \ 1} = x^7 \sqrt[4]{x}$

5) $\sqrt[6]{x^{23}} = \underbrace{x^3 \sqrt[6]{x^5}}_{23 \div 6 = 3 \ R \ 5}$

6) $\sqrt[7]{x^2 y^{20} z^{33}} = y^2 z^4 \sqrt[7]{x^2 y^6 z^5}$ since $2 \div 7 = 0 \ R \ 2$, $20 \div 7 = 2 \ R \ 6$, and $33 \div 7 = 3 \ R \ 5$.

Notice that I did not change the index in any of the above examples when I simplified. Remember to keep the index the same.

7) $\left(\sqrt[4]{2}\right)\left(\sqrt[4]{8}\right) = \sqrt[4]{2 \times 8} = \sqrt[4]{16} = 2$

8) $\left(\sqrt[5]{-4}\right)\left(\sqrt[5]{8}\right) = \sqrt[5]{(-4) \times 8} = \sqrt[5]{-32} = -2$

9) $\left(\sqrt[4]{6xy^3}\right)\left(\sqrt[4]{8x^4 y^5}\right) = \sqrt[4]{(6xy^3)(8x^4 y^5)} = \underbrace{\sqrt[4]{48 x^5 y^8} = 2x^1 y^2 \sqrt[4]{3x^1}}_{\sqrt[4]{48} = \sqrt[4]{16}\sqrt[4]{3} = 2\sqrt[4]{3}, \ 5 \div 4 = 1 \ R \ 1, \text{ and } 8 \div 4 = 2 \ R \ 0.} = 2xy^2 \sqrt[4]{3x}$

10) $\dfrac{\sqrt[6]{192 a^{25} b^2}}{\sqrt[6]{3 a^8 b^{15}}} = \sqrt[6]{\dfrac{192 a^{25} b^2}{3 a^8 b^{15}}} = \underbrace{\sqrt[6]{\dfrac{64 a^{17}}{b^{13}}} = \dfrac{2a^2}{b^2} \sqrt[6]{\dfrac{a^5}{b}}}_{\sqrt[6]{64} = 2, \ 17 \div 6 = 2 \ R \ 5, \text{ and } 13 \div 6 = 2 \ R \ 1.}$ or $\dfrac{2a^2 \sqrt[6]{a^5}}{b^2 \sqrt[6]{b}}$

11) $\sqrt[4]{3}\left(8\sqrt[4]{27} + 6\right) = \sqrt[4]{3}\left(8\sqrt[4]{27}\right) + \sqrt[4]{3}(6) = 8\underbrace{\sqrt[4]{81}}_{3} + 6\sqrt[4]{3} = 24 + 6\sqrt[4]{3}$

12) $\underbrace{\left(\sqrt[6]{16} - 5\right)\left(\sqrt[6]{4} + 2\right) = \overbrace{\sqrt[6]{64}}^{2} + 2\sqrt[6]{16} - 5\sqrt[6]{4} - 10}_{\text{Use the FOIL method.}} = -8 + 2\sqrt[6]{16} - 5\sqrt[6]{4}$

In the next chapter, we will learn that $\sqrt[6]{16} = \sqrt[3]{4}$ and $\sqrt[6]{4} = \sqrt[3]{2}$. Hence,

$$-8 + 2\sqrt[6]{16} - 5\sqrt[6]{4} = -8 + 2\sqrt[3]{4} - 5\sqrt[3]{2}.$$

13) $\underbrace{\left(\sqrt[7]{6x^5} + 1\right)^2 = \left(\sqrt[7]{6x^5}\right)^2 + 2\left(\sqrt[7]{6x^5}\right)(1) + (1)^2}_{\text{Use the formula } (A+B)^2 = A^2 + 2AB + B^2.}$

$$= \sqrt[7]{36x^{10}} + 2\sqrt[7]{6x^5} + 1 = x\sqrt[7]{36x^3} + 2\sqrt[7]{6x^5} + 1$$

14) $\underbrace{\left(\sqrt[5]{x^7} - 8\right)\left(\sqrt[5]{x^7} + 8\right) = \left(\sqrt[5]{x^7}\right)^2 - (8)^2}_{\text{Use the formula } (A+B)(A-B) = A^2 - B^2.} = \sqrt[5]{x^{14}} - 64 = x^2\sqrt[5]{x^4} - 64$

As you may have noticed, the examples on radicals are solved the same way as for square roots and cube roots. The only difference is that things get quite messy once the index is larger than three. Even though we will primarily focus on square roots and cube roots, I want you to be aware that these other radicals do exist. If you plan on taking more mathematics, such as Precalculus or Calculus, you will encounter such algebraic objects. I have supplied you with enough examples to get you through the basics. Have fun with it! In the next chapter, we will see all of this again when we learn about rational exponents.

Exercise 5.3

In Exercises 1-10, evaluate.

1. $\sqrt[4]{81}$ 2. $\sqrt[4]{16}$ 3. $\sqrt[5]{243}$ 4. $\sqrt[5]{32}$ 5. $\sqrt[5]{-32}$

6. $\sqrt[5]{-243}$ 7. $\sqrt[6]{64}$ 8. $-\sqrt[6]{64}$ 9. $\sqrt[4]{\dfrac{81}{256}}$ 10. $\sqrt[5]{\dfrac{243}{32}}$

In Exercises 11-28, simplify. Assume that all variables represent nonnegative numbers.

11. $\sqrt[4]{48}$ 12. $\sqrt[4]{162}$ 13. $-\sqrt[4]{162}$ 14. $\sqrt[4]{3^4}$ 15. $\sqrt[5]{7^5}$

16. $\sqrt[5]{(-16)^5}$ 17. $\sqrt[7]{(-25)^7}$ 18. $\sqrt[5]{-64}$ 19. $\sqrt[5]{64}$ 20. $\sqrt[4]{x^{17}}$

21. $\sqrt[6]{x^{29}}$ 22. $\sqrt[8]{a^{19}}$ 23. $\sqrt[5]{x^{14}y^8}$ 24. $\sqrt[9]{a^{13}b^4}$ 25. $\sqrt[7]{x^{24}y^2}$

26. $\sqrt[4]{x^4y^{17}}$ 27. $\sqrt[4]{48x^{12}y^3}$ 28. $\sqrt[5]{243x^{10}y^{15}}$

In Exercises 29-48, multiply and simplify. Assume that all variables represent nonnegative numbers.

29. $\sqrt[5]{3}\left(4\sqrt[5]{3} + 7\right)$ 30. $\sqrt[5]{2}\left(\sqrt[5]{2} - 8\right)$ 31. $\sqrt[7]{11}\left(2\sqrt[7]{11} - 9\sqrt[7]{5}\right)$

32. $\sqrt[4]{8}\left(3\sqrt[4]{2} + 4\sqrt[4]{5}\right)$ 33. $\left(\sqrt[5]{3} + 4\right)\left(\sqrt[5]{3} - 1\right)$ 34. $\left(\sqrt[5]{4} - 2\right)\left(\sqrt[5]{4} - 5\right)$

35. $\left(\sqrt[7]{6}+7\right)^2$

36. $\left(\sqrt[5]{4}-9\right)^2$

37. $\left(\sqrt[5]{3}+2\right)\left(\sqrt[5]{3}-2\right)$

38. $\left(\sqrt[5]{6}-7\right)\left(\sqrt[5]{6}+7\right)$

39. $\left(\sqrt[3]{x}+4\right)\left(\sqrt[3]{x}+5\right)$

40. $\left(\sqrt[7]{t}-6\right)\left(\sqrt[7]{t}+7\right)$

41. $\left(\sqrt[5]{m}+n\right)^2$

42. $\left(s-\sqrt[5]{t}\right)^2$

43. $\left(\sqrt[9]{x}-\sqrt[9]{y}\right)\left(\sqrt[9]{x}+\sqrt[9]{y}\right)$

44. $\left(\sqrt[3]{a}+\sqrt[3]{b}\right)\left(\sqrt[3]{a}-\sqrt[3]{b}\right)$

45. $\sqrt[5]{x^2}\left(\sqrt[5]{x^3}+5x\right)$

46. $\sqrt[4]{x^3}\left(4x^2+\sqrt[4]{x}\right)$

47. $12\sqrt[5]{x^3}\left(x-3\sqrt[5]{x^2}\right)$

48. $-9\sqrt[6]{x^5}\left(\sqrt[6]{x}-5x^2\right)$

END OF CHAPTER 5   QUIZ

1. $\sqrt{25}+\sqrt[3]{64}=$
   a) 13   b) 9   c) $\dfrac{203}{6}$ d) $\sqrt[5]{89}$ e) 1

2. $\sqrt{\dfrac{81}{100}}-\sqrt[4]{\dfrac{1}{16}}=$
   a) $\dfrac{2}{5}$ b) $\dfrac{7}{5}$ c) $-\sqrt[3]{\dfrac{20}{21}}$ d) 0   e) $\dfrac{9}{5}$

3. $\sqrt{50}=$
   a) $5\sqrt{2}$ b) $2\sqrt{5}$ c) 25   d) $5\sqrt{5}$ e) $2\sqrt{2}$

4. If $x \geq 0$ and y is any real number, then $\sqrt{44x^3y^8}=$
   a) $4xy^4\sqrt{11x}$ b) $2x^2y^4\sqrt{11x}$ c) $2xy^8\sqrt{11x}$ d) $4x^2y^4\sqrt{11x}$ e) $2xy^4\sqrt{11x}$

5. $-\sqrt{6}+8\sqrt{6}-12\sqrt{6}=$
   a) $-5\sqrt{18}$ b) 0   c) $-5\sqrt{6}$ d) $5\sqrt{6}$ e) $-4\sqrt{6}$

6. $9\sqrt{12}+6\sqrt{27}=$
   a) $15\sqrt{39}$ b) $36\sqrt{6}$ c) $15\sqrt{6}$ d) $36\sqrt{3}$ e) $27\sqrt{2}+18\sqrt{3}$

7. $-2\sqrt[3]{16}+12\sqrt[3]{128}-$
   a) $10\sqrt[3]{144}$ b) $44\sqrt[3]{2}$ c) $44\sqrt[3]{3}$ d) $52\sqrt[3]{2}$ e) $-44\sqrt[3]{2}$

8. If $x \geq 0$, then $\sqrt{10x}\cdot\sqrt{10x^4}=$
   a) $10x^2$ b) $10x\sqrt{x}$ c) $50x^2\sqrt{x}$ d) $x^2\sqrt{10x}$ e) $10x^2\sqrt{x}$

9. If $a > 0$ and $b > 0$, then $\dfrac{\sqrt{148a^9b^4}}{\sqrt{4ab^3}}=$
   a) $\sqrt{37a^9b}$ b) $a^8\sqrt{37b}$ c) $a^4\sqrt{37b}$ d) $6a^4\sqrt{b}$ e) $a^5b^3\sqrt{37b}$

10. $4\sqrt{7}\left(2\sqrt{7}+7\sqrt{2}\right)=$

   a) $56+28\sqrt{14}$ b) $8\sqrt{7}+28\sqrt{14}$ c) $56+7\sqrt{2}$ d) $108\sqrt{7}$ e) $84\sqrt{14}$

11. $\left(\sqrt{5}-2\right)\left(\sqrt{5}+6\right)=$

   a) $-3\sqrt{5}$ b) $5\sqrt{5}-12$ c) $4\sqrt{5}-7$ d) $-7-4\sqrt{5}$ e) -7

12. $\left(2\sqrt{10}+3\right)^{2}=$

   a) 49 b) $49+12\sqrt{10}$ c) $61\sqrt{10}$ d) $49+24\sqrt{5}$ e) $122\sqrt{5}$

13. Rationalize the denominator: $\dfrac{4}{3\sqrt{18}}=$

   a) $\dfrac{4}{3}$ b) $\dfrac{2\sqrt{2}}{9}$ c) $\dfrac{9\sqrt{2}}{2}$ d) $\dfrac{4}{9\sqrt{2}}$ e) $\dfrac{4\sqrt{2}}{9}$

14. Rationalize the denominator: $\dfrac{1-\sqrt{3}}{3+\sqrt{3}}=$

   a) $\dfrac{1}{3}$ b) $\dfrac{6-4\sqrt{3}}{9}$ c) $1-4\sqrt{3}$ d) $\dfrac{6-2\sqrt{3}}{3}$ e) $\dfrac{3-2\sqrt{3}}{3}$

15. Rationalize the numerator: $\dfrac{2\sqrt{2}+\sqrt{11}}{1+\sqrt{10}}=$

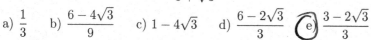

   a) $\dfrac{4\sqrt{2}-11}{2\sqrt{2}-\sqrt{11}+4\sqrt{5}-\sqrt{110}}$ b) $\dfrac{-3}{4\sqrt{106}}$ c) $\dfrac{-3}{2\sqrt{2}-\sqrt{11}+4\sqrt{5}-\sqrt{110}}$

   d) $\dfrac{2\sqrt{2}-4\sqrt{5}+\sqrt{11}-\sqrt{110}}{-9}$ e) $\dfrac{-3}{2\sqrt{2}+\sqrt{11}+4\sqrt{5}+\sqrt{110}}$

16. $\dfrac{4\sqrt{32}-\sqrt{2}}{5}=$

   a) $3\sqrt{2}$ b) $\dfrac{3\sqrt{30}}{5}$ c) $\dfrac{16\sqrt{2}}{5}$ d) $\sqrt{2}$ e) $\dfrac{13\sqrt{2}}{8}$

17. $\dfrac{4\sqrt{20}+2\sqrt{5}}{8}=$

   a) $\sqrt{5}+\dfrac{\sqrt{5}}{4}$ b) $\dfrac{15}{4}$ c) $\dfrac{5\sqrt{5}}{4}$ d) $\dfrac{5\sqrt{10}}{4}$ e) $\dfrac{\sqrt{5}}{4}$

18. If x and y are any real numbers, then $\sqrt[3]{-81x^{14}y}=$

   a) $-9x^{4}\sqrt[3]{3x^{2}y}$ b) $-3x^{4}\sqrt[3]{3x^{2}y}$ c) $-3x^{14}\sqrt[3]{3y}$ d) $-3x^{4}y^{3}\sqrt[3]{3x^{2}}$ e) $3x^{4}\sqrt[3]{3x^{2}y}$

19. If $x\geq 0$, then $\left(\sqrt[4]{x}-5\right)\left(\sqrt[4]{x^{3}}+3\right)=$

   a) $x-15$ b) $x-2\sqrt[4]{x^{2}}-15$ c) $x+\sqrt[4]{3x}-\sqrt[4]{5x^{3}}-15$ d) $x+3\sqrt[4]{x}-5\sqrt[4]{x^{3}}-15$

   e) $x^{2}+3\sqrt[4]{x}-5\sqrt[4]{x^{3}}-15$

20. If x is any real number, then $\sqrt[5]{x^{11}}-3\sqrt[5]{32x}=$

   a) $\sqrt[5]{x}-6x^{2}\sqrt[5]{x}$ b) $-2\sqrt[5]{32x}$ c) $-6x^{2}\sqrt[5]{x}$ d) $x^{2}-6\sqrt[5]{x}$ e) $\left(x^{2}-6\right)\sqrt[5]{x}$

ANSWERS FOR QUIZ 5
  1. b   2. a   3. a   4. e   5. c
  6. d   7. b   8. e   9. c   10. a
11. c   12. b   13. b   14. e   15. c
16. a   17. c   18. b   19. d   20. e

Chapter 6: Rational Exponents

In the previous chapter, we learned about radicals. The important thing to remember about a radical is that it is just the opposite of exponentiation. For example, $\sqrt{16} = 4$ comes from the fact that $16 = 4^2$. Similarly, $\sqrt[3]{-27} = -3$ because $-27 = (-3)^3$. Now, since we have this relationship between radicals and exponentiation, there should be a way of working with radicals by using only exponents. In this chapter, we will define a **rational exponent** to serve this purpose. Rational exponents will allow us to work with radicals by using our properties of exponents which were discussed in Chapter 2. In Section 6.1, the definition of a rational exponent will be given. After doing numerous examples, we will see how to use our exponent properties to work with radicals in an easy way (Section 6.2).

Section 6.1 Definition and Examples of Rational Exponents

We want to somehow link a radical to an exponent. How should we do this? Well, remember that we have a list of properties which exponents satisfy when the exponent is an integer (see Chapter 2). If we define a new type of exponent, we would like all of these properties to work for the new exponent as well. In particular, recall that if a is any real number and m and n are integers, then

$$(a^m)^n = a^{mn}$$

(the only exception is if $a = 0$ and either $m = 0$ or $n = 0$, in which case the above is undefined).

Let $m = 1/2$ and $n = 2$. If the property above is to be satisfied, we must have

$$\left(a^{\frac{1}{2}}\right)^2 = a^{\left(\frac{1}{2}\right)(2)} = a^{\left(\frac{1}{2}\right)\left(\frac{2}{1}\right)} = a^1 = a.$$

Hence, $a^{\frac{1}{2}}$ has the property that when it is squared, the answer is a. Notice that $a \geq 0$ for this to make sense. Similarly, if $m = 1/3$ and $n = 3$, then

$$\left(a^{\frac{1}{3}}\right)^3 = a^{\left(\frac{1}{3}\right)(3)} = a^{\left(\frac{1}{3}\right)\left(\frac{3}{1}\right)} = a^1 = a.$$

And so $a^{\frac{1}{3}}$ has the property that when it is cubed, the answer is a. In this case, a can be real number.

In general, if $n > 1$ is an integer, then

$$\left(a^{\frac{1}{n}}\right)^n = a^{\left(\frac{1}{n}\right)(n)} = a^{\left(\frac{1}{n}\right)\left(\frac{n}{1}\right)} = a^1 = a.$$

And so $a^{\frac{1}{n}}$ has the property that when it is raised to the nth power, the answer is a. Observe that $a \geq 0$ when n is even and a can be any real number when n is odd.

We know from our properties of radicals that $(\sqrt[n]{a})^n = a$, where $\sqrt[n]{a}$ is the principal n^{th} root of a. From what we've just observed, it makes sense to define $a^{\frac{1}{n}} = \sqrt[n]{a}$ (provided that $\sqrt[n]{a}$ is a real number) since both expressions equal a when raised to the nth power.

Definition 1: Let a be a real number and suppose that $n > 1$ is an integer. Then $a^{\frac{1}{n}} = \sqrt[n]{a}$, provided that $\sqrt[n]{a}$ is a real number.

Since $\frac{1}{n}$ is a rational number, we call it a **rational exponent**. Notice that the denominator of the exponent becomes the index of the radical. Hence, we have

$$a^{\frac{1}{2}} = \sqrt{a}, a^{\frac{1}{3}} = \sqrt[3]{a}, a^{\frac{1}{4}} = \sqrt[4]{a}, \text{etc.}$$

Examples. Evaluate.

1) $1^{\frac{1}{2}} = \sqrt{1} = 1$

2) $49^{\frac{1}{2}} = \sqrt{49} = 7$

3) $8^{\frac{1}{3}} = \sqrt[3]{8} = 2$

4) $16^{\frac{1}{4}} = \sqrt[4]{16} = 2$

5) $\underbrace{-25^{\frac{1}{2}} = -\sqrt{25}}\ = -5$

The $\frac{1}{2}$ only applies to the 35.

6) $\underbrace{(-25)^{\frac{1}{2}} = \sqrt{-25}}$ which is not a real number.

The $\frac{1}{2}$ applies to the -25.

7) $\underbrace{(-216)^{\frac{1}{3}} = \sqrt[3]{-216}}\ = -6$

The $\frac{1}{3}$ applies to the -216.

8) $\underbrace{-216^{\frac{1}{3}} = -\sqrt[3]{216}}\ = -6$

The $\frac{1}{3}$ only applies to the 216.

9) $\left(\frac{81}{4}\right)^{\frac{1}{2}} = \sqrt{\frac{81}{4}} = \frac{9}{2}$

10) $40^{\frac{1}{2}} = \sqrt{40} = 2\sqrt{10}$

We would like to define the expression $a^{\frac{m}{n}}$, where $m > 1$ is a positive integer. Let m and n be positive integers and suppose that $a^{\frac{1}{n}}$ is a real number (that is, the principal n^{th} root of a exists). We would like to define the expression $a^{\frac{m}{n}}$. Observe that

$$\left(a^{\frac{1}{n}}\right)^m = \left(\sqrt[n]{a}\right)^m$$
$$a^{\left(\frac{1}{n}\right)\left(\frac{m}{1}\right)} = \left(\sqrt[n]{a}\right)^m$$
$$a^{\frac{m}{n}} = \left(\sqrt[n]{a}\right)^m$$

and

$$\left(a^m\right)^{\frac{1}{n}} = \sqrt[n]{a^m}$$
$$a^{\left(\frac{m}{1}\right)\left(\frac{1}{n}\right)} = \sqrt[n]{a^m}$$
$$a^{\frac{m}{n}} = \sqrt[n]{a^m}.$$

Definition 2: Let a be a real number and suppose that $n > 1$ is any integer. If m is a positive integer and $\sqrt[n]{a}$ exists, then

$$a^{\frac{m}{n}} = \left(\sqrt[n]{a}\right)^m = \left(\sqrt[n]{a^m}\right).$$

Since $\frac{m}{n}$ is a rational number, we call it a **rational exponent**. Notice that the numerator of the exponent becomes the exponent of the radical, whereas the denominator of the exponent becomes the index of the radical. Furthermore, notice that if $m = 1$, we get Definition 1.

Definition 3: Let $a \neq 0$ be a real number and suppose that $n > 1$ is any integer. Then

$$a^{-\frac{m}{n}} = \frac{1}{\left(\sqrt[n]{a}\right)^m} = \frac{1}{\sqrt[n]{a^m}},$$

provided that $\sqrt[n]{a}$ exists, is well-defined.

Observe that the negative exponent 'flips' the radical into the denominator of the fraction whose numerator equals 1. We've seen this before when learning about the properties of exponents (Chapter 2, Property IV). From this, it follows that all of the things that we learned with regards to the 'flipping technique' will now work for rational exponents as well.

148

When you do an example which requires you to evaluate an expression, the easiest way to do it is to use $a^{\frac{m}{n}} = (\sqrt[n]{a})^m$, leaving the exponent m on the outside of the radical.

Examples. Evaluate.

1) $4^{\frac{3}{2}} = \left(\sqrt{4}\right)^3 = (2)^3 = 8$

2) $27^{\frac{2}{3}} = \left(\sqrt[3]{27}\right)^2 = (3)^2 = 9$

3) $64^{\frac{4}{3}} = \left(\sqrt[3]{64}\right)^4 = (4)^4 = 256$

4) $16^{\frac{7}{4}} = \left(\sqrt[4]{16}\right)^7 = (2)^7 = 128$

5) $\underbrace{-36^{\frac{3}{2}} = -\left(\sqrt{36}\right)^3}_{\frac{3}{2}\text{ only applies to 36.}} = \underbrace{-(6)^3 = -216}_{3\text{ only applies to 6.}}$

6) $\underbrace{(-36)^{\frac{3}{2}} = \left(\sqrt{-36}\right)^3}_{\frac{3}{2}\text{ applies to }-36.}$ is not a real number since $\sqrt{-36}$ is not a real number.

7) $\underbrace{-125^{\frac{2}{3}} = -\left(\sqrt[3]{125}\right)^2}_{\frac{2}{3}\text{ only applies to 125.}} = \underbrace{-(5)^2 = -25}_{2\text{ only applies to 5.}}$

8) $\underbrace{(-125)^{\frac{2}{3}} = \left(\sqrt[3]{-125}\right)^2}_{\frac{2}{3}\text{ applies to }-125.} = (-5)^2 = 25$

9) $4^{-\frac{1}{2}} = \dfrac{1}{4^{\frac{1}{2}}} = \dfrac{1}{\sqrt{4}} = \dfrac{1}{2}$

10) $64^{-\frac{2}{3}} = \dfrac{1}{64^{\frac{2}{3}}} = \dfrac{1}{\left(\sqrt[3]{64}\right)^2} = \dfrac{1}{(4)^2} = \dfrac{1}{16}$

11) $(-27)^{-\frac{4}{3}} = \dfrac{1}{(-27)^{\frac{4}{3}}} = \dfrac{1}{\left(\sqrt[3]{-27}\right)^4} = \dfrac{1}{(-3)^4} = \dfrac{1}{81}$

12) $\underbrace{-27^{-\frac{4}{3}} = -\left(27^{-\frac{4}{3}}\right)}_{-\frac{4}{3}\text{ only applies to 27.}} = -\dfrac{1}{27^{\frac{4}{3}}} = -\dfrac{1}{\left(\sqrt[3]{27}\right)^4} = -\dfrac{1}{(3)^4} = -\dfrac{1}{81}$

13) $\dfrac{4^{-\frac{1}{2}}}{25^{\frac{1}{2}}} = \dfrac{1}{4^{\frac{1}{2}} \cdot 25^{\frac{1}{2}}} = \dfrac{1}{\sqrt{4} \cdot \sqrt{25}} = \dfrac{1}{2 \cdot 5} = \dfrac{1}{10}$

14) $\dfrac{64^{\frac{2}{3}}}{49^{-\frac{1}{2}}} = \dfrac{49^{\frac{1}{2}} \cdot 64^{\frac{2}{3}}}{1} = \dfrac{\sqrt{49} \cdot \left(\sqrt[3]{64}\right)^2}{1} = \dfrac{7 \cdot (4)^2}{1} = \dfrac{112}{1} = 112$

15) $\dfrac{36^{\frac{1}{2}} \cdot 25^{-\frac{3}{2}}}{16^{-\frac{3}{4}}} = \dfrac{36^{\frac{1}{2}} \cdot 16^{\frac{3}{4}}}{25^{\frac{3}{2}}} = \dfrac{\sqrt{36} \cdot \left(\sqrt[4]{16}\right)^3}{\left(\sqrt{25}\right)^3} = \dfrac{6 \cdot (2)^3}{(5)^3} = \dfrac{48}{125}$

16) $\dfrac{(-1,000)^{-\frac{1}{3}} \cdot 4^{-\frac{3}{2}}}{27^{-\frac{1}{3}}} = \dfrac{27^{\frac{1}{3}}}{(-1,000)^{\frac{1}{3}} \cdot 4^{\frac{3}{2}}} = \dfrac{\sqrt[3]{27}}{\sqrt[3]{-1,000} \cdot \left(\sqrt{4}\right)^3} = \dfrac{3}{-10 \cdot (2)^3} = -\dfrac{3}{80}$

Examples. Rewrite each of the expressions with positive integer exponents only and simplify. Assume that all variables represent positive numbers.

1) $x^{\frac{1}{2}} = \sqrt{x}$

2) $y^{\frac{2}{3}} = \sqrt[3]{y^2}$

3) $a^{-\frac{4}{5}} = \dfrac{1}{a^{\frac{4}{5}}} = \dfrac{1}{\sqrt[5]{a^4}}$

4) $b^{-\frac{5}{9}} = \dfrac{1}{b^{\frac{5}{9}}} = \dfrac{1}{\sqrt[9]{b^5}}$

5) $m^{\frac{1}{2}} n^{\frac{4}{9}} = \sqrt{m} \cdot \sqrt[9]{n^4}$

6) $x^{\frac{2}{3}} y^{-\frac{3}{4}} = \dfrac{x^{\frac{2}{3}} y^{-\frac{3}{4}}}{1} = \dfrac{x^{\frac{2}{3}}}{y^{\frac{3}{4}}} = \dfrac{\sqrt[3]{x^2}}{\sqrt[4]{y^3}}$

7) $m^{-\frac{1}{4}} n^{-\frac{5}{6}} = \dfrac{m^{-\frac{1}{4}} n^{-\frac{5}{6}}}{1} = \dfrac{1}{m^{\frac{1}{4}} n^{\frac{5}{6}}} = \dfrac{1}{\sqrt[4]{m} \cdot \sqrt[6]{n^5}}$

8) $x(x+3)^{\frac{1}{2}} = x\sqrt{x+3}$

9) $[x(x+3)]^{\frac{1}{2}} = \sqrt{x(x+3)} = \sqrt{x^2+3x}$

10) $7y(4y-3)^{-\frac{1}{3}} = \dfrac{7y(4y-3)^{-\frac{1}{3}}}{1} = \dfrac{7y}{(4y-3)^{\frac{1}{3}}} = \dfrac{7y}{\sqrt[3]{4y-3}}$

Examples. Rewrite each of the expressions using rational exponents.

1) $\sqrt{a} = a^{\frac{1}{2}}$

2) $\sqrt[4]{b^3} = b^{\frac{3}{4}}$

3) $\sqrt[5]{x^{12}} = x^{\frac{12}{5}}$

4) $\sqrt[4]{y} = y^{\frac{1}{4}}$

5) $\dfrac{\sqrt{x}}{7} = \dfrac{x^{\frac{1}{2}}}{7}$

6) $\sqrt{\dfrac{x}{7}} = \left(\dfrac{x}{7}\right)^{\frac{1}{2}}$

7) $p^2 \sqrt[6]{(p-1)^5} = p^2 (p-1)^{\frac{5}{6}}$

8) $\sqrt[6]{[p^2(p-1)]^5} = [p^2(p-1)]^{\frac{5}{6}}$

Try These (Set 1):

I) Evaluate.

1) $36^{\frac{1}{2}}$

2) $8^{\frac{5}{3}}$

3) $32^{-\frac{3}{5}}$

4) $81^{\frac{1}{2}} \cdot 100^{-\frac{1}{2}}$

5) $\dfrac{(-64)^{-\frac{1}{3}}}{-49^{-\frac{1}{2}}}$

II) Rewrite each of the expressions with positive integer exponents only and simplify. Assume that all variables represent non-zero numbers.

1) $x^{\frac{1}{3}}$

2) $y^{-\frac{3}{5}}$

3) $3x^{\frac{2}{3}}$

4) $(3x)^{\frac{2}{3}}$

5) $\dfrac{(9a)^{\frac{2}{5}}}{2b^{-\frac{1}{3}}}$

III) Rewrite each of the expressions using rational exponents.

1) $\sqrt{t}$

2) $\sqrt[3]{\dfrac{9}{y}}$

3) $\dfrac{\sqrt[3]{9}}{y}$

4) $x\sqrt{2x+3}$

5) $\sqrt{x(2x+3)}$

Section 6.2   Radical Problems Made Easy

In Section 6.1, we learned how to write expressions containing rational exponents as radicals and vice versa. For reference purposes, recall that if a is a real number for which $\sqrt[n]{a}$ is well-defined, $n > 1$ is an integer, and m is an integer, then:

$$1.\ a^{\frac{1}{n}} = \sqrt[n]{a}$$

$$2.\ a^{\frac{m}{n}} = \left(\sqrt[n]{a}\right)^m = \sqrt[n]{a^m}$$

$$3.\ a^{-\frac{m}{n}} = \dfrac{1}{\left(\sqrt[n]{a}\right)^m} = \dfrac{1}{\sqrt[n]{a^m}},\ a \neq 0$$

In this section, we will use the properties of exponents to work with radicals. Let's state the properties for **rational exponents**:

Let a and b be (non-zero) real numbers and let m and n be any **rational numbers**. Then:

Property I: $\qquad a^m \cdot a^n = a^{m+n}$ $\qquad\qquad$ **Property V:** $\qquad (a^m)^n = a^{mn}$

Property II: $\qquad \dfrac{a^m}{a^n} = a^{m-n}$ $\qquad\qquad$ **Property VI:** $\qquad (ab)^n = a^n b^n$

Property III: $\qquad a^0 = 1$ $\qquad\qquad$ **Property VII:** $\qquad \left(\dfrac{a}{b}\right)^n = \dfrac{a^n}{b^n}$

Property IV: $\qquad a^{-n} = \dfrac{1}{a^n}$ $\qquad\qquad$ **Property VIII:** $\qquad \left(\dfrac{a}{b}\right)^{-n} = \dfrac{b^n}{a^n}$

Examples. Simplify. Assume that all variables represent positive numbers.

1) $\underbrace{5^{\frac{1}{4}} \cdot 5^{\frac{1}{2}} = 5^{\frac{1}{4}+\frac{1}{2}} = 5^{\frac{1}{4}+\frac{2}{4}} = 5^{\frac{3}{4}}}_{\text{by Property I}}$
$\qquad$
2) $\underbrace{x^{-\frac{1}{3}} \cdot x^{\frac{5}{9}} = x^{-\frac{1}{3}+\frac{5}{9}} = x^{-\frac{3}{9}+\frac{5}{9}} = x^{\frac{2}{9}}}_{\text{by Property I}}$

3) $\underbrace{\dfrac{9^{\frac{1}{7}}}{9^{\frac{2}{3}}} = 9^{\frac{1}{7}-\frac{2}{3}} = 9^{\frac{3}{21}-\frac{14}{21}} = 9^{-\frac{11}{21}}}_{\text{by Property II}}$
$\qquad$
4) $\underbrace{\dfrac{y^{-\frac{1}{4}}}{y^{\frac{1}{10}}} = y^{-\frac{1}{4}-\frac{1}{10}} = y^{-\frac{5}{20}-\frac{2}{20}} = y^{-\frac{7}{20}}}_{\text{by Property II}}$

5) $\underbrace{\left(10^{\frac{5}{6}}\right)^{12} = 10^{\left(\frac{5}{6}\right)\left(\frac{12}{1}\right)} = 10^{10}}_{\text{by Property V}}$
$\qquad$
6) $\underbrace{\left(x^{\frac{1}{5}}\right)^{\frac{1}{3}} = x^{\left(\frac{1}{5}\right)\left(\frac{1}{3}\right)} = x^{\frac{1}{15}}}_{\text{by Property V}}$

7) $\underbrace{\left(3^{\frac{7}{8}} \cdot 4^{\frac{1}{3}}\right)^{\frac{1}{2}} = \left(3^{\frac{7}{8}}\right)^{\frac{1}{2}} \cdot \left(4^{\frac{1}{3}}\right)^{\frac{1}{2}} = 3^{\frac{7}{16}} \cdot 4^{\frac{1}{6}}}_{\text{by Property VI}}$
$\qquad$
8) $\underbrace{\left(x^{-\frac{2}{7}} y^{\frac{10}{3}}\right)^{\frac{4}{5}} = \left(x^{-\frac{2}{7}}\right)^{\frac{4}{5}} \left(y^{\frac{10}{3}}\right)^{\frac{4}{5}} = x^{-\frac{8}{35}} y^{\frac{8}{3}}}_{\text{by Properties VI and V}}$

9) $\underbrace{\left(\dfrac{a^{\frac{1}{9}}}{b^{\frac{4}{3}}}\right)^{\frac{3}{11}} = \dfrac{\left(a^{\frac{1}{9}}\right)^{\frac{3}{11}}}{\left(b^{\frac{4}{3}}\right)^{\frac{3}{11}}} = \dfrac{a^{\frac{1}{33}}}{b^{\frac{4}{11}}}}_{\text{by Properties VI and V}}$
$\qquad$
10) $\underbrace{\left(\dfrac{x^{12} y^{\frac{1}{5}}}{z^4}\right)^{\frac{10}{3}} = \dfrac{\left(x^{\frac{12}{1}}\right)^{\frac{10}{3}} \left(y^{\frac{1}{5}}\right)^{\frac{10}{3}}}{\left(z^{\frac{4}{1}}\right)^{\frac{10}{3}}} = \dfrac{x^{40} y^{\frac{2}{3}}}{z^{\frac{40}{3}}}}_{\text{by Properties VII, VI, and V}}$

We are now prepared to do some examples with radicals. The first step is to convert the radicals into expressions containing rational exponents. The second step is to use the properties of exponents to perform whatever operation is being required. When we get your answer (in simplified form), we'll convert it back into radical form.

Examples. Perform the indicated operation and write the answer as a simplified, single radical. Assume that all variables represent positive numbers.

1) $\underbrace{\left(\sqrt{a}\right)\left(\sqrt[4]{a}\right) = \left(a^{\frac{1}{2}}\right)\left(a^{\frac{1}{4}}\right) = a^{\frac{1}{2}+\frac{1}{4}} = a^{\frac{2}{4}+\frac{1}{4}} =}_{\text{Go to exponents and use Property I.}} \underbrace{a^{\frac{3}{4}} = \sqrt[4]{a^3}}_{\text{Go back to radicals.}}$

2) $\underbrace{\dfrac{\sqrt[10]{x^7}}{\sqrt[4]{x^3}} = \dfrac{x^{\frac{7}{10}}}{x^{\frac{3}{4}}} = x^{\frac{7}{10}-\frac{3}{4}}}_{\text{Go to exponents and use Property II.}} = x^{\frac{14}{20}-\frac{15}{20}} = \underbrace{x^{-\frac{1}{20}} = \dfrac{1}{\sqrt[20]{x}}}_{\text{Go back to radicals.}}$

151

3) $\underbrace{\left(\sqrt[8]{t^3}\right)^{16} = \left(t^{\frac{3}{8}}\right)^{16} = t^{\left(\frac{3}{8}\right)\left(\frac{16}{1}\right)} = t^6}_{\text{Go to exponents and use Property V.}}$

4) $\underbrace{\left(\sqrt[18]{b}\right)^9 = \left(b^{\frac{1}{18}}\right)^9 = b^{\left(\frac{1}{18}\right)\left(\frac{9}{1}\right)} =}_{\text{Go to exponents and use Property V.}} \underbrace{b^{\frac{1}{2}} = \sqrt{b}}_{\text{Go back to radicals.}}$

5) $\sqrt[4]{25} = 25^{\frac{1}{4}} = \left(5^2\right)^{\frac{1}{4}} = 5^{\left(\frac{2}{1}\right)\left(\frac{1}{4}\right)} = 5^{\frac{1}{2}} = \sqrt{5}$

6) $\sqrt[6]{27} = 27^{\frac{1}{6}} = \left(3^3\right)^{\frac{1}{6}} = 3^{\left(\frac{3}{1}\right)\left(\frac{1}{6}\right)} = 3^{\frac{1}{2}} = \sqrt{3}$

7) $\underbrace{\sqrt[3]{\sqrt[3]{x}} = \left(x^{\frac{1}{3}}\right)^{\frac{1}{3}} = x^{\left(\frac{1}{3}\right)\left(\frac{1}{3}\right)} =}_{\text{Go to exponents and use Property V.}} \underbrace{x^{\frac{1}{9}} = \sqrt[9]{x}}_{\text{Go back to radicals.}}$

8) $\underbrace{\sqrt[5]{\sqrt[4]{\sqrt[3]{y^{24}}}} = \left(\left(y^{\frac{24}{3}}\right)^{\frac{1}{4}}\right)^{\frac{1}{5}} = y^{\left(\frac{24}{3}\right)\left(\frac{1}{4}\right)\left(\frac{1}{5}\right)} =}_{\text{Go to exponents and use Property V.}} \underbrace{y^{\frac{2}{5}} = \sqrt[5]{y^2}}_{\text{Go back to radicals.}}$

9) $\underbrace{\left(\sqrt[8]{a^3} \cdot \sqrt[10]{a^3}\right)^{20} = \left(a^{\frac{3}{8}} \cdot a^{\frac{3}{10}}\right)^{20} = \left(a^{\frac{3}{8}+\frac{3}{10}}\right)^{20} = \left(a^{\frac{15}{40}+\frac{12}{40}}\right)^{20} = \left(a^{\frac{27}{40}}\right)^{20} = a^{\left(\frac{27}{40}\right)\left(\frac{20}{1}\right)} =}_{\text{Go to exponents and use Properties I and V.}} \underbrace{a^{\frac{27}{2}} = \sqrt{a^{27}}}_{\text{Go back to radicals.}}$

Notice that $\dfrac{27}{2} = 13 + \dfrac{1}{2}$, so we can write $a^{\frac{27}{2}} = \underbrace{a^{13+\frac{1}{2}} = a^{13} \cdot a^{\frac{1}{2}}}_{\text{Property I going \textbf{backwards}.}} = a^{13} \cdot \sqrt{a}$. In other words, $\sqrt{a^{27}} = a^{13}\sqrt{a}$. Do you remember when we used a division problem to simplify radicals? Well, it turns out that we were doing exactly what was just done above. Recall that to simplify $\sqrt{a^{27}}$, we divide $27 \div 2 = 13\ R\ 1$. And so 13 of the a's come out and 1 of the a's stays in, giving us $a^{13}\sqrt{a}$ as above.

10) $\underbrace{\left(\dfrac{\sqrt[10]{x^3}}{\sqrt[15]{x^2}}\right)^3 = \left(\dfrac{x^{\frac{3}{10}}}{x^{\frac{2}{15}}}\right)^3 = \left(x^{\frac{3}{10}-\frac{2}{15}}\right)^3 = \left(x^{\frac{9}{30}-\frac{4}{30}}\right)^3 = \left(x^{\frac{5}{30}}\right)^3 = x^{\left(\frac{5}{30}\right)\left(\frac{3}{1}\right)} =}_{\text{Go to exponents and use Properties II and V.}} \underbrace{x^{\frac{1}{2}} = \sqrt{x}}_{\text{Go back to radicals.}}$

Try These (Set 2):

I) Simplify.

1) $x^{\frac{1}{4}} \cdot x^{\frac{2}{3}}$ 2) $\left(x^{\frac{1}{8}}\right)\left(x^{-\frac{3}{4}}\right)$ 3) $\dfrac{y^{\frac{1}{2}}}{y^{\frac{1}{6}}}$ 4) $\left(m^{-2}n^{\frac{1}{12}}\right)^6$ 5) $\left(\dfrac{a^{-\frac{7}{10}}}{b^{\frac{3}{5}}}\right)^{\frac{5}{6}}$

II) Perform the indicated operation and write the answer as a simplified, single radical. Assume that all variables represent positive numbers.

1) $\sqrt[4]{t} \cdot \sqrt{t}$ 2) $\dfrac{\sqrt[5]{y}}{\sqrt[10]{y}}$ 3) $\sqrt{\sqrt[4]{a^3}}$ 4) $\sqrt[60]{a^{20}}$ 5) $\left(\sqrt[8]{x^3} \cdot \sqrt[6]{x}\right)^{12}$

Exercise 6

In Exercises 1-58, evaluate and simplify.

1. $4^{\frac{1}{2}}$ 2. $9^{\frac{1}{2}}$ 3. $36^{\frac{1}{2}}$ 4. $121^{\frac{1}{2}}$

5. $49^{\frac{3}{2}}$ 6. $81^{\frac{3}{2}}$ 7. $100^{\frac{3}{2}}$ 8. $64^{\frac{3}{2}}$

9. $27^{\frac{1}{3}}$ 10. $64^{\frac{1}{3}}$ 11. $8^{\frac{2}{3}}$ 12. $1^{\frac{2}{3}}$

13. $1,000^{\frac{2}{3}}$ 14. $1,000^{\frac{1}{3}}$ 15. $81^{\frac{3}{4}}$ 16. $16^{\frac{3}{4}}$

17. $-16^{\frac{1}{2}}$ 18. $(-16)^{\frac{1}{2}}$ 19. $(-125)^{\frac{1}{3}}$ 20. $-125^{\frac{1}{3}}$

21. $-64^{\frac{2}{3}}$ 22. $(-64)^{\frac{2}{3}}$ 23. $(-25)^{\frac{3}{2}}$ 24. $-25^{\frac{3}{2}}$

25. $36^{-\frac{1}{2}}$ 26. $100^{-\frac{1}{2}}$ 27. $216^{-\frac{1}{3}}$ 28. $125^{-\frac{1}{3}}$

29. $125^{-\frac{2}{3}}$ 30. $8^{-\frac{4}{3}}$ 31. $16^{-\frac{3}{4}}$ 32. $81^{-\frac{3}{4}}$

33. $\left(\dfrac{16}{9}\right)^{\frac{1}{2}}$ 34. $\left(\dfrac{36}{49}\right)^{\frac{1}{2}}$ 35. $\left(\dfrac{216}{125}\right)^{\frac{2}{3}}$ 36. $\left(\dfrac{16}{81}\right)^{\frac{5}{4}}$

37. $\left(\dfrac{1}{27}\right)^{-\frac{1}{3}}$ 38. $\left(\dfrac{27}{64}\right)^{-\frac{1}{3}}$ 39. $\left(\dfrac{343}{1,000}\right)^{-\frac{2}{3}}$ 40. $\left(\dfrac{1}{8}\right)^{-\frac{2}{3}}$

41. $-81^{-\frac{1}{2}}$ 42. $(-81)^{-\frac{1}{2}}$ 43. $(-8)^{-\frac{1}{3}}$ 44. $-8^{-\frac{1}{3}}$

45. $-64^{-\frac{2}{3}}$ 46. $(-64)^{-\frac{2}{3}}$ 47. $9^{\frac{3}{2}} \cdot 4^{\frac{1}{2}}$ 48. $27^{\frac{1}{3}} \cdot 4^{\frac{1}{2}}$

49. $81^{\frac{1}{4}} \cdot 144^{-\frac{1}{2}}$ 50. $121^{\frac{1}{2}} \cdot 125^{-\frac{1}{3}}$ 51. $\dfrac{16^{-\frac{1}{2}}}{27^{\frac{1}{3}}}$ 52. $\dfrac{1,000^{\frac{1}{3}}}{25^{-\frac{1}{2}}}$

53. $\dfrac{169^{\frac{1}{2}}}{8^{-\frac{1}{3}}}$ 54. $\dfrac{49^{-\frac{1}{2}}}{16^{\frac{1}{4}}}$ 55. $\dfrac{81^{-\frac{1}{2}}}{8^{-\frac{2}{3}}}$ 56. $\dfrac{16^{-\frac{3}{4}}}{100^{-\frac{1}{2}}}$

57. $\dfrac{1^{\frac{1}{2}} + 8^{-\frac{1}{3}}}{4^{-\frac{1}{2}} + 27^{\frac{1}{3}}}$ 58. $\dfrac{8^{\frac{2}{3}} + 1^{\frac{4}{3}}}{25^{-\frac{1}{2}} - 9^{\frac{1}{2}}}$

In Exercises 59–100, rewrite each of the expressions with positive integer exponents only and simplify. Assume that all variables represent positive numbers.

59. $x^{\frac{1}{4}}$ 60. $x^{\frac{1}{5}}$ 61. $y^{\frac{1}{2}}$ 62. $y^{\frac{1}{10}}$ 63. $a^{\frac{2}{5}}$

64. $a^{\frac{2}{9}}$ 65. $b^{\frac{4}{5}}$ 66. $b^{\frac{3}{8}}$ 67. $t^{\frac{5}{9}}$ 68. $t^{\frac{8}{9}}$

69. $x^{-\frac{1}{2}}$ 70. $m^{-\frac{1}{4}}$ 71. $m^{-\frac{1}{3}}$ 72. $n^{-\frac{2}{3}}$ 73. $y^{-\frac{3}{10}}$

74. $p^{-\frac{5}{6}}$ 75. $a^{\frac{1}{2}} b^{\frac{1}{2}}$ 76. $x^{\frac{1}{2}} y^{\frac{1}{2}} z^{\frac{1}{2}}$ 77. $25^{\frac{1}{2}} p^{\frac{1}{2}}$

78. $8^{\frac{1}{3}} q^{\frac{1}{3}}$ 79. $a^{\frac{1}{2}} b^{\frac{3}{4}}$ 80. $x^{\frac{2}{3}} y^{\frac{1}{5}}$ 81. $m^{\frac{2}{5}} n^{\frac{3}{4}}$

82. $p^{\frac{2}{3}} q^{\frac{1}{7}}$ 83. $x(x-3)^{\frac{1}{2}}$ 84. $y(y+5)^{\frac{1}{2}}$ 85. $x^2(2x+3)^{-\frac{1}{2}}$

86. $t^2(-4t+1)^{-\frac{1}{3}}$ 87. $\dfrac{1}{2}x^{-\frac{1}{2}}$ 88. $\dfrac{1}{3}x^{-\frac{2}{3}}$ 89. $\dfrac{1}{4}\left(x^2 - 7x + 3\right)^{-\frac{3}{4}}$

90. $\dfrac{4}{9}\left(y^2 + y - 2\right)^{-\frac{5}{9}}$ 91. $\left(\dfrac{x}{36}\right)^{\frac{1}{2}}$ 92. $\left(\dfrac{121}{y}\right)^{\frac{1}{2}}$ 93. $\dfrac{x^{\frac{1}{2}}}{144}$

94. $\dfrac{9^{\frac{1}{2}}}{y}$ 95. $\left(\dfrac{t}{16}\right)^{-\frac{1}{2}}$ 96. $\left(\dfrac{64}{y}\right)^{-\frac{1}{2}}$ 97. $\left(\dfrac{x}{125}\right)^{-\frac{2}{3}}$

98. $\left(\dfrac{t}{64}\right)^{-\frac{2}{3}}$ 99. $\dfrac{x^{-\frac{2}{3}}}{125}$ 100. $\dfrac{t^{-\frac{2}{3}}}{164}$

In Exercises 101-120, rewrite each of the expressions using rational exponents.

101. $\sqrt{x}$ 102. $\sqrt[3]{y}$ 103. $\sqrt[3]{a^2}$ 104. $\sqrt{b}$

105. $\sqrt[6]{m}$ 106. $\sqrt[4]{k}$ 107. $\sqrt[3]{n^7}$ 108. $\sqrt[5]{y^2}$

109. $\sqrt[3]{a}\sqrt{b}$ 110. $\sqrt[6]{a^5}\sqrt{b}$ 111. $\sqrt{\dfrac{x}{6}}$ 112. $\sqrt[5]{\dfrac{y}{4}}$

113. $\dfrac{\sqrt{x}}{6}$ 114. $\dfrac{\sqrt[5]{y}}{4}$ 115. $\left(\sqrt[7]{u^2 v}\right)^4$ 116. $\left(\sqrt[8]{uv^5}\right)^7$

117. $m^4\sqrt[4]{n}$ 118. $x\sqrt[6]{y}$ 119. $\dfrac{\left(\sqrt[3]{m}\right)^2}{9}$ 120. $\left(\sqrt[3]{\dfrac{m}{9}}\right)^2$

In Exercises 121-148, perform the indicated operation and simplify. Leave your answer in terms of **positive rational exponents**. Assume that all variables represent positive numbers.

121. $x^{\frac{1}{6}} \cdot x^{\frac{1}{8}}$ 122. $y^{\frac{1}{6}} \cdot y^{\frac{1}{4}}$ 123. $b^{-\frac{4}{5}} \cdot b^{\frac{2}{5}}$ 124. $a^{-\frac{4}{3}} \cdot a^{\frac{7}{3}}$

125. $y^{-\frac{5}{6}} \cdot y^{-\frac{1}{9}}$ 126. $m^{-\frac{1}{8}} \cdot m^{-\frac{3}{4}}$ 127. $\left(x^{-\frac{2}{3}}\right)\left(x^{\frac{5}{6}}\right)\left(x^{\frac{1}{3}}\right)$ 128. $\left(y^{\frac{3}{10}}\right)\left(y^{-\frac{2}{5}}\right)\left(y^{\frac{1}{10}}\right)$

129. $\dfrac{u^{\frac{9}{10}}}{u^{\frac{1}{10}}}$ 130. $\dfrac{v^{\frac{8}{9}}}{v^{\frac{2}{9}}}$ 131. $\dfrac{n^{\frac{1}{2}}}{n^{-\frac{3}{4}}}$ 132. $\dfrac{k^{\frac{5}{6}}}{k^{-\frac{1}{12}}}$

133. $\dfrac{x^{-\frac{3}{2}}}{x^{-\frac{7}{6}}}$ 134. $\dfrac{y^{-\frac{4}{5}}}{y^{-\frac{2}{15}}}$ 135. $\left(a^{\frac{1}{2}}\right)^2$ 136. $\left(b^{\frac{2}{3}}\right)^3$

137. $\left(s^{\frac{4}{13}}\right)^{26}$ 138. $\left(t^{\frac{4}{9}}\right)^{27}$ 139. $\left(a^8 b^2\right)^{\frac{3}{2}}$ 140. $\left(a^6 b^3\right)^{\frac{2}{3}}$

141. $\left(x^{\frac{8}{11}} y^{\frac{2}{7}}\right)^{\frac{22}{3}}$ 142. $\left(x^{\frac{6}{5}} y^{\frac{1}{3}}\right)^{\frac{10}{3}}$ 143. $\left(s^8 t^{-2}\right)^{-\frac{3}{4}}$ 144. $\left(a^{-2} b^{15}\right)^{-\frac{4}{5}}$

145. $\left(\dfrac{p^{\frac{2}{5}}}{q^{-\frac{3}{5}}}\right)^{\frac{1}{4}}$ 146. $\left(\dfrac{s^{-\frac{1}{10}}}{t^{\frac{9}{10}}}\right)^3$ 147. $\left(\dfrac{a^5 b}{c^{-\frac{1}{6}}}\right)^{\frac{1}{5}}$ 148. $\left(\dfrac{xy^{\frac{1}{3}}}{z^{-\frac{2}{5}}}\right)^{\frac{1}{6}}$

In Exercises 149-176, perform the indicated operation and write your answer as a **simplified, single radical**. Assume that all variables represent positive numbers.

149. $\left(\sqrt[4]{x}\right)\left(\sqrt{x}\right)$ 150. $\left(\sqrt[5]{y}\right)\left(\sqrt[3]{y}\right)$ 151. $\left(\sqrt[9]{a^2}\right)\left(\sqrt[3]{a^2}\right)$ 152. $\left(\sqrt[3]{b^2}\right)\left(\sqrt[6]{b^5}\right)$

153. $\left(\sqrt[8]{x}\right)\left(\sqrt[8]{x}\right)$ 154. $\left(\sqrt[4]{b}\right)\left(\sqrt[4]{b}\right)$ 155. $\dfrac{\sqrt[5]{m}}{\sqrt[10]{m^3}}$ 156. $\dfrac{\sqrt[6]{n^5}}{\sqrt[4]{n}}$

157. $\left(\sqrt[9]{x^2}\right)^{18}$ 158. $\left(\sqrt[8]{x^3}\right)^{24}$ 159. $\sqrt[21]{a^7}$ 160. $\sqrt[24]{b^{12}}$

161. $\sqrt[4]{t^2}$ 162. $\sqrt[16]{s^4}$ 163. $\sqrt[3]{\sqrt{t}}$ 164. $\sqrt{\sqrt{t}}$

165. $\sqrt[5]{\sqrt[5]{b}}$ 166. $\sqrt[10]{\sqrt[3]{t}}$ 167. $\sqrt[3]{\sqrt[8]{x^{12}}}$ 168. $\sqrt[6]{\sqrt[3]{x^{36}}}$

169. $\left(\sqrt[10]{x^3} \cdot \sqrt[5]{x^2}\right)^5$ 170. $\left(\sqrt[4]{x^3} \cdot \sqrt[8]{x}\right)^2$ 171. $\left(\dfrac{\sqrt[14]{a}}{\sqrt[7]{a}}\right)^{21}$ 172. $\left(\dfrac{\sqrt[4]{a}}{\sqrt[8]{a}}\right)^{21}$

173. $\left(\dfrac{\sqrt{m} \cdot \sqrt[3]{m}}{\sqrt[6]{m^5}}\right)^9$ 174. $\left(\dfrac{\sqrt[18]{n^5} \cdot \sqrt[6]{n}}{\sqrt[36]{n^7}}\right)^8$ 175. $\sqrt[3]{\sqrt{a} \cdot \sqrt[5]{a^2}}$ 176. $\sqrt{\sqrt[3]{b^2} \cdot \sqrt[4]{b^3}}$

END OF CHAPTER 6   QUIZ

1. $36^{\frac{1}{2}} =$
   a) 6   b) 18   c) $\dfrac{1}{72}$ d) $1{,}276$ e) 12

2. $(-8)^{\frac{5}{3}} =$
   a) $\dfrac{-40}{3}$ b) $\dfrac{40}{3}$ c) 32 d) -32 e) -10

3. $\left(\dfrac{16}{25}\right)^{\frac{3}{2}} =$
   a) $\dfrac{64}{25}$ b) $\dfrac{64}{125}$ c) $\dfrac{48}{75}$ d) $\dfrac{16}{125}$ e) $\dfrac{4}{5}$

4. $216^{-\frac{2}{3}} =$
   a) -36 b) $\dfrac{1}{36}$ c) $-\dfrac{1}{36}$ d) -144 e) $\dfrac{1}{216\sqrt{216}}$

5. $4^{-\frac{1}{2}} \cdot 27^{\frac{1}{3}} =$
   a) -18 b) $\dfrac{1}{6}$ c) $\dfrac{3}{2}$ d) $108^{-\frac{1}{6}}$ e) $\dfrac{3}{\sqrt[3]{2}}$

6. $\dfrac{100^{-\frac{1}{2}} \cdot 8^{\frac{1}{3}}}{49^{-\frac{3}{2}}} =$
   a) $\dfrac{343}{5}$ b) $\dfrac{343}{20}$ c) $\dfrac{7\sqrt{7}}{5}$ d) $\dfrac{\sqrt[3]{7}}{10}$ e) $\dfrac{5}{343}$

7. If $x \geq 0$ and $y \geq 0$, then $x^{\frac{1}{4}} y^{\frac{3}{4}} =$
   a) $\sqrt[4]{x} + \sqrt[4]{y^3}$ b) $x^4 \sqrt[3]{y^4}$ c) $\left(\sqrt[4]{xy}\right)^3$ d) $\left(\sqrt[3]{xy}\right)^4$ e) $\sqrt[4]{xy^3}$

8. If $a > 0$ and $b > 0$, then $\left(\dfrac{a^2}{20b}\right)^{-\frac{1}{2}} =$
   a) $\dfrac{a}{2\sqrt{5b}}$ b) $\dfrac{2b\sqrt{5}}{a}$ c) $\dfrac{a}{2\sqrt{10b}}$ d) $\dfrac{10\sqrt{b}}{a}$ e) $\dfrac{2\sqrt{5b}}{a}$

9. If $n \neq 0$ and m is any real number, then $m^{\frac{2}{3}} n^{-\frac{1}{5}} =$
   a) $-\sqrt[3]{m^2}\sqrt[5]{n}$ b) $\dfrac{\sqrt[3]{m^2}}{\sqrt[5]{n}}$ c) $\dfrac{\sqrt{m^3}}{\sqrt[5]{n}}$ d) $\dfrac{1}{\sqrt[5]{m^2 n}}$ e) $\dfrac{\sqrt[3]{m^2}}{n^5}$

10. $9^{\frac{1}{4}} \cdot 9^{\frac{5}{8}} =$
    a) 729 b) $9^{\frac{5}{8}}$ c) $81^{\frac{7}{8}}$ d) $9^{\frac{7}{8}}$ e) $9^{\frac{5}{32}}$

11. If $x > 0$, then $\dfrac{x^{\frac{5}{6}}}{x^{\frac{3}{8}}} =$
    a) $x^{\frac{20}{9}}$ b) 1 c) $x^{\frac{11}{24}}$ d) $x^{\frac{29}{24}}$ e) $x^{\frac{5}{12}}$

12. $\left(x^{\frac{16}{5}}\right)^{15} =$
    a) $x^{\frac{91}{5}}$ b) $x^{\frac{16}{75}}$ c) x^{48} d) x^{28} e) $x^{\frac{31}{5}}$

13. If $b > 0$ and a is any real number, then $\left(\dfrac{a^{\frac{6}{7}}}{b^{\frac{1}{4}}}\right)^8 =$

   a) $\dfrac{a^{\frac{48}{7}}}{b^2}$ b) $\dfrac{a^{\frac{48}{7}}}{b^{\frac{1}{4}}}$ c) $\dfrac{a^{\frac{62}{7}}}{b^{\frac{33}{4}}}$ d) $a^8 b^8$ e) $\dfrac{a^{\frac{48}{7}}}{b^{\frac{1}{32}}}$

14. If $x > 0$ and $y > 0$, then $\left(25 x^{-\frac{1}{2}} y^{\frac{3}{2}}\right)^{\frac{1}{2}} =$

   a) $5 \sqrt[4]{xy^3}$ b) $25 \sqrt[4]{\dfrac{y^3}{x}}$ c) $\dfrac{5}{\sqrt[4]{xy^3}}$ d) $5 \sqrt[4]{\dfrac{y^3}{x}}$ e) $5 \sqrt[4]{\dfrac{x}{y^3}}$

15. If $a > 0$, then $\left(\sqrt[3]{\sqrt[4]{a}}\right)^8 =$

   a) $a \sqrt[7]{a}$ b) $\sqrt[3]{a^2}$ c) $\sqrt[7]{a^8}$ d) $\sqrt[8]{a^7}$ e) $a \sqrt{a}$

16. If $x \geq 0$, then $\sqrt{x} \cdot \sqrt[3]{x^2} =$

   a) $\sqrt[6]{x^3}$ b) $\sqrt[5]{x^2}$ c) $\sqrt[7]{x^6}$ d) $\sqrt[3]{x}$ e) $x \sqrt[6]{x}$

17. If $y > 0$, then $\dfrac{\sqrt[10]{y^7}}{\sqrt[15]{y^2}} =$

   a) $\sqrt[30]{y^{17}}$ b) $y \sqrt[17]{y^{13}}$ c) $\sqrt[6]{y^5}$ d) $\dfrac{1}{y}$ e) $\dfrac{1}{\sqrt[30]{y^{17}}}$

18. $\left(a^2 \sqrt[3]{a^2}\right)^{12} =$

   a) a^{30} b) a^{16} c) a^{32} d) $a^{24} \sqrt[3]{a^2}$ e) $a^{24} \sqrt[36]{a^2}$

19. If $x \geq 0$, then $\sqrt[7]{\sqrt[3]{x} \cdot \sqrt[4]{x}} =$

   a) $\sqrt[14]{x}$ b) $\sqrt[49]{x^2}$ c) $\sqrt[12]{x}$ d) $x^4 \sqrt[12]{x}$ e) $\sqrt[12]{x^5}$

20. If $x \geq 0$ and $y \geq 0$, then $\sqrt[24]{x^6 y^8} =$

   a) $\sqrt[4]{xy}$ b) $\sqrt[3]{xy}$ c) $\sqrt[3]{x} \cdot \sqrt[4]{y}$ d) $\sqrt[4]{x} \cdot \sqrt[3]{y}$ e) $\sqrt[12]{xy}$

ANSWERS FOR QUIZ 6   1. a   2. d   3. b   4. b   5. c

                             6. a   7. e   8. e   9. b   10. d

                             11. c   12. c   13. a   14. d   15. b

                             16. e   17. a   18. c   19. c   20. d

SOLUTIONS TO 'TRY THESE' EXAMPLES

Chapter 1, Set 1

1a) 0.75 is a terminating decimal.
1b) 0.625 is a terminating decimal.
1c) $0.\overline{2}$ is a non-terminating, repeating.
1d) 0 is a terminating decimal.

2) a only
3) a, b, c, and e
4) b and e

Chapter 1, Set 2

I) 1) $12 + 8$ 2) 5×2 3) $17 - 2$

4) $\dfrac{x}{4} = 3$ 5) $y + 1 = 8\,(4)$ 6) $7 - x = \dfrac{x}{11}$

II) 1) 15 plus 3 2) 7 minus 4 3) the product of 6 and 8

4) The sum of x and 7 is 19. 5) 2 less than the product of 3 and a is a.

6) y divided by 4 equals the sum of 9 times y and 1.

Chapter 1, Set 3

1) 5 2) -22 3) -15 4) -6
5) -14 6) -16 7) -36 8) 15
9) 19 10) -8 11) 4 12) -16

Chapter 1, Set 4

1) $\dfrac{2}{3}$ 2) $\dfrac{1}{2}$ 3) $\dfrac{7}{9}$ 4) $-\dfrac{2}{7}$

5) $\dfrac{1}{2}$ 6) $-\dfrac{4}{15}$ 7) $-\dfrac{11}{36}$ 8) $-\dfrac{5}{8}$

9) $\dfrac{20}{7}$ 10) $\dfrac{5}{7}$ 11) $-\dfrac{132}{5}$ 12) $\dfrac{3}{7}$

Chapter 1, Set 5

1) 3.241 (both)
2) 8.906 (both)
3) 43.601 rounded off, 43.600 truncated
4) 12.333 rounded off, 12.332 truncated
5) 60.102 rounded off, 60.101 truncated
6) 0.149 (both)

Chapter 1, Set 6

1) -4 2) -6 3) 12 4) 15
5) 16 6) 20 7) 12 8) -75
9) -2 10) -51 11) 0 12) 72

Chapter 1, Set 7

I) 1) Commutative Property   2) Associative Property

    3) Commutative Property   4) Distributive Property

II) The additive inverse of 15 is -15 and the reciprocal of 15 is $\dfrac{1}{15}$.

The additive inverse of $-\dfrac{2}{5}$ is $\dfrac{2}{5}$ and the reciprocal of $-\dfrac{2}{5}$ is $-\dfrac{5}{2}$.

III) False.

IV) 1) $3x + 15$ 2) $-6a - 36$ 3) $ab - 9a$ 4) $-18 + x$

Chapter 1, Set 8

I)

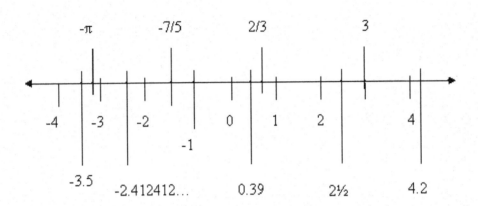

II) 1) $4 < 9$ 2) $-8 > -11$ 3) $\frac{1}{7} < \frac{1}{4}$ 4) $-3.022 > -3.0225$

5) $-1.\overline{5} < 1.\overline{5}$ 6) $\pi > 3.12$ 7) $-1.56 > -\frac{155}{99}$

Chapter 1, Set 9

I) 1) 3   2) 1   3) 20   4) 17

5) $\frac{2}{11}$ 6) $2.852\overline{3}$ 7) -15 8) -14

II) 1) 14   2) 16   3) 21   4) $\frac{29}{12}$

III) 1) x^2 2) $12\,|y|$ 3) $7b^2\,|a|$ 4) $\dfrac{1}{|x|}$ 5) $\dfrac{|t|}{8}$ 6) $\dfrac{a^2 b^2\,|a|}{10}$

Chapter 1, Set 10

I) 1) -16 2) -78 3) $\dfrac{9}{2}$ 4) -10 5) $\dfrac{1}{6}$ 6) -68

II) 1) All real numbers except 1.

2) All real numbers except -5.

3) All real numbers except 9.

Chapter 2, Set 1

I) 1) 3^2 has exponent 2 and base 3. 2) 7^4 has exponent 4 and base 7.

3) $(2.19)^3$ has exponent 3 and base 2.19. 4) 12^4 has exponent 4 and base 12.

5) x^5 has exponent 5 and base x. 6) $(-5y)^3$ has exponent 3 and base $-5y$.

II) 1) 64   2) 27   3) 9   4) -9

5) $\dfrac{4}{25}$ 6) $\dfrac{1}{625}$ 7) $-\dfrac{1}{625}$ 8) $-\dfrac{216}{343}$

9) $-\dfrac{216}{343}$ 10) 122   11) 0.1521   12) -0.000125

Chapter 2, Set 2

I) 1) x^8 2) y^{14} 3) $-14a^{14}$

4) $27x^5y^4$ 5) $-9a^6b^{14}$ 6) $216x^{15}$

II) 1) x^{11} 2) a 3) $6n^7$ 4) $-7x^5y^8$

5) $\dfrac{5a^3b^{17}c^6}{3} = \dfrac{5}{3}a^3b^{17}c^6$ 6) $7^2 = 49$

Chapter 2, Set 3

1) 1   2) 10   3) 1   4) 1

5) 1   6) $-7a^3$ 7) 1   8) -1

Chapter 2, Set 4

1) $\dfrac{1}{9}$ 2) $\dfrac{1}{125}$ 3) $\dfrac{1}{2}$ 4) $\dfrac{1}{121}$

5) $\dfrac{1}{16}$ 6) $-\dfrac{1}{16}$ 7) $\dfrac{1}{x^3}$ 8) $\dfrac{1}{y^8}$

9) $-\dfrac{1}{64}$ 10) $-\dfrac{1}{64}$

Chapter 2, Set 5

1) x^{16} 2) y^{21} 3) a^9 4) b^{-30} 5) 1   6) x^{-36}

Chapter 2, Set 6

1) a^5b^5 2) $9x^2y^2$ 3) $16x^6y^{10}$

4) $81x^{20}y^{20}z^4$ 5) $-\dfrac{343}{64}a^9b^{24}$ 6) $32x^5y^{25}z^{10}$

Chapter 2, Set 7

1) $\dfrac{64}{9}$ 2) $-\dfrac{1}{125}$ 3) $\dfrac{y^{10}}{144}$

4) $\dfrac{64x^{27}}{y^{12}}$ 5) $\dfrac{x^{14}}{9y^2}$ 6) $\dfrac{1,000}{27n^{18}}$

Chapter 2, Set 8

1) $72x^9$ 2) $49x^6$ 3) $-25x^{22}y^{38}$

4) $\dfrac{8x^{24}}{27y^6}$ 5) $\dfrac{9s^9t^{12}}{4}$ 6) $\dfrac{7a^{11}}{125}$

Chapter 2, Set 9

1) 4 2) $\dfrac{64}{27}$ 3) -11

4) 81 5) $\dfrac{1}{288}$ 6) $\dfrac{1}{100}$

7) $\dfrac{81}{4}$ 8) 2 9) $-\dfrac{45}{2}$

Chapter 2, Set 10

1) $\dfrac{100}{x^2}$ 2) $\dfrac{8}{49x^9}$ 3) $\dfrac{13a^6}{b^2}$ 4) $\dfrac{x^6y^{16}}{25}$

5) $\dfrac{a^{18}}{125b^{12}}$ 6) $\dfrac{25x^3y^2}{16}$ 7) $-\dfrac{s^2t^5}{6}$ 8) $\dfrac{x^{10}y^{14}}{36}$

Chapter 2, Set 11

I) 1) 4.993×10^3 2) 5.28901×10^2
3) 1.20026×10^{-1} 4) 1.3890111×10^4
5) 7.7691×10^{-2} 6) 1.0×10^0

II) 1) 680 2) $80,012$
3) 51.6 4) 0.00634
5) 0.75002 6) 0.0001

Chapter 2, Set 12

1) 6.0×10^{10} 2) 4.0×10^{-7}
3) 5.12×10^{32} 4) 1.0×10^{-24}
5) 1.92×10^2 6) 3.0×10^{-10}

Chapter 3, Set 1

1) $y + 13$

2) $11x^2 + 6x + 21$

3) $6x^2 - 4xy + 10y^2$

4) $-4a - 5ab - 2 + a^2$

5) $-13x^2 + 7x - 12$

6) $-t^2 + \dfrac{6}{25}t - \dfrac{13}{6}$

Chapter 3, Set 2

1) $-5x$

2) $-3x^2 + 2x - 1$

3) $8a^2 - 7ab^2$

4) $-x^2 + 3y$

5) $\dfrac{x}{6} - \dfrac{8x^2}{11}$

Chapter 3, Set 3

1) $10x - 9y$

2) $-5a^2 + 9ab - 12b^2$

3) $-2s^2 - 8st - 3t^2$

4) $-x^2 - 20xy + 3$

5) $-14a^2 + a + 10$

6) $n - m$

Chapter 3, Set 4

1) $10a^6$

2) $12x^5y^{10}$

3) $\dfrac{3}{4}x^6y^8$

4) $-12m^7n^6$

Chapter 3, Set 5

1) $3x^2 - 24x$

2) $-15y^4 + 5y^3 - 30y^2$

3) $18a^3 - 12a^2b - 6ab^2$

4) $14p^3q^9 - 21p^4q^9 - 56p^3q^8$

Chapter 3, Set 6

1) $13x^2 + 18x$

2) $2a^3 - 17a^2 - 22a$

3) $20y^3 + 10xy^2 - 60y^2 + 10x^2y - 5x^3 + 55x^2$

4) $-22x^2 - 13x$

5) $18a^2 - 42ab + 5b^2 - ab^2$

6) $-47 + 57x + 25y$

Chapter 3, Set 7

1) $x^2 - 6x - 16$

2) $16a^2 - 32a + 15$

3) $3y^3 - 2y^2 - 16y$

4) $33 - 17x + 2x^2$

5) $4y^2 - 49$

6) $4a^2 + 48a + 144$

Chapter 3, Set 8

1) $x^3 + 6x^2 + 7x - 2$

2) $2y^3 - 11y^2 + 11y - 3$

3) $10a^3 - 3a^2b - 16ab^2 - 3b^3$

4) $x^3 + 5x^2 - 25x - 125$

5) $8t^3 - 36t^2 + 54t - 27$

6) $m^4 - 4m^3 + 2m^2 + 4m + 1$

Chapter 3, Set 9

1) $7x^3$

2) $-6ab^2$

3) $8x^9 y^{14}$

4) $\dfrac{-5t^4}{s^3}$

5) $\dfrac{7}{mn^2}$

6) $\dfrac{-6}{z^6}$

Chapter 3, Set 10

1) $3x + 5$

2) $5a^2 - 3a$

3) $5x^3 y^5 + 2y^8 - x^4 y$

4) $-11m^6 + 6 - \dfrac{7}{4m}$

5) $\dfrac{2}{y} - \dfrac{7}{2}y + \dfrac{y^2}{4}$

Chapter 3, Set 11

1) $y - 5$ R 11

2) $x + 2$ R 7

3) $x^2 + 3x - 13$ R 42

4) $3x + 21$ R 149

5) $a^2 - 3a + 12$ R $-36a + 11$

Chapter 3, Set 12

1) $4x^3 (4x + 5)$

2) $a (12a^2 - 11)$

3) $y (y^4 - 6y + 2)$

4) $2xy^3 (8x^3 - 5y^3)$

5) $7st^2 (3t^6 - s^2t^2 + 2s)$

6) $xy (x + y - 1)$

7) $(x + 5) (x - 4)$

8) $(x - 3) (x + 1)$

Chapter 3, Set 13

1) $(a + 2) (a - 2)$

2) $(b + 5) (b - 5)$

3) $(12x + 1) (12x - 1)$

4) $(5 + 13y) (5 - 13y)$

5) $(s + 6t) (s - 6t)$

6) $\left(9x + \frac{10}{11}y\right) \left(9x - \frac{10}{11}y\right)$

7) prime

8) prime

Chapter 3, Set 14

1) $(x - 1) (x^2 + x + 1)$

2) $(a + 2) (a^2 - 2a + 4)$

3) $(4y - 1) (16y^2 + 4y + 1)$

4) $(3x + y) (9x^2 - 3xy + y^2)$

5) $(6 + 5t) (36 - 30t + 25t^2)$

6) $\left(x - \dfrac{1}{2}\right) \left(x^2 + \dfrac{1}{2}x + \dfrac{1}{4}\right)$

162

Chapter 3, Set 15

1) $6(x+2)(x-2)$

2) $5y(y+4)(y-4)$

3) $a^2(y-3)(y^2+3y+9)$

4) $9s^2t(t-2)(t^2+2t+4)$

5) $(x^2+16)(x+4)(x-4)$

6) $(y+1)(y^2-y+1)(y-1)(y^2+y+1)$

Chapter 3, Set 16

1) $(x+4)(x+2)$

2) $(k+7)^2$

3) $(y-5)(y-4)$

4) prime

5) prime

6) $(m+12)^2$

7) $(y+6)(y-5)$

8) $(n+14)(n-3)$

9) $(x-11)^2$

Chapter 3, Set 17

1) $(3x+2)(x+4)$

2) $(4y-3)^2$

3) $(5a-1)(4a-3)$

4) $(3t-8)(3t-2)$

5) $(6x+5)(2x-1)$

6) $(10y-9)^2$

Chapter 3, Set 18

1) $(t^2+2)(t+3)$

2) $(x^3+7)(x-3)$

3) $(2y^2-1)(y-5)$

4) $(9a^3+2)(2a+3)$

5) $(2p^3+5)(4p^2-3)$

6) $(x+7+10y)(x+7-10y)$

Chapter 3, Set 19

1) $3x(x+4)(x+1)$

2) $2(2y-7)(2y+1)$

3) $-3x^3(8x+5)(x-2)$

4) $(x^2-2)(x+5)(x-5)$

5) $7y^3(y-1)(y^2+y+1)(y+2)$

6) $(4a+5b)(8a+3b)$

Chapter 4, Set 1

1) $\dfrac{4(2x-1)}{2x+3}$

2) $\dfrac{y-5}{9y+1}$

3) $\dfrac{2}{x+2}$

4) $\dfrac{1}{3x+2}$

5) $\dfrac{13}{7x-12}$

6) $-\dfrac{1}{y+6}$

Chapter 4, Set 2

1) 120

2) 196

3) $75x^5y^3$

4) $10x^2(2x-1)(4x-1)$

5) $(x+3)(x-3)(x-5)$

6) $120x^4(x+1)^3(x-2)(x-3)^3$

Chapter 4, Set 3

1) $\dfrac{10y + 21}{14y}$

2) $\dfrac{1}{4t}$

3) $\dfrac{2x - 7}{(x + 2)(x - 9)}$

4) $\dfrac{-a + 19}{a(a - 3)(a + 5)}$

5) $\dfrac{2(y + 3)(y - 2)}{y(y + 4)(y - 4)}$

6) $\dfrac{5x^2 + 44x + 8}{(x + 2)(x + 8)^2}$

7) $\dfrac{5u^2 + 28u + 9}{u + 7}$

Chapter 5, Set 1

1) $2\sqrt{6}$

2) $3\sqrt{5}$

3) $\sqrt{110}$

4) $7\sqrt{2}$

5) $\sqrt{29}$

Chapter 5, Set 2

1) x^2

2) $y^6\sqrt{y}$

3) $t\sqrt{t}$

4) x^{14}

5) $p^{10}\sqrt{p}$

Chapter 5, Set 3

1) $2x^2y\sqrt{3x}$

2) $3x^2y^3\sqrt{6y}$

3) $10p^3q^4\sqrt{q}$

4) $-7a^2c^5\sqrt{2bc}$

5) $y^6\sqrt{15x}$

Chapter 5, Set 4

1) $11xy^3\sqrt{x}$

2) $2x\sqrt{2}$

3) $6a^6\sqrt{a}$

Chapter 5, Set 5

1) $11\sqrt{13}$

2) $\dfrac{\sqrt{3}}{2}$

3) $13\sqrt{6}$

4) $12 - \sqrt{2}$

5) $-8\sqrt{13} + 8$

6) $\dfrac{11\sqrt{3}}{5}$

Chapter 5, Set 6

1) $12\sqrt{15}$

2) $-26\sqrt{6} - 48$

3) 120

4) $4 + 4y\sqrt{10} + 10y^2$

Chapter 5, Set 7

1) $\dfrac{6\sqrt{5}}{35}$

2) $\sqrt{6}$

3) $13 - \sqrt{78}$

4) $\dfrac{7 + 3\sqrt{6}}{5}$

Chapter 5, Set 8

1) $\dfrac{6}{\sqrt{15}}$

2) $\dfrac{7}{4\sqrt{14}}$

3) $\dfrac{2}{\sqrt{34} + \sqrt{14}}$

4) $-\dfrac{1}{7 - 3\sqrt{6}}$

Chapter 5, Set 9

1) $2\sqrt[3]{7}$ 　　　 2) $-4x^2y^6\sqrt[3]{2y^2}$ 　　　 3) $10 + 7\sqrt[3]{5}$ 　　　 4) $2\sqrt[3]{2} - 2\sqrt[3]{4} + 1$

Chapter 6, Set 1

I) 1) 6 　　 2) 32 　　 3) $\dfrac{1}{8}$ 　　 4) $\dfrac{729}{10}$ 　　 5) $\dfrac{7}{4}$

II) 1) $\sqrt[3]{x}$ 　　 2) $\dfrac{1}{\sqrt[5]{y^3}}$ 　　 3) $3\sqrt[3]{x^2}$ 　　 4) $\sqrt[3]{9x^2}$ 　　 5) $\dfrac{\sqrt[5]{81a^2} \cdot \sqrt[3]{b}}{2}$

III) 1) $t^{\frac{1}{2}}$ 　　 2) $\left(\dfrac{9}{y}\right)^{\frac{1}{3}}$ 　　 3) $\dfrac{9^{\frac{1}{3}}}{y}$ 　　 4) $x(2x+3)^{\frac{1}{2}}$ 　　 5) $[x(2x+3)]^{\frac{1}{2}}$

Chapter 6, Set 2

I) 1) $x^{\frac{11}{12}}$ 　　 2) $x^{-\frac{5}{8}}$ 　　 3) $y^{\frac{1}{3}}$ 　　 4) $m^{-12}n^{\frac{1}{2}}$ 　　 5) $\dfrac{a^{-\frac{7}{12}}}{b^{\frac{1}{2}}}$

II) 1) $\sqrt[4]{t^3}$ 　　 2) $\sqrt[10]{y}$ 　　 3) $\sqrt[8]{a^3}$ 　　 4) $\sqrt[3]{a}$ 　　 5) $x^6\sqrt{x}$

SOLUTIONS TO ODD NUMBERED EXERCISES

Chapter 1 Exercises

1. 4 is a natural number, an integer, and a rational number.
3. +12 is a natural number, an integer, and a rational number.
5. $-4.2\overline{36}$ is a rational number.
7. 9.5523 is a rational number.
9. 18.070770777... is an irrational number.
11. 16.0 is a natural number, an integer, and a rational number.

13. $\dfrac{3}{4} = 0.75$

$$
\begin{array}{r}
0.75 \\
4\overline{)\,3.00} \\
-\,28 \\
\hline
20 \\
-\,20 \\
\hline
0
\end{array}
$$

15. $\dfrac{5}{2} = 2.5$

$$
\begin{array}{r}
2.5 \\
2\overline{)\,5.0} \\
-4 \\
\hline
10 \\
-\,10 \\
\hline
0
\end{array}
$$

17. $\dfrac{7}{8} = 0.875$

$$
\begin{array}{r}
0.875 \\
8\overline{)\,7.000} \\
-\,64 \\
\hline
60 \\
-\,56 \\
\hline
40 \\
-\,40 \\
\hline
0
\end{array}
$$

19. $-\dfrac{7}{10} = -0.7$

$$
\begin{array}{r}
0.7 \\
10\overline{)\,7.0} \\
-70 \\
\hline
0
\end{array}
$$

21. $\dfrac{17}{3} = 5.\overline{6}$

```
         5.66...
    3) 17.00...
      −15
       2 0
       −1 8
         20
        −18
          2
          ⋮
```

23. $-\dfrac{2}{9} = -0.\overline{2}$

```
         0.22...
    9)  2.00...
       − 18
         20
        − 18
          2
          ⋮
```

25. $\dfrac{16}{5} = 3.2$

```
         3.2
    5) 16.00
      −15
       10
      − 10
        0
```

27. $\dfrac{16}{99} = 0.\overline{16}$

```
          0.1616...
    99) 16.000...
       − 9 9
        6 10
       − 5 94
         1 60
       −    99
          610
       −   594
           16
           ⋮
```

167

29. $\dfrac{100}{999} = 0.\overline{100}$

$$
\begin{array}{r}
0.100100... \\
999\overline{)\,100.000000...} \\
-\underline{99\ 9} \\
1000 \\
-\underline{999} \\
1000 \\
-\underline{999} \\
1 \\
\vdots
\end{array}
$$

31. $\dfrac{209}{990} = 0.2\overline{1}$

$$
\begin{array}{r}
0.211... \\
990\overline{)\,209.000...} \\
-\underline{1980} \\
1100 \\
-\underline{990} \\
1100 \\
-\underline{990} \\
110 \\
\vdots
\end{array}
$$

33. $-\dfrac{12}{25} = -0.48$

$$
\begin{array}{r}
0.48 \\
25\overline{)\,12.00} \\
-\underline{100} \\
200 \\
-\underline{200} \\
0
\end{array}
$$

35. $\dfrac{35}{6} = 5.8\overline{3}$

$$
\begin{array}{r}
5.833... \\
6\overline{)\,35.0000...} \\
-\underline{30} \\
5\ 0 \\
-\underline{4\ 8} \\
20 \\
-\underline{18} \\
20 \\
-\underline{18} \\
2 \\
\vdots
\end{array}
$$

168

37. $\dfrac{24}{6} = 4$ 39. $\dfrac{0}{6} = 0$ 41. $\dfrac{87}{87} = 1$

43. $9 + 3$ 45. $12 - 3$ 47. 9×5

49. $18 \div 3$ 51. $x + 10 = 12$ 53. $25 - 4 = y$

55. $n\,(3) = 14 \div 2$ 57. $11 + x = 2x - 28$ 59. The sum of 8 and 4 is 12.

61. 23 minus 6 is 17.   63. The product of 2 and 7 is 14.   65. 36 divided by 9 equals 4.

67. x plus 5 is 12.   69. a subtracted from 14 is 2.   71. 6 added to 5 times y is 12.

73. 72 divided by 9 is n minus 6.   75. Addition   77. Subtraction

79. Multiplication   81. Division   83. Division

85. Addition   87. Subtraction   89. Division

91. Multiplication   93. $11 + (+4) = 15$ 95. $(-7) + (-11) = -18$

97. $(-22) + (+5) = -17$ 99. $(+15) + (-3) = 12$ 101. $26 + (-13) = 13$

103. $-30 + 9 = -21$ 105. $-7 + 13 = 6$ 107. $-17 - 1 = (-17) + (-1) = -18$

109. $-19 - 5 = (-19) + (-5) = -24$ 111. $10 - 12 = 10 + (-12) = -2$ 113. $31 + (-31) = 0$

115. $-13 + 13 = 0$ 117. $(-2)(+7) = -14$ 119. $(+4)(-11) = -44$

121. $(7)(-10) = -70$ 123. $(-2)(16) = -32$ 125. $(-8)(-4) = 32$

127. $(-18)(-1) = 18$ 129. $(24) \div (-6) = -4$ 131. $(-49) \div 7 = -7$

133. $36 \div (-18) = -2$ 135. $(-90) \div (-9) = 10$ 137. $(-56) \div (-8) = 7$

139. $\dfrac{-42}{+2} = -21$ 141. $\dfrac{-88}{+11} = -8$ 143. $\dfrac{-52}{4} = -13$

145. $\dfrac{-100}{-10} = 10$ 147. $\dfrac{-121}{-11} = 11$ 149. $\dfrac{6}{11} + \dfrac{2}{11} = \dfrac{8}{11}$

151. $\dfrac{14}{5} - \dfrac{11}{5} = \dfrac{3}{5}$ 153. $\dfrac{5}{16} + \dfrac{3}{16} = \dfrac{8}{16} = \dfrac{1}{2}$ 155. $\dfrac{9}{15} - \dfrac{4}{15} = \dfrac{5}{15} = \dfrac{1}{3}$

157. $\dfrac{1}{5} + \dfrac{1}{10} = \dfrac{1\,(2)}{5\,(2)} + \dfrac{1}{10} = \dfrac{2}{10} + \dfrac{1}{10} = \dfrac{3}{10}$ 159. $\dfrac{1}{21} + \dfrac{1}{7} = \dfrac{1}{21} + \dfrac{1\,(3)}{7\,(3)} = \dfrac{1}{21} + \dfrac{3}{21} = \dfrac{4}{21}$

161. $\dfrac{1}{6} - \dfrac{1}{18} = \dfrac{1\,(3)}{6\,(3)} - \dfrac{1}{18} = \dfrac{3}{18} - \dfrac{1}{18} = \dfrac{2}{18} = \dfrac{1}{9}$ 163. $\dfrac{1}{7} - \dfrac{1}{14} = \dfrac{1\,(2)}{7\,(2)} - \dfrac{1}{14} = \dfrac{2}{14} - \dfrac{1}{14} = \dfrac{1}{14}$

165. $\dfrac{5}{7} + \dfrac{1}{3} = \dfrac{5\,(3)}{7\,(3)} + \dfrac{1\,(7)}{3\,(7)} = \dfrac{15}{21} + \dfrac{7}{21} = \dfrac{22}{21}$ 167. $\dfrac{7}{10} + \dfrac{5}{8} = \dfrac{7\,(4)}{10\,(4)} + \dfrac{5\,(5)}{8\,(5)} = \dfrac{28}{40} + \dfrac{25}{40} = \dfrac{53}{40}$

169. $\dfrac{9}{13} - \dfrac{1}{2} = \dfrac{9\,(2)}{13\,(2)} - \dfrac{1\,(13)}{2\,(13)} = \dfrac{18}{26} - \dfrac{13}{26} = \dfrac{5}{26}$ 171. $\dfrac{8}{9} - \dfrac{5}{6} = \dfrac{8\,(2)}{9\,(2)} - \dfrac{5\,(3)}{6\,(3)} = \dfrac{16}{18} - \dfrac{15}{18} = \dfrac{1}{18}$

173. $\left(-\dfrac{3}{7}\right) + \dfrac{2}{7} = -\dfrac{1}{7}$

175. $\dfrac{8}{15} + \left(-\dfrac{1}{15}\right) = \dfrac{7}{15}$

177. $\left(-\dfrac{2}{9}\right) + \left(-\dfrac{7}{9}\right) = \dfrac{-9}{9} = -1$

179. $\left(-\dfrac{1}{5}\right) + \left(-\dfrac{7}{20}\right) = \dfrac{-1(4)}{5(4)} + \left(\dfrac{-7}{20}\right) = \dfrac{-4}{20} + \left(\dfrac{-7}{20}\right) = \dfrac{-11}{20} = -\dfrac{11}{20}$

181. $-\dfrac{1}{12} - \dfrac{1}{12} = \dfrac{-1}{12} + \left(\dfrac{-1}{12}\right) = \dfrac{-\overset{1}{\cancel{2}}}{\underset{6}{\cancel{12}}} = -\dfrac{1}{6}$

183. $-\dfrac{2}{3} - \dfrac{5}{24} = \dfrac{-2(8)}{3(8)} + \left(\dfrac{-5}{24}\right) = \dfrac{-16}{24} + \left(\dfrac{-5}{24}\right) = -\dfrac{\overset{7}{\cancel{21}}}{\underset{8}{\cancel{24}}} = -\dfrac{7}{8}$

185. $-\dfrac{7}{12} - \dfrac{5}{16} = \dfrac{-7(4)}{12(4)} - \dfrac{5(3)}{16(3)} = \dfrac{-28}{48} + \left(\dfrac{-15}{48}\right) = \dfrac{-43}{48} = -\dfrac{43}{48}$

187. $-\dfrac{9}{10} + \dfrac{9}{10} = \dfrac{0}{10} = 0$

189. $\left(\dfrac{1}{5}\right)\left(\dfrac{3}{5}\right) = \dfrac{3}{25}$

191. $\left(\dfrac{8}{9}\right)\left(\dfrac{4}{5}\right) = \dfrac{32}{45}$

193. $\left(\dfrac{\overset{2}{\cancel{6}}}{\underset{1}{\cancel{11}}}\right)\left(\dfrac{\overset{2}{\cancel{22}}}{\underset{1}{\cancel{3}}}\right) = \dfrac{4}{1} = 4$

195. $\left(\dfrac{\overset{1}{\cancel{7}}}{\underset{4}{\cancel{12}}}\right)\left(\dfrac{\overset{3}{\cancel{9}}}{\underset{2}{\cancel{14}}}\right) = \dfrac{3}{8}$

197. $\left(-\dfrac{1}{2}\right)\left(\dfrac{1}{3}\right) = -\dfrac{1}{6}$

199. $\left(\dfrac{6}{7}\right)\left(-\dfrac{8}{5}\right) = -\dfrac{48}{35}$

201. $\left(-\dfrac{13}{\underset{3}{\cancel{12}}}\right)\left(\dfrac{\overset{2}{\cancel{8}}}{5}\right) = -\dfrac{26}{15}$

203. $\left(\dfrac{1}{\underset{8}{\cancel{16}}}\right)\left(-\dfrac{\overset{5}{\cancel{10}}}{11}\right) = -\dfrac{5}{88}$

205. $(24)\left(\dfrac{7}{8}\right) = \left(\dfrac{\overset{3}{\cancel{24}}}{1}\right)\left(\dfrac{7}{\underset{1}{\cancel{8}}}\right) = 21$

207. $(-10)\left(\dfrac{7}{12}\right) = \left(\dfrac{-\overset{5}{\cancel{10}}}{1}\right)\left(\dfrac{7}{\underset{6}{\cancel{12}}}\right) = -\dfrac{35}{6}$

209. $\left(-\dfrac{\overset{}{\cancel{10}}}{\underset{3}{\cancel{21}}}\right)\left(-\dfrac{\overset{1}{\cancel{7}}}{\underset{1}{\cancel{10}}}\right) = \dfrac{1}{3}$

211. $\left(-\dfrac{9}{16}\right)(-12) = \left(-\dfrac{9}{\underset{4}{\cancel{16}}}\right)\left(\dfrac{-\overset{3}{\cancel{12}}}{1}\right) = \dfrac{27}{4}$

213. $\left(-\dfrac{\overset{1}{\cancel{13}}}{\underset{4}{\cancel{12}}}\right)\left(-\dfrac{\overset{9}{\cancel{27}}}{\underset{2}{\cancel{26}}}\right) = \dfrac{9}{8}$

215. $\dfrac{2}{3} \div \dfrac{1}{3} = \dfrac{2}{\underset{1}{\cancel{3}}} \times \dfrac{\overset{1}{\cancel{3}}}{1} = \dfrac{2}{1} = 2$

217. $\dfrac{2}{7} \div \dfrac{4}{5} = \dfrac{\overset{1}{\cancel{2}}}{7} \times \dfrac{5}{\underset{2}{\cancel{4}}} = \dfrac{5}{14}$

219. $\dfrac{9}{10} \div \dfrac{3}{4} = \dfrac{\overset{3}{\cancel{9}}}{\underset{5}{\cancel{10}}} \times \dfrac{\overset{2}{\cancel{4}}}{\underset{1}{\cancel{3}}} = \dfrac{6}{5}$

221. $\dfrac{1}{4} \div 3 = \dfrac{1}{4} \div \dfrac{3}{1} = \dfrac{1}{4} \times \dfrac{1}{3} = \dfrac{1}{12}$

223. $6 \div \dfrac{3}{7} = \dfrac{6}{1} \div \dfrac{3}{7} = \dfrac{\overset{2}{\cancel{6}}}{1} \times \dfrac{7}{\underset{1}{\cancel{3}}} = 14$

225. $\left(-\dfrac{1}{22}\right) \div \dfrac{4}{11} = \left(-\dfrac{1}{\underset{2}{\cancel{22}}}\right) \times \dfrac{\overset{1}{\cancel{11}}}{4} = -\dfrac{1}{8}$

227. $\left(-\dfrac{1}{2}\right) \div \dfrac{1}{2} = \left(-\dfrac{1}{2}\right) \times \dfrac{2}{1} = -1$

229. $\dfrac{2}{5} \div \left(-\dfrac{10}{9}\right) = \dfrac{\overset{1}{\cancel{2}}}{5} \times \left(-\dfrac{9}{\underset{5}{\cancel{10}}}\right) = -\dfrac{9}{25}$

231. $\dfrac{7}{10} \div (-5) = \dfrac{7}{10} \div \left(\dfrac{-5}{1}\right) = \dfrac{7}{10} \times \left(\dfrac{1}{-5}\right) = -\dfrac{7}{50}$

233. $\left(-\dfrac{9}{20}\right) \div \left(-\dfrac{1}{20}\right) = \left(-\dfrac{9}{\cancel{20}}\right) \times \left(-\dfrac{\overset{1}{\cancel{20}}}{1}\right) = 9$ 235. $\left(-\dfrac{3}{8}\right) \div \left(-\dfrac{1}{12}\right) = \left(-\dfrac{3}{\underset{2}{\cancel{8}}}\right) \times \left(-\dfrac{\overset{3}{\cancel{12}}}{1}\right) = \dfrac{9}{2}$

237. $(-2) \div \left(-\dfrac{1}{2}\right) = (-2) \times \left(-\dfrac{2}{1}\right) = 4$

239. $\left(-\dfrac{5}{14}\right) \div (-3) = \left(-\dfrac{5}{14}\right) \div \left(\dfrac{-3}{1}\right) = \left(-\dfrac{5}{14}\right) \times \left(\dfrac{1}{-3}\right) = \dfrac{5}{42}$

241: $\left(-\dfrac{7}{16}\right) \div (-1) = \left(-\dfrac{7}{16}\right) \times (-1) = \dfrac{7}{16}$ 243. $1 \div \left(-\dfrac{2}{5}\right) = 1 \times \left(-\dfrac{5}{2}\right) = -\dfrac{5}{2}$

245. $0 \div \left(-\dfrac{5}{22}\right) = 0$ 247. $\underbrace{7(3)}+11 = 21+11 = 32$ 249. $\underbrace{7(-5)}+26 = -35+26 = -9$

251. $\underbrace{4(-4)}-4 = -16-4 = -20$ 253. $5 - \underbrace{6 \times 3} = 5-18 = -13$ 255. $8\underbrace{(6-3)} = 8(3) = 24$

257. $\underbrace{(3+11)} \times 2 = (14) \times 2 = 28$ 259. $\underbrace{(5-11)} \times (-5) = (-6) \times (-5) = 30$

261. $(-9) + \underbrace{11 \div 11} = (-9)+1 = -8$ 263. $-5 - \underbrace{24 \div 6} = -5-4 = -9$

265. $\underbrace{(-3-24)} \div 3 = (-27) \div 3 = -9$ 267. $\underbrace{6+2}-12-5 = \underbrace{8-12}-5 = -4-5 = -9$

269. $\underbrace{12 \times 4} \div 2 \times 3 = \underbrace{48 \div 2} \times 3 = 24 \times 3 = 72$ 271. $\underbrace{(6+2)} - \underbrace{(12-5)} = 8-7 = 1$

273. $\underbrace{(28 \div 2)} \times \underbrace{(14 \div 7)} = 14 \times 2 = 28$ 275. $\underbrace{7^2}-6 = 49-6 = 43$

277. $(5-8)^2 = (-3)^2 = 9$ 279. $14 - \underbrace{18 \div 3}+\underbrace{5 \times 2} = 14-\underbrace{6}+10 = 8+10 = 18$

281. $\underbrace{(12-18)} \div 3 + \underbrace{6 \times 2} = \underbrace{(-6) \div 3}+12 = -2+12 = 10$

283. $\underbrace{(13-7)^2}\underbrace{(4-5)} = \underbrace{(6)^2}(-1) = 36\,(-1) = -36$

285. $\underbrace{6^2} \div (-18) - 9 = \underbrace{36 \div (-18)}-9 = -2-9 = -11$

287. $\dfrac{1+2\overbrace{(4-15)}}{\underbrace{2^2}+3} = \dfrac{1+\overbrace{2(-11)}}{\underbrace{4+3}} = \dfrac{1+(-22)}{7} = \dfrac{-21}{7} = -3$

289. $9 - 4\left\{1 + 2\underbrace{(6 \div 3)}\right\} = 9 - 4\left\{1 + \underbrace{2\,(2)}\right\} = 9 - 4\underbrace{\{1+4\}} = 9 - \underbrace{4\{5\}} = 9-20 = -11$

291. $\underbrace{4 \cdot 9}+5\underbrace{(2)^2} = 36 + \underbrace{5\,(4)} = 36+20 = 56$

293. $(-12)\left(-\dfrac{3}{2}\right)\left(\dfrac{1}{4}\right) = \left(\dfrac{-\overset{3}{\cancel{12}}}{1}\right)\left(-\dfrac{3}{2}\right)\left(\dfrac{1}{\underset{1}{\cancel{4}}}\right) = \dfrac{9}{2}$

171

295. $5 + 3\left(-\dfrac{1}{12}\right) = 5 + \dfrac{3}{1}\left(-\dfrac{1}{12}\right) = 5 + \left(-\dfrac{\overset{1}{\cancel{3}}}{\underset{4}{\cancel{12}}}\right) = \dfrac{5}{1} + \left(-\dfrac{1}{4}\right) = \dfrac{20}{4} + \left(-\dfrac{1}{4}\right) = \dfrac{19}{4}$

297. $(5+3)\left(-\dfrac{1}{12}\right) = (8)\left(-\dfrac{1}{12}\right) = \left(\dfrac{\overset{2}{\cancel{8}}}{1}\right)\left(-\dfrac{1}{\underset{3}{\cancel{12}}}\right) = -\dfrac{2}{3}$

299. $\dfrac{4}{5} - \left(\dfrac{1}{30} - \dfrac{2}{3}\right) = \dfrac{4}{5} - \left(\dfrac{1}{30} - \dfrac{2(10)}{3(10)}\right) = \dfrac{4}{5} - \left(\dfrac{1}{30} - \dfrac{20}{30}\right) = \dfrac{4}{5} - \left(-\dfrac{19}{30}\right)$

$\qquad = \dfrac{4}{5} + \dfrac{19}{30} = \dfrac{4(6)}{5(6)} + \dfrac{19}{30} = \dfrac{24}{30} + \dfrac{19}{30} = \dfrac{43}{30}$

301. $\dfrac{4}{5} - \dfrac{1}{30} - \dfrac{2}{3} = \dfrac{4(6)}{5(6)} - \dfrac{1}{30} - \dfrac{2(10)}{3(10)} = \dfrac{24}{30} - \dfrac{1}{30} - \dfrac{20}{30} = \dfrac{23}{30} - \dfrac{20}{30} = \dfrac{3}{30} = \dfrac{1}{10}$

303. $\dfrac{1}{4} \times \left(4 - \dfrac{8}{9}\right) = \dfrac{1}{4} \times \left(\dfrac{4}{1} - \dfrac{8}{9}\right) = \dfrac{1}{4} \times \left(\dfrac{4(9)}{1(9)} - \dfrac{8}{9}\right) = \dfrac{1}{4} \times \left(\dfrac{36}{9} - \dfrac{8}{9}\right) = \dfrac{1}{\underset{1}{\cancel{4}}} \times \left(\dfrac{\overset{7}{\cancel{28}}}{9}\right) = \dfrac{7}{9}$

305. $\left(\dfrac{1}{4} \times 4\right) - \dfrac{8}{9} = \left(\dfrac{1}{4} \times \dfrac{4}{1}\right) - \dfrac{8}{9} = 1 - \dfrac{8}{9} = \dfrac{9}{9} - \dfrac{8}{9} = \dfrac{1}{9}$

307. $\dfrac{2}{5} + \dfrac{2}{5} - \dfrac{2}{5} \times \dfrac{2}{5} = \dfrac{2}{5} + \dfrac{2}{5} - \dfrac{4}{25} = \dfrac{4}{5} - \dfrac{4}{25} = \dfrac{4(5)}{5(5)} - \dfrac{4}{25} = \dfrac{20}{25} - \dfrac{4}{25} = \dfrac{16}{25}$

309. $\dfrac{2}{5} + \left(\dfrac{2}{5} - \dfrac{2}{5}\right) \times \dfrac{2}{5} = \dfrac{2}{5} + (0) \times \dfrac{2}{5} = \dfrac{2}{5} + 0 = \dfrac{2}{5}$

311. 0.984 : rounded off **and** truncated to two decimals is 0.98.

313. 8.9342 : rounded off **and** truncated to two decimals is 8.93.

315. 10.4162 : rounded off to two decimals is 10.42 and truncated to two decimals is 10.41.

317. 78.98502 : rounded off to two decimals is 78.99 and truncated to two decimals is 78.98.

319. 68.79933 : rounded off to two decimals is 68.80 and truncated to two decimals is 68.79.

321. 0.0007 : rounded off **and** truncated to two decimals is 0.00.

323. 29.9982 : rounded off to two decimals is 30.00 and truncated to two decimals is 29.99.

325. 96.3154 : rounded off to two decimals is 96.32 and truncated to two decimals is 96.31.

327. $8 + y = y + \underline{8}$ is the Commutative Property (for addition).

329. $2(x + 1) = 2(\underline{x}) + 2(1)$ is the Distributive Property.

331. $9 + (3 + \underline{7}) = (9 + 3) + 7$ is the Associative Property (for addition).

333. $(\underline{4})[(-3)(0)] = [(4)(-3)](0)$ is the Associative Property (for multiplication).

335. $(t - \underline{1})(12) = t(12) - 1(12)$ is the Distributive Property.

337. $\underline{3} + (-3) = 0$ is the Additive Inverse Property.

339. $\left(\dfrac{9}{7}\right)\left(\dfrac{7}{9}\right) = 1$ is the Multiplicative Inverse (or Reciprocal) Property.

341. $a + \underline{0} = a$ is the Additive Identity Property.

343. $(y)\,(\underline{18}) = (18)\,(y)$ is the Commutative Property (for multiplication).

345. $14 > 3$

347. $\dfrac{4}{5} > \dfrac{1}{10}$

349. $-7 < 16$

351. $-16 > -30$

353. $-8 < -3$

355. $\dfrac{1}{9} > 0.11$

357. $0.623 < \dfrac{62}{99}$

359. $0.435 > \dfrac{43}{99}$

361. $-3.226 > -3.2262$

363. $-\dfrac{2}{9} < -0.0\overline{2}$

365. $-\pi > -3.16$

367. $|12| = 12$

369. $|-23| = 23$

371. $|-14| = 14$

373. $|+17| = 17$

375. $\left|+\dfrac{10}{13}\right| = \dfrac{10}{13}$

377. $|-29.5893| = 29.5893$

379. $|24 - 16| = |8| = 8$

381. $|11 - 32| = |-21| = 21$

383. $|-22 - 4| = |-26| = 26$

385. $|0 + 5 - 27| = |-22| = 22$

387. $\underbrace{|-14|} - \underbrace{|+6|} = 14 - 6 = 8$

389. $\underbrace{|+13|} + \underbrace{|-19|} = 13 + 19 = 32$

391. $\left|\dfrac{1}{4} + \left(-\dfrac{3}{5}\right)\right| = \left|\dfrac{1\,(5)}{4\,(5)} - \dfrac{3\,(4)}{5\,(4)}\right| = \left|\dfrac{5}{20} - \dfrac{12}{20}\right| = \left|-\dfrac{7}{20}\right| = \dfrac{7}{20}$

393. $\underbrace{\left|\dfrac{1}{4}\right|} + \underbrace{\left|-\dfrac{3}{5}\right|} = \dfrac{1}{4} + \dfrac{3}{5} = \dfrac{1\,(5)}{4\,(5)} + \dfrac{3\,(4)}{5\,(4)} = \dfrac{5}{20} + \dfrac{12}{20} = \dfrac{17}{20}$

395. The distance between $\underbrace{12}_{a}$ and $\underbrace{3}_{b}$ is $|b - a| = |3 - 12| = |-9| = 9$.

397. The distance between $\underbrace{-7}_{a}$ and $\underbrace{0}_{b}$ is $|b - a| = |0 - (-7)| = |7| = 7$.

399. The distance between $\underbrace{-3}_{a}$ and $\underbrace{20}_{b}$ is $|b - a| = |20 - (-3)| = |23| = 23$.

401. The distance between $\underbrace{-\dfrac{5}{6}}_{a}$ and $\underbrace{\dfrac{3}{8}}_{b}$ is $|b - a| = \left|\dfrac{3}{8} - \left(-\dfrac{5}{6}\right)\right| = \left|\dfrac{3\,(3)}{8\,(3)} + \dfrac{5\,(4)}{6\,(4)}\right|$

$$= \left|\dfrac{9}{24} + \dfrac{20}{24}\right| = \left|\dfrac{29}{24}\right| = \dfrac{29}{24}.$$

403. The distance between $\underbrace{-18}_{a}$ and $\underbrace{-27}_{b}$ is $|b - a| = |-27 - (-18)| = |-27 + 18| = |-9| = 9$.

405. The distance between $\underbrace{-\dfrac{3}{16}}_{a}$ and $\underbrace{-\dfrac{7}{6}}_{b}$ is $|b - a| = \left|-\dfrac{7}{6} - \left(-\dfrac{3}{16}\right)\right| = \left|-\dfrac{7\,(8)}{6\,(8)} + \dfrac{3\,(3)}{16\,(3)}\right|$

$$= \left|-\dfrac{56}{48} + \dfrac{9}{48}\right| = \left|\dfrac{-47}{48}\right| = \dfrac{47}{48}.$$

407. $|11y| = |11| \cdot |y| = 11\,|y|$ 409. $|-2b| = |-2| \cdot |b| = 2\,|b|$ 411. $|5y^2| = |5| \cdot |y^2| = 5y^2$

413. $|-8y^2| = |-8| \cdot |y^2| = 8y^2$ 415. $\left|\dfrac{27}{t}\right| = \dfrac{|27|}{|t|} = \dfrac{27}{|t|}$ 417. $\left|\dfrac{b^2}{-4}\right| = \dfrac{|b^2|}{|-4|} = \dfrac{b^2}{4}$

419. $4(4) - (-3) + 5(0) = 16 + 3 + 0 = 19$

421. $-(4) + 3(0)^2 - 2(-3) = -4 + 0 + 6 = 2$

423. $-9(4) - (-3) + 7(-3)(0) = -36 + 3 + 0 = -33$

425. $\dfrac{(4) - 7(-3)}{(0) + 3(4)} = \dfrac{4 + 21}{0 + 12} = \dfrac{25}{12}$ 427. $(-3)^2 + 4(-3) - 9 = 9 - 12 - 9 = -12$

429. $6 + 5(0) - 9(0)^2 = 6 + 0 - 0 = 6$ 431. $\dfrac{1}{4} + \dfrac{1}{-3} = \dfrac{3}{12} + \dfrac{-4}{12} = \dfrac{-1}{12} = -\dfrac{1}{12}$

433. $|-3(4) + 11(0)| = |-12 + 0| = |-12| = 12$ 435. $|-3(4)| + |11(0)| = |-12| + |0| = 12 + 0 = 12$

437. The domain of the variable x for the expression $\dfrac{6}{x-1}$ is the set of all real numbers except 1:

$$
\begin{aligned}
x - \cancel{1} &= 0 \quad \text{(which is bad)} \\
\underline{+1 \;\; +1} & \\
x &= 1
\end{aligned}
$$

439. The domain of the variable x for the expression $\dfrac{-10}{x+8}$ is the set of all real numbers except -8:

$$
\begin{aligned}
x + \cancel{8} &= 0 \quad \text{(which is bad)} \\
\underline{-8 \;\; -8} & \\
x &= -8
\end{aligned}
$$

441. The domain of the variable x for the expression $\dfrac{10}{10-x}$ is the set of all real numbers except 10:

$$
\begin{aligned}
10 - \cancel{x} &= 0 \quad \text{(which is bad)} \\
\underline{+x \;\; +x} & \\
10 &= x
\end{aligned}
$$

443. The domain of the variable x for the expression $\dfrac{1}{9+x}$ is the set of all real numbers except -9:

$$
\begin{aligned}
\cancel{9} + x &= 0 \quad \text{(which is bad)} \\
\underline{-9 \;\;\;\; -9} & \\
x &= -9
\end{aligned}
$$

445. The area is $A = \dfrac{1}{2}bh = \dfrac{1}{2}(6)(4) = \dfrac{1}{2}(24) = 12 \text{ in}^2$.

447. The volume is $V = s^3 = 7^3 = 7 \times 7 \times 7 = 343 \text{ ft}^3$.

449. $C = \dfrac{5}{9}(F - 32) = \dfrac{5}{9}(212 - 32) = \dfrac{5}{9}(180) = \dfrac{5}{\cancel{9}}\left(\dfrac{\overset{20}{\cancel{180}}}{1}\right) = 100^\circ\, C.$

Chapter 2 Exercise 2.1

1. $4 \times 4 = 4^2$ has exponent 2 and base 4.

3. $8 \cdot 8 \cdot 8 \cdot 8 = 8^4$ has exponent 4 and base 8.

5. $(-6)(-6)(-6) = (-6)^3$ has exponent 3 and base -6.

7. $\left(\frac{2}{9}\right)\left(\frac{2}{9}\right)\left(\frac{2}{9}\right)\left(\frac{2}{9}\right) = \left(\frac{2}{9}\right)^4$ has exponent 4 and base $\frac{2}{9}$.

9. $x \cdot x \cdot x \cdot x \cdot x = x^5$ has exponent 5 and base x.

11. $(a)(a)(a)(a)(a) = a^5$ has exponent 5 and base a.

13. $(4n)(4n) = (4n)^2$ has exponent 2 and base $4n$.

15. $\left(x^2y\right)\left(x^2y\right)\left(x^2y\right)\left(x^2y\right) = \left(x^2y\right)^4$ has exponent 4 and base x^2y.

17. $8^2 = (8)(8) = 64$ 19. $\left(\frac{3}{4}\right)^3 = \left(\frac{3}{4}\right)\left(\frac{3}{4}\right)\left(\frac{3}{4}\right) = \frac{27}{64}$ 21. $\left(-\frac{3}{11}\right)^2 = \left(-\frac{3}{11}\right)\left(-\frac{3}{11}\right) = \frac{9}{121}$

23. $-7^2 = -(7)(7) = -49$ 25. $\left(-\frac{1}{2}\right)^5 = \left(-\frac{1}{2}\right)\left(-\frac{1}{2}\right)\left(-\frac{1}{2}\right)\left(-\frac{1}{2}\right)\left(-\frac{1}{2}\right) = -\frac{1}{32}$

27. $-1^3 = -(1)(1)(1) = -1$ 29. $6^0 = 1$ 31. $(-12)^0 = 1$

33. $\frac{9^6}{9^5} = 9^{6-5} = 9^1 = 9$ 35. $\frac{(-3)^{12}}{(-3)^9} = (-3)^{12-9} = (-3)^3 = (-3)(-3)(-3) = -27$

37. $\frac{6^5}{6^7} = 6^{5-7} = 6^{-2} = \frac{1}{6^2} = \frac{1}{(6)(6)} = \frac{1}{36}$ 39. $\frac{(-4)^5}{(-4)^6} = (-4)^{5-6} = (-4)^{-1} = \frac{1}{(-4)^1} = \frac{1}{-4} = -\frac{1}{4}$

41. $11^{-1} = \frac{1}{11^1} = \frac{1}{11}$ 43. $3^{-2} = \frac{1}{3^2} = \frac{1}{(3)(3)} = \frac{1}{9}$ 45. $5^{-3} = \frac{1}{5^3} = \frac{1}{(5)(5)(5)} = \frac{1}{125}$

47. $-7^{-2} = -\frac{1}{7^2} = -\frac{1}{(7)(7)} = -\frac{1}{49}$ 49. $(-8)^{-3} = \frac{1}{(-8)^3} = \frac{1}{(-8)(-8)(-8)} = \frac{1}{-512} = -\frac{1}{512}$

51. $(-2)^{-2} = \frac{1}{(-2)^2} = \frac{1}{(-2)(-2)} = \frac{1}{4}$ 53. $\left(3^3\right)^2 = 3^{3(2)} = 3^6 = (3)(3)(3)(3)(3)(3) = 729$

55. $\left(3^4\right)^{-1} = 3^{4(-1)} = 3^{-4} = \frac{1}{3^4} = \frac{1}{(3)(3)(3)(3)} = \frac{1}{81}$

57. $\frac{800^2}{100^2} = \left(\frac{800}{100}\right)^2 = 8^2 = (8)(8) = 64$ 59. $\frac{100^5}{(-100)^5} = \left(\frac{100}{-100}\right)^5 = (-1)^5 = -1$

61. $y^2 \cdot y^5 = y^{2+5} = y^7$ 63. $s \cdot s^3 = s^{1+3} = s^4$ 65. $\left(a^5\right)\left(a^5\right)\left(a^2\right) = a^{5+5+2} = a^{12}$

67. $\left(-2x^5\right)\left(6x^3\right) = -12x^{5+3} = -12x^8$ 69. $\left(2x^3y\right)\left(x^9y^{12}\right) = 2x^{3+9}y^{1+12} = 2x^{12}y^{13}$

71. $\left(4a^2b^2\right)\left(5a^{10}b^9\right) = 20a^{2+10}b^{2+9} = 20a^{12}b^{11}$ 73. $\frac{x^{10}}{x^3} = x^{10-3} = x^7$

75. $\frac{-35s^8t^5}{-5s^4t} = 7s^{8-4}t^{5-1} = 7s^4t^4$

77. $\frac{\overset{5}{\cancel{25}}x^{18}y^{16}}{\underset{2}{\cancel{-10}}x^4y^5} = -\frac{5}{2}x^{18-4}y^{16-5} = -\frac{5}{2}x^4y^{11}$ 79. $3x^0 = 3(1) = 3$

81. $-12t^4 \left(10s^8 t^{10}\right)^0 = -12t^4(1) = -12t^4$　　　83. $y^{-3} = \dfrac{1}{y^3}$　　　85. $-x^{-5} = -\dfrac{1}{x^5}$

87. $x^{-6} \cdot x^{-2} = x^{-6+(-2)} = x^{-8} = \dfrac{1}{x^8}$　　　89. $t^{-4} \cdot t^7 = t^{-4+7} = t^3$

91. $\dfrac{y^9}{y^{-1}} = y^{9-(-1)} = y^{10}$　　　93. $\underbrace{\dfrac{32x^0 y^{-1}}{16x^5 y^{-4}} = \dfrac{2y^{-1-(-4)}}{x^5}}_{\frac{32}{16}=2,\ x^0=1,\ \text{and}\ \frac{y^{-1}}{y^{-4}}=y^{-1-(-4)}.} = \dfrac{2y^3}{x^5}$

95. $\left(x^9\right)^2 = x^{9(2)} = x^{18}$　　　97. $\left(s^8\right)^{-5} = s^{8(-5)} = s^{-40} = \dfrac{1}{s^{40}}$　　　99. $\left(x^0\right)^{-7} = (1)^{-7} = \dfrac{1}{1^7} = \dfrac{1}{1} = 1$

101. $(3x)^4 = 3^4 x^4 = 81x^4$　　　103. $\left(-4x^7 y^8\right)^3 = (-4)^3 \left(x^7\right)^3 \left(y^8\right)^3 = -64x^{7(3)} y^{8(3)} = -64x^{21} y^{24}$

105. $(7s)^{-3} = \dfrac{1}{(7s)^3} = \dfrac{1}{7^3 s^3} = \dfrac{1}{343s^3}$　　　107. $\left(16x^4 y\right)^{-1} = \dfrac{1}{\left(16x^4 y\right)^1} = \dfrac{1}{16x^4 y}$

109. $\left(\dfrac{7}{3} a^2 b^6\right)^2 = \left(\dfrac{7}{3}\right)^2 \left(a^2\right)^2 \left(b^6\right)^2 = \dfrac{49}{9} a^{2(2)} b^{6(2)} = \dfrac{49}{9} a^4 b^{12}$　　　111. $\left(\dfrac{x}{y}\right)^9 = \dfrac{x^9}{y^9}$

113. $\left(-\dfrac{6}{a^7}\right)^2 = \dfrac{(-6)^2}{\left(a^7\right)^2} = \dfrac{36}{a^{7(2)}} = \dfrac{36}{a^{14}}$　　　115. $\left(\dfrac{5x^6}{y^5}\right)^4 = \dfrac{5^4 \left(x^6\right)^4}{\left(y^5\right)^4} = \dfrac{625x^{6(4)}}{y^{5(4)}} = \dfrac{625x^{24}}{y^{20}}$

117. $\left(-\dfrac{m^7}{8n^3}\right)^2 = \dfrac{\left(m^7\right)^2}{8^2 \left(n^3\right)^2} = \dfrac{m^{7(2)}}{64n^{3(2)}} = \dfrac{m^{14}}{64n^6}$

119. $-9a^3 \left(2a^7\right)^2 = -9a^3 \left(2^2 \left(a^7\right)^2\right) = -9a^3 \left(4a^{7(2)}\right) = -9a^3 \left(4a^{14}\right) = -36a^{3+14} = -36a^{17}$

121. $\left(13x^5\right)^2 \left(2x^5\right)^0 = 13^2 \left(x^5\right)^2 (1) = 169x^{5(2)} = 169x^{10}$

123. $\left(m^2 n^7\right)^3 \left(-6mn^8\right)^3 = \left(m^2\right)^3 \left(n^7\right)^3 (-6)^3 m^3 \left(n^8\right)^3 = -216m^{2(3)} n^{7(3)} m^3 n^{8(3)}$

$$= -216m^6 n^{21} m^3 n^{24} = -216m^{6+3} n^{21+24} = -216m^9 n^{45}$$

125. $\left(\dfrac{-11a^5}{3b^4}\right)^2 \cdot \dfrac{(-2a)^0}{11b^3} = \dfrac{(-11)^2 \left(a^5\right)^2}{3^2 \left(b^4\right)^2} \cdot \dfrac{1}{11b^3} = \dfrac{121a^{5(2)}}{9b^{4(2)}} \cdot \dfrac{1}{11b^3}$

$$= \dfrac{121a^{10}}{9b^8} \cdot \dfrac{1}{11b^3} = \dfrac{11a^{10}}{9b^{8+3}} = \dfrac{11a^{10}}{9b^{11}}$$

127. $\dfrac{\left(-9x^0 y^{11}\right)^2}{-3\left(3x^2 y\right)^3} \cdot \dfrac{\left(-5x^0 y^4\right)^0}{(-2x)^3} = \dfrac{(-9)^2 \left(y^{11}\right)^2}{-3\left(3^3 \left(x^2\right)^3 y^3\right)} \cdot \dfrac{1}{(-2)^3 x^3} = \dfrac{81y^{11(2)}}{-3\left(27x^{2(3)} y^3\right)} \cdot \dfrac{1}{-8x^3}$

$$= \dfrac{81y^{22}}{-3\left(27x^6 y^3\right)} \cdot \dfrac{1}{-8x^3} = \dfrac{\overset{1}{\cancel{81}}y^{22}}{\underset{1}{\cancel{-81}}x^6 y^3} \cdot \dfrac{1}{-8x^3}$$

$$= \dfrac{y^{22}}{-x^6 y^3} \cdot \dfrac{1}{-8x^3} = \dfrac{y^{22}}{8x^6 y^3 x^3} = \dfrac{y^{22-3}}{8x^{6+3}} = \dfrac{y^{19}}{8x^9}$$

Chapter 2 Exercise 2.2

1. $\left(\dfrac{1}{4}\right)^{-1} = \left(\dfrac{4}{1}\right)^1 = 4^1 = 4$　　　3. $\left(\dfrac{5}{3}\right)^{-1} = \left(\dfrac{3}{5}\right)^1 = \dfrac{3}{5}$　　　5. $\left(\dfrac{7}{8}\right)^{-2} = \left(\dfrac{8}{7}\right)^2 = \dfrac{64}{49}$

7. $\left(\dfrac{2}{7}\right)^{-3} = \left(\dfrac{7}{2}\right)^3 = \dfrac{343}{8}$

9. $\dfrac{2^2}{5^{-1}} = \dfrac{2^2 \cdot 5^1}{1} = \dfrac{4 \cdot 5}{1} = \dfrac{20}{1} = 20$

11. $\dfrac{2^{-2}}{4^2} = \dfrac{1}{2^2 \cdot 4^2} = \dfrac{1}{4 \cdot 16} = \dfrac{1}{64}$

13. $\dfrac{(-10)^{-2}}{(-3)^1} = \dfrac{1}{(-10)^2(-3)^1} = \dfrac{1}{100(-3)} = -\dfrac{1}{300}$

15. $\dfrac{5^{-2}}{3^{-4}} = \dfrac{3^4}{5^2} = \dfrac{81}{25}$

17. $\dfrac{(-9)^{-2}}{-2^{-3}} = -\dfrac{2^3}{(-9)^2} = -\dfrac{8}{81}$

19. $\dfrac{4^1 \cdot 3^{-2}}{4^{-1} \cdot 3^2} = \dfrac{4^1 \cdot 4^1}{3^2 \cdot 3^2} = \dfrac{4 \cdot 4}{9 \cdot 9} = \dfrac{16}{81}$

21. $\dfrac{9^{-3} \cdot 2^0}{9^{-2} \cdot 2^{-5}} = \dfrac{9^2 \cdot 2^5}{9^3} = \dfrac{1 \cdot 32}{9^1} = \dfrac{32}{9}$

23. $5^0 \cdot 2^{-4} \cdot 6 = \dfrac{5^0 \cdot 2^{-4} \cdot 6}{1} = \dfrac{1 \cdot 6}{2^4} = \dfrac{\overset{3}{\cancel{6}}}{\underset{8}{\cancel{16}}} = \dfrac{3}{8}$

25. $\dfrac{12^0}{7^{-3}} = \dfrac{1}{7^{-3}} = \dfrac{7^3}{1} = \dfrac{343}{1} = 343$

27. $\dfrac{6^{-2}}{16^0} = \dfrac{6^{-2}}{1} = \dfrac{1}{6^2} = \dfrac{1}{36}$

29. $\dfrac{3^2 \cdot (-5)^{-1}}{(-4)^{-2} \cdot 2^{-1}} = \dfrac{(-4)^2 \cdot 3^2 \cdot 2^1}{(-5)^1} = \dfrac{16 \cdot 9 \cdot 2}{-5} = -\dfrac{288}{5}$

31. $\left(\dfrac{5}{2}\right)^{-2} + \left(\dfrac{2}{3}\right)^{-1} = \left(\dfrac{2}{5}\right)^2 + \left(\dfrac{3}{2}\right)^1 = \dfrac{4}{25} + \dfrac{3}{2} = \dfrac{4(2)}{25(2)} + \dfrac{3(25)}{2(25)} = \dfrac{8}{50} + \dfrac{75}{50} = \dfrac{83}{50}$

33. $2\left(\dfrac{4}{5}\right)^{-2} + \left(\dfrac{2}{5}\right)^{-3} = 2\left(\dfrac{5}{4}\right)^2 + \left(\dfrac{5}{2}\right)^3 = \dfrac{\overset{1}{\cancel{2}}}{1}\left(\dfrac{25}{\underset{8}{\cancel{16}}}\right) + \dfrac{125}{8} = \dfrac{25}{8} + \dfrac{125}{8} = \dfrac{\overset{75}{\cancel{150}}}{\underset{4}{\cancel{8}}} = \dfrac{75}{4}$

35. $\dfrac{7}{18}\left(\dfrac{5}{6}\right)^{-2} + \left(\dfrac{4}{7}\right)^0 = \dfrac{7}{18}\left(\dfrac{6}{5}\right)^2 + 1 = \dfrac{7}{\underset{1}{\cancel{18}}}\left(\dfrac{\overset{2}{\cancel{36}}}{25}\right) + 1 = \dfrac{14}{25} + 1 = \dfrac{14}{25} + \dfrac{25}{25} = \dfrac{39}{25}$

37. $\left(\dfrac{a}{6}\right)^{-1} = \left(\dfrac{6}{a}\right)^1 = \dfrac{6}{a}$

39. $\left(\dfrac{a}{7}\right)^{-2} = \left(\dfrac{7}{a}\right)^2 = \dfrac{49}{a^2}$

41. $\left(\dfrac{7a}{5}\right)^{-2} = \left(\dfrac{5}{7a}\right)^2 = \dfrac{25}{49a^2}$

43. $\left(\dfrac{9}{4x^2}\right)^{-3} = \left(\dfrac{4x^2}{9}\right)^3 = \dfrac{64x^6}{729}$

45. $\left(\dfrac{10m^2}{3n^{12}}\right)^{-2} = \left(\dfrac{3n^{12}}{10m^2}\right)^2 = \dfrac{9n^{24}}{100m^4}$

47. $13x^{-4}y^0z^5 = \dfrac{13x^{-4}y^0z^5}{1} = \dfrac{13z^5}{x^4}$

49. $\left(5a^5b^{-1}\right)^{-2} = \dfrac{\left(5a^5b^{-1}\right)^{-2}}{1} = \dfrac{1}{\left(5a^5b^{-1}\right)^2} = \dfrac{1}{25a^{10}b^{-2}} = \dfrac{b^2}{25a^{10}}$

51. $\left(\dfrac{a^{-3}}{b^6}\right)^{-2} = \left(\dfrac{b^6}{a^{-3}}\right)^2 = \dfrac{b^{12}}{a^{-6}} = \dfrac{a^6b^{12}}{1} = a^6b^{12}$

53. $\left(\dfrac{a^0}{b^{-7}}\right)^{-2} = \left(\dfrac{1}{b^{-7}}\right)^{-2} = \left(\dfrac{b^{-7}}{1}\right)^2 = b^{-14} = \dfrac{1}{b^{14}}$

55. $\left(\dfrac{3x^{-1}}{4x^0}\right)^{-1} = \left(\dfrac{4x^0}{3x^{-1}}\right)^1 = \dfrac{4x^0}{3x^{-1}} = \dfrac{4}{3x^{-1}} = \dfrac{4x}{3}$

57. $\left(\dfrac{x^2}{6}\right)^{-2} \cdot \left(\dfrac{x^4}{2}\right)^{-1} = \left(\dfrac{6}{x^2}\right)^2 \cdot \left(\dfrac{2}{x^4}\right)^1 = \dfrac{36}{x^4} \cdot \dfrac{2}{x^4} = \dfrac{72}{x^8}$

59. $\left(\dfrac{10}{m^3}\right)^{-3} \cdot \left(\dfrac{m^2}{100}\right)^{-1} = \left(\dfrac{m^3}{10}\right)^3 \cdot \left(\dfrac{100}{m^2}\right)^1 = \dfrac{m^9}{\underset{10}{1,000}} \cdot \dfrac{\overset{1}{100}}{m^2} = \dfrac{m^7}{10}$

61. $\dfrac{a^7b^4}{8} \cdot \dfrac{\left(ab^6\right)^{-1}}{4} = \dfrac{a^7b^4}{8} \cdot \dfrac{1}{4\left(ab^6\right)^1} = \dfrac{a^7b^4}{8} \cdot \dfrac{1}{4ab^6} = \dfrac{a^7b^4}{32ab^6} = \dfrac{a^6}{32b^2}$

63. $\dfrac{\left(s^8t^{-1}\right)^{-1}}{s^2t^5} = \dfrac{1}{s^2t^5\left(s^8t^{-1}\right)^1} = \dfrac{1}{s^2t^5s^8t^{-1}} = \dfrac{1}{s^{10}t^4}$

65. $\dfrac{x^3y^{-3}}{\left(x^{-3}y^7\right)^{-1}} = \dfrac{x^3y^{-3}\left(x^{-3}y^7\right)^1}{1} = x^3y^{-3}x^{-3}y^7 = y^4$

67. $\dfrac{x^9y^{-8}}{\left(x^{-2}y^{10}\right)^{-1}} = \dfrac{x^9y^{-8}\left(x^{-2}y^{10}\right)^1}{1} = x^9y^{-8}x^{-2}y^{10} = x^7y^2$

69. $6x^4y^{-5}(3xy^3)^2 = 6x^4y^{-5}(9x^2y^6) = 54x^6y^1 = 54x^6y$

71. $(3a^{-3}b^2)^0(9a^{-3}b^6)^2 = 1(81a^{-6}b^{12}) = 81a^{-6}b^{12} = \dfrac{81b^{12}}{a^6}$

73. $(16ab^{-2}c^6)^0(-2a^{-1}b^0c^4)^{-3} = 1(-2a^{-1}c^4)^{-3} = \dfrac{(-2a^{-1}c^4)^{-3}}{1} = \dfrac{1}{(-2a^{-1}c^4)^3} = \dfrac{1}{-8a^{-3}c^{12}} = -\dfrac{a^3}{8c^{12}}$

75. $\dfrac{\left(5x^8y^{-1}\right)^2\left(3x^0y\right)}{\left(xy^2\right)\left(-4x^6y^4\right)^0} = \dfrac{\left(25x^{16}y^{-2}\right)\left(3y\right)}{\left(xy^2\right)\left(1\right)} = \dfrac{75x^{16}y^{-1}}{xy^2} = \dfrac{75x^{15}}{y^3}$

77. $\dfrac{\left(4x^5y^{-9}\right)^0}{\left(3x^2\right)^3\left(y^{-1}\right)^2} \cdot \dfrac{9x^5}{x^{-6}y^{-7}} = \dfrac{1}{\underset{3}{27}x^6y^{-2}} \cdot \dfrac{\overset{1}{9}x^5}{x^{-6}y^{-7}} = \dfrac{x^5}{3y^{-9}} = \dfrac{x^5y^9}{3}$

79. $\left[\left(25x^3y^{-2}\right)^{-1}\left(5x^0y^{-5}\right)^3\right]^{-2} = \left[\dfrac{\left(25x^3y^{-2}\right)^{-1}\left(5x^0y^{-5}\right)^3}{1}\right]^{-2} = \left[\dfrac{\left(5x^0y^{-5}\right)^3}{\left(25x^3y^{-2}\right)^1}\right]^{-2} = \left[\dfrac{\overset{5}{125}y^{-15}}{\underset{1}{25}x^3y^{-2}}\right]^{-2}$

$= \left[\dfrac{5y^2}{x^3y^{15}}\right]^{-2} = \left[\dfrac{5}{x^3y^{13}}\right]^{-2} = \left[\dfrac{x^3y^{13}}{5}\right]^2 = \dfrac{x^6y^{26}}{25}$

Chapter 2 Exercise 2.3

1. $0.2 = 2 \times 10^{-1}$ 3. $0.00982 = 9.82 \times 10^{-3}$ 5. $0.0010111001 = 1.0111001 \times 10^{-3}$

7. $6 = 6 \times 10^0$ 9. $4.23 = 4.23 \times 10^0$ 11. $3.14 = 3.14 \times 10^0$

13. $60 = 6.0 \times 10^1$ 15. $26.19 = 2.619 \times 10^1$ 17. $935.112 = 9.35112 \times 10^2$

19. $4,502 = 4.502 \times 10^3$ 21. $65,782.001 = 6.5782001 \times 10^4$

23. $52,402,437.86 = 5.240243786 \times 10^7$ 25. $5 \times 10^1 = 50.0$ 27. $3.9 \times 10^2 = 390.0$

29. $7.26 \times 10^1 = 72.6$ 31. $6.403 \times 10^4 = 64,030.0$ 33. $4.82777 \times 10^4 = 48,277.7$

35. $7.0 \times 10^5 = 700,000.0$ 37. $3 \times 10^8 = 300,000,000.0$ 39. $2.53911 \times 10^8 = 253,911,000.0$

41. $7.16562 \times 10^1 = 71.6562$ 43. $8 \times 10^{-1} = 0.8$ 45. $1.113 \times 10^{-2} = 0.01113$

47. $8.22762 \times 10^{-3} = 0.00822762$ 49. $1 \times 10^{-9} = 0.000000001$ 51. $\left(3 \times 10^1\right)\left(3 \times 10^2\right) = 9 \times 10^3$

53. $\left(2.5 \times 10^8\right)\left(5 \times 10^1\right) = 12.5 \times 10^9 = 1.25 \times 10^{10}$ 55. $\left(5 \times 10^{-7}\right)\left(1 \times 10^{-1}\right) = 5 \times 10^{-8}$

57. $\left(6 \times 10^{-5}\right)\left(6 \times 10^{11}\right) = 36 \times 10^6 = 3.6 \times 10^7$ 59. $\left(7 \times 10^{-2}\right)\left(9 \times 10^{-6}\right) = 63 \times 10^{-8} = 6.3 \times 10^{-7}$

61. $\dfrac{8 \times 10^5}{4 \times 10^3} = 2 \times 10^2$ 63. $\dfrac{150 \times 10^{12}}{15 \times 10^2} = 10 \times 10^{10} = 1.0 \times 10^{11}$

65. $\dfrac{65 \times 10^{-2}}{5 \times 10^6} = 13 \times 10^{-8} = 1.3 \times 10^{-7}$

67. $\dfrac{144 \times 10^{-1}}{6 \times 10^{-9}} = 24 \times 10^8 = 2.4 \times 10^9$ 69. $\left(2 \times 10^4\right)^2 = 4 \times 10^8$

71. $\left(5 \times 10^4\right)^3 = 125 \times 10^{12} = 1.25 \times 10^{14}$ 73. $\left(7 \times 10^{-4}\right)^2 = 49 \times 10^{-8} = 4.9 \times 10^{-7}$

75. $\left(2 \times 10^{-2}\right)^{-2} = 2^{-2} \times 10^4 = \dfrac{1}{4} \times 10^4 = 0.25 \times 10^4 = 2.5 \times 10^3$

77. $\left(5 \times 10^2\right)\left(4 \times 10^6\right)^2 = \left(5 \times 10^2\right)\left(16 \times 10^{12}\right) = 80 \times 10^{14} = 8.0 \times 10^{15}$

79. $\left(2 \times 10^4\right)^3\left(3 \times 10^{-7}\right)^2 = \left(8 \times 10^{12}\right)\left(9 \times 10^{-14}\right) = 72 \times 10^{-2} = 7.2 \times 10^{-1}$

81. $\dfrac{\left(4 \times 10^2\right)\left(5 \times 10^{-1}\right)^{-1}}{2 \times 10^0} = \dfrac{4 \times 10^2}{\left(2 \times 10^0\right)\left(5 \times 10^{-1}\right)^1} = \dfrac{4 \times 10^2}{\left(2 \times 10^0\right)\left(5 \times 10^{-1}\right)}$

$$= \dfrac{4 \times 10^2}{10 \times 10^{-1}} = \dfrac{4 \times 10^2}{1} = 4 \times 10^2$$

83. $\dfrac{\left(2 \times 10^4\right)^2\left(9 \times 10^3\right)^1}{4 \times 10^4} = \dfrac{\overset{1}{\left(\cancel{4} \times 10^8\right)}\left(9 \times 10^3\right)}{\underset{1}{\cancel{4}} \times 10^4} = \dfrac{9 \times 10^{11}}{1 \times 10^4} = 9 \times 10^7$

85. $\dfrac{\left(2 \times 10^7\right)^{-2}}{\left(2 \times 10^5\right)^{-3}} = \dfrac{\left(2 \times 10^5\right)^3}{\left(2 \times 10^7\right)^2} = \dfrac{8 \times 10^{15}}{4 \times 10^{14}} = 2 \times 10^1$

87. $\dfrac{\left(1 \times 10^{10}\right)^{-2}}{1 \times 10^{-5}} = \dfrac{1}{\left(1 \times 10^{-5}\right)\left(1 \times 10^{10}\right)^2} = \dfrac{1}{\left(1 \times 10^{-5}\right)\left(1 \times 10^{20}\right)} = \dfrac{1}{1 \times 10^{15}} = 1 \times 10^{-15}$

89. $\dfrac{8 \times 10^4}{\left(7 \times 10^{-3}\right)^{-1}} = \dfrac{\left(8 \times 10^4\right)\left(7 \times 10^{-3}\right)^1}{1} = \left(8 \times 10^4\right)\left(7 \times 10^{-3}\right) = 56 \times 10^1 = 5.6 \times 10^2$

Chapter 3 Exercise 3.1

1. 2 has the coefficient 2 and the degree 0.   3. $-6x$ has the coefficient -6 and the degree 1.

5. $9y^2$ has the coefficient 9 and the degree 2.   7. $7x^3y^5$ has the coefficient 7 and the degree 8 $(= 3 + 5)$.

9. $\dfrac{15x^3}{14} = \dfrac{15}{14}x^3$ has the coefficient $\dfrac{15}{14}$ and the degree 3.

11. $-\dfrac{2y^{10}}{7} = -\dfrac{2}{7}y^{10}$ has the coefficient $-\dfrac{2}{7}$ and the degree 10.

13. $8a^3 - a^2$ is a polynomial. The coefficients of the terms are 8 and -1.

15. $\dfrac{3x}{13} + \dfrac{x^2}{12} - \dfrac{1}{2} = \dfrac{3}{13}x + \dfrac{1}{12}x^2 - \dfrac{1}{2}$ is a polynomial. The coefficients of the terms are $\dfrac{3}{13}$, $\dfrac{1}{12}$, and $-\dfrac{1}{2}$.

17. $\dfrac{9}{x^4} + 12 - 3x$ is not a polynomial since $\dfrac{9}{x^4}$ is not a monomial.

19. $\dfrac{3xy}{4} - \dfrac{4x^8}{5y}$ is not a polynomial since $\dfrac{4x^8}{5y}$ is not a monomial.

21. $\dfrac{12x^2 - 5}{3} = \dfrac{12x^2}{3} - \dfrac{5}{3} = 4x^2 - \dfrac{5}{3}$ is a polynomial. The coefficients of the terms are 4 and $-\dfrac{5}{3}$.

23. $\dfrac{x^2 + 12y^2 - 24}{12} = \dfrac{x^2}{12} + \dfrac{12y^2}{12} - \dfrac{24}{12} = \dfrac{1}{12}x^2 + y^2 - 2$ is a polynomial. The coefficients are $\dfrac{1}{12}$, 1, and -2.

25. $7 + 2x = 2x + 7$ has the leading term $2x$, the leading coefficient 2, and the degree 1.

27. $8 - 3x = -3x + 8$ has the leading term $-3x$, the leading coefficient -3, and the degree 1.

29. $2x^2 + 12 - 5x = 2x^2 - 5x + 12$ has the leading term $2x^2$, the leading coefficient 2, and the degree 2.

31. $t^2 - 6t^3 + \dfrac{2}{9} = -6t^3 + t^2 + \dfrac{2}{9}$ has the leading term $-6t^3$, the leading coefficient -6, and the degree 3.

33. $-\dfrac{14}{13} + 9t - 2t^2 = -2t^2 + 9t - \dfrac{14}{13}$ has the leading term $-2t^2$, the leading coefficient -2, and the degree 2.

35. $\dfrac{-x^2}{3} - \dfrac{1}{4}x^5 + x^3 = -\dfrac{1}{4}x^5 + x^3 - \dfrac{x^2}{3}$ has the leading term $-\dfrac{1}{4}x^5$, the leading coefficient $-\dfrac{1}{4}$, and the degree 5.

37. $-8x = -8x^1$ has the degree 1, so it is linear.   39. $3a = 3a^1$ has the degree 1, so it is linear.

41. $5x^2$ has the degree 2, so it is quadratic.   43. $2x - 5$ has the degree 1, so it is linear.

45. $6 - 11x = -11x + 6$ has the degree 1, so it is linear.   47. $13x + 2$ has the degree 1, so it is linear.

49. $y^2 + 5y - 1$ has the degree 2, so it is quadratic.

51. $8 + 8x^2 = 8x^2 + 8$ has the degree 2, so it is quadratic.

53. $2t + 5t^3 = 5t^3 + 2t$ has the degree 3, so it is neither.

55. $\dfrac{3a^4 + 12a^2 - 2a}{3} = \dfrac{3a^4}{3} + \dfrac{12a^2}{3} - \dfrac{2}{3}a = a^4 + 4a^2 - \dfrac{2}{3}a$ has the degree 4, so it is neither.

57. $4y + 7x + \underbrace{6y^2}_{\text{degree 2}}$ has the degree 2   59. $\underbrace{6y^4}_{\text{degree 3}} - x^3 - 8x$ has the degree 4

61. $x^2 + \underbrace{2x^2y}_{\text{degree 3}} - \underbrace{y^3}_{\text{degree 3}}$ has the degree 3   63. $\underbrace{12x^7}_{\text{degree 7}} - 5xy^3 + 3x^2y^3$ has the degree 7

Chapter 3 Exercise 3.2

1. $9x + 7x = 16x$

3. $-12y^2 + 7y^2 = -5y^2$

5. $-6x - 6x = -12x$

7. $6ab^3 + (-11ab^3) = -5ab^3$

9. $(-18ab) - (-4ab) = -14ab$

11. $-6a^2b^2 - a^2b^2 + 9a^2b^2 = 2a^2b^2$

13. $7q + 14q - 8q + q = 14q$

15. $(11a + 3) + (-8a + 4) = 3a + 7$

17. $\left(a^2 - 4a - 3\right) + \left(8a^2 - 2a + 7\right) = 9a^2 - 6a + 4$

19. $\left(-x^2 - 2xy - 8y^2\right) + \left(-x^2 + 2xy + 15y^2\right) = -2x^2 + 7y^2$

21. $(p + 3q - 5) + (7 + 9p + 4pq) = 10p + 3q + 2 + 4pq$

23. $\left(9x^2 - z^2\right) + \left(4z^2 - 12xz + 9x^2\right) = 18x^2 + 3z^2 - 12xz$

25. $(8x + 1) - (3x + 7) = 8x + 1 - 3x - 7 = 5x - 6$

27. $(-3a + 8b) - (4a - b) = -3a + 8b - 4a + b = -7a + 9b$

29. $\left(-x^2 + 5x + 8\right) - \left(3x^2 - 2x - 6\right) = -x^2 + 5x + 8 - 3x^2 + 2x + 6 = -4x^2 + 7x + 14$

31. $\left(8a^2 - 4ab + b^2\right) - \left(-2a^2 + 10b^2\right) = 8a^2 - 4ab + b^2 + 2a^2 - 10b^2 = 10a^2 - 4ab - 9b^2$

33. $(12p + pq - q) - \left(-3p + 2pq - 9q^2\right) = 12p + pq - q + 3p - 2pq + 9q^2 = 15p - pq - q + 9q^2$

35. $\left(-6x^2 + 10\right) - \left(18 - 8x^2 + 3y^2\right) = -6x^2 + 10 - 18 + 8x^2 - 3y^2 = 2x^2 - 3y^2 - 8$

37. $(6x + 2y) + (9x - 3y) + (-7x + y) = 8x$

39. $\left(5x^2 - 9x\right) + \left(-8x^2 + 2\right) + (x + 15) = -3x^2 - 8x + 17$

41. $(7m + 4) + (12m - 3) - (-7m + 8) = 7m + 4 + 12m - 3 + 7m - 8 = 26m - 7$

43. $\left(x^2 + 9\right) + \left(x^2 - 5x\right) - (-7x + 14) = x^2 + 9 + x^2 - 5x + 7x - 14 = 2x^2 + 2x - 5$

45. $\left(2y^2 - 5\right) - \left(4y^2 + 2y - 2\right) + (y + 8) = 2y^2 - 5 - 4y^2 - 2y + 2 + y + 8 = -2y^2 - y + 5$

47. $\left(6t^2 + 12\right) - \left(-t^2 - 11t\right) - (7t - 14) = 6t^2 + 12 + t^2 + 11t - 7t + 14 = 7t^2 + 4t + 26$

49. The additive inverse of $8x$ is $-8x$.

51. The additive inverse of $6n - 7$ is $-(6n - 7) = -6n + 7$.

53. The additive inverse of $-a^2 - 6a + 4$ is $-\left(-a^2 - 6a + 4\right) = a^2 + 6a - 4$.

55. The additive inverse of $-x^2 - 9xy + 4y^2$ is $-\left(-x^2 - 9xy + 4y^2\right) = x^2 + 9xy - 4y^2$.

Chapter 3 Exercise 3.3

1. $\left(4x^2\right)\left(5x^3\right) = 20x^{2+3} = 20x^5$

3. $\left(-9a^5\right)\left(-7a^6\right) = 63a^{5+6} = 63a^{11}$

5. $\left(-\dfrac{\overset{1}{\cancel{5}}}{\underset{1}{\cancel{6}}}y^5\right)\left(\dfrac{\overset{2}{\cancel{12}}}{\underset{5}{\cancel{25}}}y^7\right) = -\dfrac{2}{5}y^{5+7} = -\dfrac{2}{5}y^{12}$

7. $\left(-8y^2\right)\left(\dfrac{-9}{16}y^8\right) = \left(\dfrac{\overset{1}{\cancel{-8}}}{1}y^2\right)\left(\dfrac{-9}{\underset{2}{\cancel{16}}}y^8\right) = \dfrac{9}{2}y^{2+8} = \dfrac{9}{2}y^{10}$

9. $\left(3a^{13}b^{16}\right)\left(-ab^{12}\right) = -3a^{13+1}b^{16+12} = -3a^{14}b^{28}$

11. $\left(\dfrac{9x^5y^{12}}{\underset{1}{\cancel{3}}}\right)\left(\dfrac{\overset{3}{\cancel{-24}}xy^{11}}{5}\right) = -\dfrac{27x^{5+1}y^{12+11}}{5} = -\dfrac{27x^6y^{23}}{5}$

13. $5a(4a+7) = 5a\,(4a) + 5a\,(7) = 20a^2 + 35a$

15. $9x^4(8x^3 - 2x) = 9x^4\left(8x^3\right) + 9x^4\left(-2x\right) = 72x^7 - 18x^5$

17. $-2p^3(-12p + 8p^3) = -2p^3\left(-12p\right) + \left(-2p^3\right)\left(8p^3\right) = 24p^4 - 16p^6$

19. $6x^3y^4(2x^2y^5 - 5xy^2) = 6x^3y^4\left(2x^2y^5\right) + 6x^3y^4\left(-5xy^2\right) = 12x^5y^9 - 30x^4y^6$

21. $5(2a^2 + 7a - 1) = 5\left(2a^2\right) + 5\left(7a\right) + 5\left(-1\right) = 10a^2 + 35a - 5$

23. $8x^2(5x^3 - 4x^2 - 15) = 8x^2\left(5x^3\right) + 8x^2\left(-4x^2\right) + 8x^2\left(-15\right) = 40x^5 - 32x^4 - 120x^2$

25. $-2x^5y^3(5x^4 - 8x^2y^2 + y^2) = -2x^5y^3\left(5x^4\right) + \left(-2x^5y^3\right)\left(-8x^2y^2\right) + \left(-2x^5y^3\right)\left(y^2\right)$
$$= -10x^9y^3 + 16x^7y^5 - 2x^5y^5$$

27. $9a^3b^2(-a^2b^4 + 3a^5b^2 - 4a^6b^7) = 9a^3b^2\left(-a^2b^4\right) + 9a^3b^2\left(3a^5b^2\right) + 9a^3b^2\left(-4a^6b^7\right)$
$$= -9a^5b^6 + 27a^8b^4 - 36a^9b^9$$

29. $5xy^2z^9(x^3y + 7xy^6 - 2yz^{13}) = 5xy^2z^9\left(x^3y\right) + 5xy^2z^9\left(7xy^6\right) + 5xy^2z^9\left(-2yz^{13}\right)$
$$= 5x^4y^3z^9 + 35x^2y^8z^9 - 10xy^3z^{22}$$

31. $(x+2)(x+3) = x^2 \underbrace{+2x + 3x}\ +6 = x^2 + 5x + 6$

33. $(y-8)(y+3) = y^2 \underbrace{+3y - 8y}\ -24 = y^2 - 5y - 24$

35. $(t-8)(t-7) = t^2 \underbrace{-7t - 8t}\ +56 = t^2 - 15t + 56$

37. $(2x+1)(5x+3) = 10x^2 \underbrace{+6x + 5x}\ +3 = 10x^2 + 11x + 3$

39. $(5t+9)(3t-4) = 15t^2 \underbrace{-20t + 27t}\ -36 = 15t^2 + 7t - 36$

41. $(3-4n)(11+3n) = 33 \underbrace{+9n - 44n}\ -12n^2 = 33 - 35n - 12n^2$

43. $(2-7t)(3-2t) = 6 \underbrace{-4t - 21t}\ +14t^2 = 6 - 25t + 14t^2$

45. $\left(5x^2 + 2x\right)(3x+1) = 15x^3 \underbrace{+5x^2 + 6x^2}\ +2x = 15x^3 + 11x^2 + 2x$

47. $\left(4t^2 - 7\right)(-5t+5) = -20t^3 + 20t^2 + 35t - 35$

49. $\left(n^3 - 7n\right)(6n-2) = 6n^4 - 2n^3 - 42n^2 + 14n$

51. $(x+1)(x-1) = (x)^2 - (1)^2 = x^2 - 1$

53. $(8-y)(8+y) = (8)^2 - (y)^2 = 64 - y^2$

55. $(4x+3)(4x-3) = (4x)^2 - (3)^2 = 16x^2 - 9$

57. $(10a - 9b)(10a + 9b) = (10a)^2 - (9b)^2 = 100a^2 - 81b^2$

59. $(x+2)^2 = (x)^2 + 2\,(x)\,(2) + (2)^2 = x^2 + 4x + 4$

61. $(p-8)^2 = (p)^2 - 2\,(p)\,(8) + (8)^2 = p^2 - 16p + 64$

63. $(2y+3)^2 = (2y)^2 + 2\,(2y)\,(3) + (3)^2 = 4y^2 + 12y + 9$

65. $(8x - 5y)^2 = (8x)^2 - 2(8x)(5y) + (5y)^2 = 64x^2 - 80xy + 25y^2$

67. $(4 - 13x)^2 = (4)^2 - 2(4)(13x) + (13x)^2 = 16 - 104x + 169x^2$

69. $(x + 3)\left(x^2 + 2x - 2\right)$

$$
\begin{array}{r}
x^2 + 2x - 2 \\
x + 3 \\
\hline
3x^2 + 6x - 6 \\
+ x^3 + 2x^2 - 2x \\
\hline
x^3 + 5x^2 + 4x - 6
\end{array}
$$

71. $(2y - 3)\left(y^2 - y - 3\right)$

$$
\begin{array}{r}
y^2 - y - 3 \\
2y - 3 \\
\hline
- 3y^2 + 3y + 9 \\
+ 2y^3 - 2y^2 - 6y \\
\hline
2y^3 - 5y^2 - 3y + 9
\end{array}
$$

73. $(4b + 2)\left(16b^2 - 8b + 4\right)$

$$
\begin{array}{r}
16b^2 - 8b + 4 \\
4b + 2 \\
\hline
32b^2 - 16b + 8 \\
+ 64b^3 - 32b^2 + 16b \\
\hline
64b^3 \qquad\qquad + 8
\end{array}
$$

75. $(x + 2y + 5)(6x - 5)$

$$
\begin{array}{r}
x + 2y + 5 \\
6x - 5 \\
\hline
- 5x - 10y - 25 \\
+ 6x^2 + 12xy + 30x \\
\hline
6x^2 + 12xy + 25x - 10y - 25
\end{array}
$$

77. $(t + 2)^3 = \underbrace{(t + 2)(t + 2)}(t + 2) = \left(t^2 + 2t + 2t + 4\right)(t + 2) = \left(t^2 + 4t + 4\right)(t + 2)$

$\qquad = t^3 + 2t^2 + 4t^2 + 8t + 4t + 8 = t^3 + 6t^2 + 12t + 8$

79. $(2m - 3n)^3 = \underbrace{(2m - 3n)(2m - 3n)}(2m - 3n) = \left(4m^2 - 6mn - 6mn + 9n^2\right)(2m - 3n)$

$\qquad = \left(4m^2 - 12mn + 9n^2\right)(2m - 3n)$

$\qquad = 8m^3 - 12m^2n - 24m^2n + 36mn^2 + 18mn^2 - 27n^3 = 8m^3 - 36m^2n + 54mn^2 - 27n^3$

81. $(x + 3)^2(x - 3) = (x + 3) \underbrace{(x + 3)(x - 3)}_{\text{Easier to do these first.}} = (x + 3)\left((x)^2 - (3)^2\right)$

$\qquad = (x + 3)\left(x^2 - 9\right) = x^3 - 9x + 3x^2 - 27$

83. $\underbrace{(a + 2)(3a - 2)}(2a + 1) = \left(3a^2 - 2a + 6a - 4\right)(2a + 1) = \left(3a^2 + 4a - 4\right)(2a + 1)$

$\qquad = 6a^3 + 3a^2 + 8a^2 + 4a - 8a - 4 = 6a^3 + 11a^2 - 4a - 4$

85. $(2x - 3y + 1)^2 = (2x - 3y + 1)(2x - 3y + 1)$

$$
\begin{array}{r}
2x - 3y + 1 \\
2x - 3y + 1 \\
\hline
2x - 3y + 1 \\
- 6xy + 9y^2 \qquad - 3y \\
+4x^2 - 6xy \qquad + 2x \\
\hline
4x^2 - 12xy + 9y^2 + 4x - 6y + 1
\end{array}
$$

87. $8(3x + 3) + 2(2x - 1) = 24x + 24 + 4x - 2 = 28x + 22$

89. $-x^2(8x + 2) - 2x^2(9x - 3) = -8x^3 - 2x^2 - 18x^3 + 6x^2 = -26x^3 + 4x^2$

91. $3p^2(-p^2 + 5p - 1) - 6p(p^2 - 4p) = -3p^4 + 15p^3 - 3p^2 - 6p^3 + 24p^2 = -3p^4 + 9p^3 + 21p^2$

93. $6x(4x - 1) + 5x(-x + 2) - 10(x^2 - 5) = 24x^2 - 6x - 5x^2 + 10x - 10x^2 + 50 = 9x^2 + 4x + 50$

95. $\underbrace{(x + 1)(x - 2)} + \underbrace{(x + 2)(x + 8)} = \left(x^2 - 2x + x - 2\right) + \left(x^2 + 8x + 2x + 16\right) = 2x^2 + 9x + 14$

97. $\underbrace{(2a - 3)(a + 1)} - \underbrace{(a + 2)(2a - 5)} = \left(2a^2 + 2a - 3a - 3\right) - \left(2a^2 - 5a + 4a - 10\right)$

$$= 2a^2 + 2a - 3a - 3 - 2a^2 + 5a - 4a + 10 = 7$$

99. $\underbrace{(y + 5)(y - 5)} + \underbrace{(y + 9)(y - 9)} = \left((y)^2 - (5)^2\right) + \left((y)^2 - (9)^2\right) = \left(y^2 - 25\right) + \left(y^2 - 81\right) = 2y^2 - 106$

101. $\underbrace{(3b - 2)(3b + 2)} - \underbrace{(7 + 3b)(7 - 3b)} = \left((3b)^2 - (2)^2\right) - \left((7)^2 - (3b)^2\right) = \left(9b^2 - 4\right) - \left(49 - 9b^2\right)$

$$= 9b^2 - 4 - 49 + 9b^2 = 18b^2 - 53$$

103. $\underbrace{(r + 3)^2} + \underbrace{(r - 7)^2} = \left((r)^2 + 2(r)(3) + (3)^2\right) + \left((r)^2 - 2(r)(7) + (7)^2\right)$

$$= \left(r^2 + 6r + 9\right) + \left(r^2 - 14r + 49\right) = 2r^2 - 8r + 58$$

105. $\underbrace{(x + 6)^2} - \underbrace{(x - 1)^2} = \left((x)^2 + 2(x)(6) + (6)^2\right) - \left((x)^2 - 2(x)(1) + (1)^2\right)$

$$= \left(x^2 + 12x + 36\right) - \left(x^2 - 2x + 1\right) = x^2 + 12x + 36 - x^2 + 2x - 1 = 14x + 35$$

107. $\underbrace{(2x + 5)^2} - \underbrace{(x - 1)(x + 4)} = \left((2x)^2 + 2(2x)(5) + (5)^2\right) - \left(x^2 + 4x - x - 4\right)$

$$= \left(4x^2 + 20x + 25\right) - \left(x^2 + 3x - 4\right)$$

$$= 4x^2 + 20x + 25 - x^2 - 3x + 4$$

$$= 3x^2 + 17x + 29$$

Chapter 3 Exercise 3.4

1. $\left(24x^5\right) \div \left(3x^4\right) = \dfrac{24x^5}{3x^4} = 8x^1 = 8x$

3. $\left(-20b^8\right) \div \left(4b^3\right) = \dfrac{-20b^8}{4b^3} = -5b^5$

5. $\left(-20y^{16}\right) \div \left(-5y^8\right) = \dfrac{-20y^{16}}{-5y^8} = 4y^8$

7. $\left(54x^{14}y^5\right) \div \left(9xy^2\right) = \dfrac{54x^{14}y^5}{9xy^2} = 6x^{13}y^3$

9. $\left(8m^{15}n^{18}\right) \div \left(-2m^4n^9\right) = \dfrac{8m^{15}n^{18}}{-2m^4n^9} = -4m^{11}n^9$

11. $\left(-2x^6y^{10}\right) \div \left(8x^2y^8\right) = \dfrac{\overset{1}{-\cancel{2}}x^6y^{10}}{\underset{4}{\cancel{8}}x^2y^8} = \dfrac{-x^4y^2}{4} = -\dfrac{x^4y^2}{4}$

13. $\left(-8a^2b^2\right) \div \left(-18a^8b\right) = \dfrac{\overset{4}{-\cancel{8}}a^2b^2}{\underset{9}{-\cancel{18}}a^8b} = \dfrac{4b}{9a^6}$

15. $\left(-32a^3b^4\right) \div \left(40a^2b^7\right) = \dfrac{\overset{4}{-\cancel{32}}a^3b^4}{\underset{5}{\cancel{40}}a^2b^7} = \dfrac{-4a}{5b^3} = -\dfrac{4a}{5b^3}$

17. $(12x + 21) \div 3 = \dfrac{12x + 21}{3} = \dfrac{12x}{3} + \dfrac{21}{3} = 4x + 7$

19. $\left(12x^2 - 4x\right) \div (4x) = \dfrac{12x^2 - 4x}{4x} = \dfrac{12x^2}{4x} - \dfrac{4x}{4x} = 3x - 1$

21. $\left(8x^3 - 24x\right) \div (-4x) = \dfrac{8x^3 - 24x}{-4x} = \dfrac{8x^3}{-4x} + \dfrac{-24x}{-4x} = -2x^2 + 6$

23. $\left(28x^3 - 16x^2 + 20x\right) \div (4x) = \dfrac{28x^3 - 16x^2 + 20x}{4x} = \dfrac{28x^3}{4x} - \dfrac{16x^2}{4x} + \dfrac{20x}{4x} = 7x^2 - 4x + 5$

25. $\left(-24a^5 - 30a^4 + 6a^2\right) \div \left(-3a^2\right) = \dfrac{-24a^5 - 30a^4 + 6a^2}{-3a^2} = \dfrac{-24a^5}{-3a^2} - \dfrac{30a^4}{-3a^2} + \dfrac{6a^2}{-3a^2} = 8a^3 + 10a^2 - 2$

27. $\left(24x^2 + 13x\right) \div (8x) = \dfrac{24x^2 + 13x}{8x} = \dfrac{24x^2}{8x} + \dfrac{13x}{8x} = 3x + \dfrac{13}{8}$

29. $\left(6x^3 + 8x^2 - 12x\right) \div (-6x) = \dfrac{6x^3 + 8x^2 - 12x}{-6x} = \dfrac{6x^3}{-6x} + \dfrac{8x^2}{-6x} - \dfrac{12x}{-6x} = -x^2 - \dfrac{4x}{3} + 2$

31. $\left(-36x^6y^9 + 16x^4y^5 - 24x^{11}y^8\right) \div \left(-12x^3y^4\right) = \dfrac{-36x^6y^9 + 16x^4y^5 - 24x^{11}y^8}{-12x^3y^4}$

$= \dfrac{-36x^6y^9}{-12x^3y^4} + \dfrac{16x^4y^5}{-12x^3y^4} - \dfrac{24x^{11}y^8}{-12x^3y^4}$

$= 3x^3y^5 - \dfrac{4xy}{3} + 2x^8y^4$

33. $\left(16s^4t^5 - 18s^6t^{10} - 24s^4t^9\right) \div \left(8s^{12}t^9\right) = \dfrac{16s^4t^5 - 18s^6t^{10} - 24s^4t^9}{8s^{12}t^9}$

$= \dfrac{16s^4t^5}{8s^{12}t^9} - \dfrac{18s^6t^{10}}{8s^{12}t^9} - \dfrac{24s^4t^9}{8s^{12}t^9}$

$= \dfrac{2}{s^8t^4} - \dfrac{9t}{4s^6} - \dfrac{3}{s^8}$

35. $\left(x^2 + 4x + 3\right) \div (x + 1) = x + 3$

$$
\begin{array}{r}
x + 3 \\
x + 1 \overline{)\, x^2 + 4x + 3} \\
-\ \ x^2 + x \\
\hline
3x + 3 \\
-\ \ \ \ \ \ 3x + 3 \\
\hline
0
\end{array}
$$

37. $(x^2 + x - 6) \div (x + 3) = x - 2$

$$
\begin{array}{r}
x - 2 \\
x + 3 \overline{)\ x^2 + \ x - 6} \\
-\ \underline{x^2 + 3x} \\
-2x - 6 \\
-\ \underline{-2x - 6} \\
0
\end{array}
$$

39. $(x^2 + 4x - 45) \div (x - 5) = x + 9$

$$
\begin{array}{r}
x + 9 \\
x - 5 \overline{)\ x^2 + 4x - 45} \\
-\ \underline{x^2 - 5x} \\
9x - 45 \\
-\ \underline{9x - 45} \\
0
\end{array}
$$

41. $(x^2 + 4x + 2) \div (x + 1) = x + 3 \text{ R } -1$

$$
\begin{array}{r}
x + 3 \text{ R } -1 \\
x + 1 \overline{)\ x^2 + 4x + 2} \\
-\ \underline{x^2 + \ x} \\
3x + 2 \\
-\ \underline{3x + 3} \\
-1
\end{array}
$$

43. $(y^2 - 12y + 3) \div (y + 5) = y - 17 \text{ R } 88$

$$
\begin{array}{r}
y - 17 \text{ R } 88 \\
y + 5 \overline{)\ y^2 - 12y + 3} \\
-\ \underline{y^2 + \ 5y} \\
-17y + \ 3 \\
-\ \underline{-17y - 85} \\
88
\end{array}
$$

45. $(a^2 - 7a - 9) \div (a + 4) = a - 11 \text{ R } 35$

$$
\begin{array}{r}
a - 11 \text{ R } 35 \\
a + 4 \overline{)\ a^2 - 7a - 9} \\
-\ \underline{a^2 + 4a} \\
-11a - \ 9 \\
-\ \underline{-11a - 44} \\
35
\end{array}
$$

186

47. $\left(x^2 + 10x - 6\right) \div (x - 3) = x + 13 \text{ R } 33$

$$
\begin{array}{r}
x + 13 \text{ R } 33 \\
x - 3 \overline{)\, x^2 + 10x - 6} \\
-\ \underline{x^2 - 3x} \\
13x - 6 \\
-\ \underline{13x - 39} \\
33
\end{array}
$$

49. $\left(p^2 - 4p - 14\right) \div (p + 4) = p - 8 \text{ R } 18$

$$
\begin{array}{r}
p - 8 \text{ R } 18 \\
p + 4 \overline{)\, p^2 - 4p - 14} \\
-\ \underline{p^2 + 4p} \\
-8p - 14 \\
-\ \underline{-8p - 32} \\
18
\end{array}
$$

51. $\left(3x^2 + 2x + 1\right) \div (x + 5) = 3x - 13 \text{ R } 66$

$$
\begin{array}{r}
3x - 13 \text{ R } 66 \\
x + 5 \overline{)\, 3x^2 + 2x + 1} \\
-\ \underline{3x^2 + 15x} \\
-13x + 1 \\
-\ \underline{-13x - 65} \\
66
\end{array}
$$

53. $\left(7y^2 + 3y - 1\right) \div (y + 3) = 7y - 18 \text{ R } 53$

$$
\begin{array}{r}
7y - 18 \text{ R } 53 \\
y + 3 \overline{)\, 7y^2 + 3y - 1} \\
-\ \underline{7y^2 + 21y} \\
-18y - 1 \\
-\ \underline{-18y - 54} \\
53
\end{array}
$$

55. $\left(8m^2 - 2m - 5\right) \div (m - 2) = 8m + 14 \text{ R } 23$

$$
\begin{array}{r}
8m + 14 \text{ R } 23 \\
m - 2 \overline{)\, 8m^2 - 2m - 5} \\
-\ \underline{8m^2 - 16m} \\
14m - 5 \\
-\ \underline{14m - 28} \\
23
\end{array}
$$

57. $\left(2x^2 - 3x + 4\right) \div (2x + 1) = x - 2 \text{ R } 6$

$$
\begin{array}{r}
x - 2 \text{ R } 6 \\
2x + 1 \overline{)\, 2x^2 - 3x + 4} \\
\underline{-\ \ 2x^2 +\ \ x} \\
-4x + 4 \\
\underline{-\qquad -4x - 2} \\
6
\end{array}
$$

59. $\left(3a^2 - 6a + 5\right) \div (3a - 4) = a - \frac{2}{3} \text{ R } \frac{7}{3}$

$$
\begin{array}{r}
a - \dfrac{2}{3} \text{ R } \dfrac{7}{3} \\
3a - 4 \overline{)\, 3a^2 - 6a + 5} \\
\underline{-\ \ 3a^2 - 4a} \\
-2a + 5 \\
\underline{-\qquad -2a + \dfrac{8}{3}} \\
\dfrac{7}{3}
\end{array}
$$

61. $\left(5t^2 - 10t - 6\right) \div (5t - 2) = t - \frac{8}{5} \text{ R } -\frac{46}{5}$

$$
\begin{array}{r}
t - \dfrac{8}{5} \text{ R } -\dfrac{46}{5} \\
5t - 2 \overline{)\, 5t^2 - 10t -\ \ 6} \\
\underline{-\ \ 5t^2 -\ \ 2t} \\
-8t -\ \ 6 \\
\underline{-\qquad -8t + \dfrac{16}{5}} \\
-\dfrac{46}{5}
\end{array}
$$

63. $\left(4y^2 + 2y + 3\right) \div (4y - 1) = y + \frac{3}{4} \text{ R } \frac{15}{4}$

$$
\begin{array}{r}
y + \dfrac{3}{4} \text{ R } \dfrac{15}{4} \\
4y - 1 \overline{)\, 4y^2 + 2y + 3} \\
\underline{-\ \ 4y^2 -\ \ y} \\
3y + 3 \\
\underline{-\qquad 3y - \dfrac{3}{4}} \\
\dfrac{15}{4}
\end{array}
$$

65. $\left(6y^2 - y + 4\right) \div (3y - 1) = 2y + \frac{1}{3} \text{ R } \frac{13}{3}$

$$
\begin{array}{r}
2y + \dfrac{1}{3} \text{ R } \dfrac{13}{3} \\
3y - 1 \overline{)\, 6y^2 - y + 4} \\
-\quad 6y^2 - 2y \\
\hline
y + 4 \\
-\qquad y - \dfrac{1}{3} \\
\hline
\dfrac{13}{3}
\end{array}
$$

67. $\left(x^3 + 3x^2 - 2x + 1\right) \div (x + 4) = x^2 - x + 2 \text{ R } -7$

$$
\begin{array}{r}
x^2 - x + 2 \text{ R } -7 \\
x + 4 \overline{)\, x^3 + 3x^2 - 2x + 1} \\
-\quad x^3 + 4x^2 \\
\hline
-x^2 - 2x + 1 \\
-\qquad -x^2 - 4x \\
\hline
2x + 1 \\
-\qquad 2x + 8 \\
\hline
-7
\end{array}
$$

69. $\left(y^3 - y^2 - 7y + 3\right) \div (y + 5) = y^2 - 6y + 23 \text{ R } -112$

$$
\begin{array}{r}
y^2 - 6y + 23 \text{ R } -112 \\
y + 5 \overline{)\, y^3 - y^2 - 7y + 3} \\
-\quad y^3 + 5y^2 \\
\hline
-6y^2 - 7y + 3 \\
-\qquad -6y^2 - 30y \\
\hline
23y + 3 \\
-\qquad 23y + 115 \\
\hline
-112
\end{array}
$$

71. $\left(x^3 - 4x^2 + 3x - 2\right) \div (x - 2) = x^2 - 2x - 1 \text{ R } -4$

$$
\begin{array}{r}
x^2 - 2x - 1 \text{ R } -4 \\
x - 2 \overline{)\, x^3 - 4x^2 + 3x - 2} \\
-\quad x^3 - 2x^2 \\
\hline
-2x^2 + 3x - 2 \\
-\qquad -2x^2 + 4x \\
\hline
-x - 2 \\
-\qquad -x + 2 \\
\hline
-4
\end{array}
$$

73. $\left(5a^3 - 3a^2 + a + 2\right) \div (a - 3) = 5a^2 + 12a + 37 \ \text{R} \ 113$

$$
\begin{array}{r}
5a^2 + 12a + 37 \ \text{R} \ 113 \\
a-3 \overline{)\, 5a^3 - 3a^2 + a + 2\,} \\
- \quad 5a^3 - 15a^2 \\
\hline
12a^2 + a + 2 \\
- \quad 12a^2 - 36a \\
\hline
37a + 2 \\
- \quad 37a - 111 \\
\hline
113
\end{array}
$$

75. $\left(y^2 + 5\right) \div (y - 3) = y + 3 \ \text{R} \ 14$

$$
\begin{array}{r}
y + 3 \ \text{R} \ 14 \\
y - 3 \overline{)\, y^2 + 0y + 5\,} \\
- \quad y^2 - 3y \\
\hline
3y + 5 \\
- \quad 3y - 9 \\
\hline
14
\end{array}
$$

77. $\left(-3t^2 + 4t\right) \div (t + 6) = -3t + 22 \ \text{R} \ -132$

$$
\begin{array}{r}
-3t + 22 \ \text{R} \ -132 \\
t + 6 \overline{)\, -3t^2 + 4t + 0\,} \\
- \quad -3t^2 - 18t \\
\hline
22t + 0 \\
- \quad 22t + 132 \\
\hline
-132
\end{array}
$$

79. $\left(x^2 + 5x\right) \div \left(x^2 + 6\right) = 1 \ \text{R} \ 5x - 6$

$$
\begin{array}{r}
1 \ \text{R} \ 5x - 6 \\
x^2 + 6 \overline{)\, x^2 + 5x + 0\,} \\
- \quad x^2 \quad + 6 \\
\hline
5x - 6
\end{array}
$$

81. $\left(9p^2 + 1\right) \div \left(p^2 - 8p\right) = 9 \ \text{R} \ 72p + 1$

$$
\begin{array}{r}
9 \ \text{R} \ 72p + 1 \\
p^2 - 8p \overline{)\, 9p^2 + 0p + 1\,} \\
- \quad 9p^2 - 72p \\
\hline
72p + 1
\end{array}
$$

83. $\left(4x^2 + 1\right) \div \left(x^2 - 5x\right) = 4 \ \text{R} \ 20x + 1$

$$
\begin{array}{r}
4 \ \text{R} \ 20x + 1 \\
x^2 - 5x \overline{)\, 4x^2 + 0x + 1\,} \\
- \quad 4x^2 - 20x \\
\hline
20x + 1
\end{array}
$$

85. $\left(y^3 - 4y^2 + 2\right) \div (y - 3) = y^2 - y - 3 \ \ \text{R} \ \ -7$

$$
\begin{array}{r}
y^2 - y - 3 \ \ \text{R} \ \ -7 \\
y - 3 \overline{)\, y^3 - 4y^2 + 0y + 2} \\
-\ \ \underline{y^3 - 3y^2} \\
-\ y^2 + 0y + 2 \\
-\ \ \underline{-\ y^2 + 3y} \\
-3y + 2 \\
-\ \ \underline{-3y + 9} \\
-7
\end{array}
$$

87. $\left(a^3 + 2a^2 + 4\right) \div (a + 5) = a^2 - 3a + 15 \ \ \text{R} \ \ -71$

$$
\begin{array}{r}
a^2 - 3a + 15 \ \ \text{R} \ \ -71 \\
a + 5 \overline{)\, a^3 + 2a^2 + 0a + 4} \\
-\ \ \underline{a^3 + 5a^2} \\
-3a^2 + 0a + 4 \\
-\ \ \underline{-3a^2 - 15a} \\
15a + 4 \\
-\ \ \underline{15a + 75} \\
-71
\end{array}
$$

89. $\left(4b^3 + b^2 - 3b\right) \div \left(b^2 + 3\right) = 4b + 1 \ \ \text{R} \ \ -15b - 3$

$$
\begin{array}{r}
4b + 1 \ \ \text{R} \ \ -15b - 3 \\
b^2 + 3 \overline{)\, 4b^3 + b^2 - 3b + 0} \\
-\ \ \underline{4b^3 \qquad + 12b} \\
b^2 - 15b + 0 \\
-\ \ \underline{b^2 \qquad + 3} \\
-15b - 3
\end{array}
$$

91. $\left(x^4 - 5x^2 + 9\right) \div \left(x^2 - 1\right) = x^2 - 4 \ \ \text{R} \ \ 5$

$$
\begin{array}{r}
x^2 - 4 \ \ \text{R} \ \ 5 \\
x^2 - 1 \overline{)\, x^4 + 0x^3 - 5x^2 + 0x + 9} \\
-\ \ \underline{x^4 \qquad - x^2} \\
-4x^2 + 0x + 9 \\
-\ \ \underline{-4x^2 \qquad + 4} \\
5
\end{array}
$$

93. $\left(64x^3 + 1\right) \div (4x + 1) = 16x^2 - 4x + 1$

$$
\begin{array}{r}
16x^2 - 4x + 1 \\
4x + 1 \overline{)\, 64x^3 + 0x^2 + 0x + 1} \\
-\ \ \underline{64x^3 + 16x^2} \\
-16x^2 + 0x + 1 \\
-\ \ \underline{-16x^2 - 4x} \\
4x + 1 \\
-\ \ \underline{4x + 1} \\
0
\end{array}
$$

191

95. $\left(64a^3 - 27\right) \div (4a - 3) = 16a^2 + 12a + 9$

$$
\begin{array}{r}
16a^2 + 12a + 9 \\
4a - 3\overline{)\,64a^3 + \ 0a^2 + \ 0a - 27} \\
-\quad \underline{64a^3 - 48a^2} \\
48a^2 + \ 0a - 27 \\
-\quad \underline{48a^2 - 36a} \\
36a - 27 \\
-\quad \underline{36a - 27} \\
0
\end{array}
$$

Chapter 3 Exercise 3.5

1. $2x + 18 = 2\,(x + 9)$ 3. $4a^2 + 12 = 4\left(a^2 + 3\right)$ 5. $10x^2 + 5x - 20 = 5\left(2x^2 + x - 4\right)$

7. $6x^2 + 24x = 6x\,(x + 4)$ 9. $15x^3 - 9x^2 = 3x^2\,(5x - 3)$ 11. $7q^2 + 16q^5 = q^2\left(7 + 16q^3\right)$

13. $18x^4 + 27x^3 - 9x^2 = 9x^2\left(2x^2 + 3x - 1\right)$ 15. $20a^4b^2 + 22ab^6 = 2ab^2\left(10a^3 + 11b^4\right)$

17. $6s^3t - 5s^3t^2 + s^2t^2 = s^2t\,(6s - 5st + t)$

19. $21a^5b^2c^3 - 7a^3b^5c^4 - 35a^5b^2c^8 = 7a^3b^2c^3\left(3a^2 - b^3c - 5a^2c^5\right)$

21. $36x^2y^7 + 27xy^6 - 18y^8 = 9y^6\left(4x^2y + 3x - 2y^2\right)$

23. $-3x + 6 = -3\,(x - 2)$ 25. $-4t - 36 = -4\,(t + 9)$ 27. $-16y^2 - 32y + 80 = -16\left(y^2 + 2y - 5\right)$

29. $-5n^4 - 15n^3 - 55 = -5\left(n^4 + 3n^3 + 11\right)$ 31. $-16t^2 + 32t + 64 = -16\left(t^2 - 2t - 4\right)$

33. $y^2 - 9 = (y)^2 - (3)^2 = (y + 3)\,(y - 3)$ 35. $n^2 - 36 = (n)^2 - (6)^2 = (n + 6)\,(n - 6)$

37. $b^2 - 25 = (b)^2 - (5)^2 = (b + 5)\,(b - 5)$ 39. $49 - x^2 = (7)^2 - (x)^2 = (7 + x)\,(7 - x)$

41. $81t^2 - 64 = (9t)^2 - (8)^2 = (9t + 8)\,(9t - 8)$ 43. $121a^2 - 4 = (11a)^2 - (2)^2 = (11a + 2)\,(11a - 2)$

45. $p^2 - 144q^2 = (p)^2 - (12q)^2 = (p + 12q)\,(p - 12q)$

47. $36u^2 - 49v^2 = (6u)^2 - (7v)^2 = (6u + 7v)\,(6u - 7v)$

49. $y^2 - \dfrac{1}{4} = (y)^2 - \left(\dfrac{1}{2}\right)^2 = \left(y + \dfrac{1}{2}\right)\left(y - \dfrac{1}{2}\right)$

51. $\dfrac{49}{81} - 100d^2 = \left(\dfrac{7}{9}\right)^2 - (10d)^2 = \left(\dfrac{7}{9} + 10d\right)\left(\dfrac{7}{9} - 10d\right)$

53. $\dfrac{16}{121}x^2 - 144y^2 = \left(\dfrac{4}{11}x\right)^2 - (12y)^2 = \left(\dfrac{4}{11}x + 12y\right)\left(\dfrac{4}{11}x - 12y\right)$

55. $y^3 + 27 = (y)^3 + (3)^3 = (y + 3)\left((y)^2 - (y)\,(3) + (3)^2\right) = (y + 3)\left(y^2 - 3y + 9\right)$

57. $m^3 + 8 = (m)^3 + (2)^3 = (m + 2)\left((m)^2 - (m)\,(2) + (2)^2\right) = (m + 2)\left(m^2 - 2m + 4\right)$

59. $125 - y^3 = (5)^3 - (y)^3 = (5 - y)\left((5)^2 + (5)\,(y) + (y)^2\right) = (5 - y)\left(25 + 5y + y^2\right)$

61. $q^3 - 216 = (q)^3 - (6)^3 = (q - 6)\left((q)^2 + (q)(6) + (6)^2\right) = (q - 6)\left(q^2 + 6q + 36\right)$

63. $8b^3 + 1 = (2b)^3 + (1)^3 = (2b + 1)\left((2b)^2 - (2b)(1) + (1)^2\right) = (2b + 1)\left(4b^2 - 2b + 1\right)$

65. $64x^3 - y^3 = (4x)^3 - (y)^3 = (4x - y)\left((4x)^2 + (4x)(y) + (y)^2\right) = (4x - y)\left(16x^2 + 4xy + y^2\right)$

67. $27m^3 + 1{,}000 = (3m)^3 + (10)^3 = (3m + 10)\left((3m)^2 - (3m)(10) + (10)^2\right) = (3m + 10)\left(9m^2 - 30m + 100\right)$

69. $343x^3 + 8y^3 = (7x)^3 + (2y)^3 = (7x + 2y)\left((7x)^2 - (7x)(2y) + (2y)^2\right) = (7x + 2y)\left(49x^2 - 14xy + 4y^2\right)$

71. $64a^3 - 125b^3 = (4a)^3 - (5b)^3 = (4a - 5b)\left((4a)^2 + (4a)(5b) + (5b)^2\right) = (4a - 5b)\left(16a^2 + 20ab + 25b^2\right)$

73. $7y^2 - 63 = 7\left(y^2 - 9\right) = 7(y + 3)(y - 3)$ 75. $2n^4 - 72n^2 = 2n^2\left(n^2 - 36\right) = 2n^2(n + 6)(n - 6)$

77. $\underbrace{9b^2 - 9 = 9\left(b^2 - 1\right)}_{\text{The GCF first!}} = 9(b + 1)(b - 1)$ 79. $\underbrace{64x^2 - 16y^2 = 16\left(4x^2 - y^2\right)}_{\text{The GCF first!}} = 16(2x + y)(2x - y)$

81. $5m^3 + 40 = 5\underbrace{\left(m^3 + 8\right)}_{(m)^3 + (2)^3} = 5(m + 2)\left(m^2 - 2m + 4\right)$ 83. $12u^3 - 12 = 12\underbrace{\left(u^3 - 1\right)}_{(u)^3 + (1)^3} = 12(u - 1)\left(u^2 + u + 1\right)$

85. $250t^7 - 2t^4 = 2t^4\underbrace{\left(125t^3 - 1\right)}_{(5t)^3 - (1)^3} = 2t^4(5t - 1)\left(25t^2 + 5t + 1\right)$

87. $x^4y^2 - 1{,}000xy^2 = xy^2\underbrace{\left(x^3 - 1{,}000\right)}_{(x)^3 - (10)^3} = xy^2(x - 10)\left(x^2 + 10x + 100\right)$

89. $x^2 + 4x + 3 = (x + 1)(x + 3)$ 91. $y^2 + 13y + 40 = (y + 8)(y + 5)$

93. $x^2 + 7x - 18 = (x + 9)(x - 2)$ 95. $y^2 + 8y - 20 = (y + 10)(y - 2)$

97. $a^2 - 12a + 27 = (a - 9)(a - 3)$ 99. $b^2 - 15b + 36 = (b - 12)(b - 3)$

101. $x^2 - 4x - 21 = (x + 3)(x - 7)$ 103. $q^2 + 21q + 38 = (q + 19)(q + 2)$

105. $x^2 + 4x + 4 = (x + 2)(x + 2) = (x + 2)^2$ 107. $m^2 - 18m + 81 = (m - 9)(m - 9) = (m - 9)^2$

109. $t^2 + 22t + 121 = (t + 11)(t + 11) = (t + 11)^2$ 111. $x^2 - 10x + 25 = (x - 5)(x - 5) = (x - 5)^2$

113. $x^2 + 4x + 8$ is prime.   115. $y^2 + 9y + 10$ is prime.   117. $2x^2 + 3x + 1 = (2x + 1)(x + 1)$

119. $2y^2 + y - 3 = (2y + 3)(y - 1)$ 121. $5x^2 + 19x - 4 = (5x - 1)(x + 4)$

123. $14m^2 + 11m + 2 = (7m + 2)(2m + 1)$ 125. $4s^2 - 20s + 21 = (2s - 3)(2s - 7)$

127. $4p^2 - 23p + 15 = (4p - 3)(p - 5)$ 129. $6a^2 + 31a + 35 = (2a + 7)(3a + 5)$

131. $8x^2 - 38x + 45 = (4x - 9)(2x - 5)$ 133. $30y^2 + y - 3 = (10y - 3)(3y + 1)$

135. $9u^2 + 24u + 16 = (3u + 4)(3u + 4) = (3u + 4)^2$

137. $121m^2 + 132m + 36 = (11m + 6)(11m + 6) = (11m + 6)^2$

139. $16p^2 - 40p + 25 = (4p - 5)(4p - 5) = (4p - 5)^2$ 141. $3x^2 + 5x + 4$ is prime.

143. $7a^2 - 2a + 11$ is prime.   145. $4x^2 - x + 12$ is prime.

147. $x^3 + x^2 + 4x + 4 = (x^3 + x^2) + (4x + 4) = x^2\underline{(x + 1)} + 4\underline{(x + 1)} = \underline{(x + 1)}(x^2 + 4)$

149. $y^3 - 7y^2 + 2y - 14 = (y^3 - 7y^2) + (2y - 14) = y^2\underline{(y - 7)} + 2\underline{(y - 7)} = \underline{(y - 7)}(y^2 + 2)$

151. $3a^3 + 15a^2 + 2a + 10 = (3a^3 + 15a^2) + (2a + 10) = 3a^2\underline{(a + 5)} + 2\underline{(a + 5)} = \underline{(a + 5)}(3a^2 + 2)$

153. $16m^3 - 40m^2 - 6m + 15 = (16m^3 - 40m^2) + (-6m + 15) = 8m^2\underline{(2m - 5)} - 3\underline{(2m - 5)} = \underline{(2m - 5)}(8m^2 - 3)$

155. $x^5 + x^3 + 12x^2 + 12 = (x^5 + x^3) + (12x^2 + 12) = x^3\underline{(x^2 + 1)} + 12\underline{(x^2 + 1)} = \underline{(x^2 + 1)}(x^3 + 12)$

157. $8b^5 - 48b^3 + 3b^2 - 18 = (8b^5 - 48b^3) + (3b^2 - 18) = 8b^3\underline{(b^2 - 6)} + 3\underline{(b^2 - 6)} = \underline{(b^2 - 6)}(8b^3 + 3)$

159. $2p^3 + p + 6p^2q + 3q = (2p^3 + p) + (6p^2q + 3q) = p\underline{(2p^2 + 1)} + 3q\underline{(2p^2 + 1)} = \underline{(2p^2 + 1)}(p + 3q)$

161. $80m^4 - 50m^2 - 24m^2n + 15n = (80m^4 - 50m^2) + (-24m^2n + 15n)$

$$= 10m^2\underline{(8m^2 - 5)} - 3n\underline{(8m^2 - 5)} = \underline{(8m^2 - 5)}(10m^2 - 3n)$$

163. $x^2 + 8x + 16 - y^2 = \underbrace{(x^2 + 8x + 16)}_{(x+4)(x+4)} - y^2 = \underbrace{(x + 4)^2 - (y)^2 = (x + 4 + y)(x + 4 - y)}$
      Use $A^2 - B^2 = (A+B)(A-B)$ with $A = x+4$ and $B = y$.

165. $a^2 - 14a + 49 - 9b^2 = \underbrace{(a^2 - 14a + 49)}_{(a-7)(a-7)} - 9b^2 = \underbrace{(a - 7)^2 - (3b)^2 = (a - 7 + 3b)(a - 7 - 3b)}$
      Use $A^2 - B^2 = (A+B)(A-B)$ with $A = a-7$ and $B = 3b$.

167. $x^2 + 18x + 81 - 144y^2 = \underbrace{(x^2 + 18x + 81)}_{(x+9)(x+9)} - 144y^2 = \underbrace{(x + 9)^2 - (12y)^2 = (x + 9 + 12y)(x + 9 - 12y)}$
      Use $A^2 - B^2 = (A+B)(A-B)$ with $A = x+9$ and $B = 12y$.

169. $6x^2 + 18x + 12 = 6(x^2 + 3x + 2) = 6(x + 2)(x + 1)$

171. $4a^4 - 8a^3 - 60a^2 = 4a^2(a^2 - 2a - 15) = 4a^2(a + 3)(a - 5)$

173. $5u^7 - 55u^6 + 150u^5 = 5u^5(u^2 - 11u + 30) = 5u^5(u - 6)(u - 5)$

175. $2x^3y^3 - 6x^3y^2 - 56x^3y = 2x^3y(y^2 - 3y - 28) = 2x^3y(y + 4)(y - 7)$

177. $27x^2y + 63xy + 18y = 9y(3x^2 + 7x + 2) = 9y(3x + 1)(x + 2)$

179. $56y^2 + 14y - 21 = 7(8y^2 + 2y - 3) = 7(4y + 3)(2y - 1)$

181. $48u^5 - 58u^4 + 14u^3 = 2u^3(24u^2 - 29u + 7) = 2u^3(8u - 7)(3u - 1)$

183. $8s^3t^2 - 48s^2t^2 + 72st^2 = 8st^2(s^2 - 6s + 9) = 8st^2(s - 3)(s - 3) = 8st^2(s - 3)^2$

185. $9a^4 + 6a^3 + a^2 = a^2(9a^2 + 6a + 1) = a^2(3a + 1)(3a + 1) = a^2(3a + 1)^2$

187. $20 + x - x^2 = -x^2 + x + 20 = -1(x^2 - x - 20) = -1(x + 4)(x - 5)$ or $-(x + 4)(x - 5)$

189. $-20 + 9t - t^2 = -t^2 + 9t - 20 = -1\left(t^2 - 9t + 20\right) = -1\left(t - 5\right)\left(t - 4\right)$ or $-\left(t - 5\right)\left(t - 4\right)$

191. $72 + 30x - 12x^2 = -12x^2 + 30x + 72 = -6\left(2x^2 - 5x - 12\right) = -6\left(2x + 3\right)\left(x - 4\right)$

193. $x^4 + 10x^2 + 25 = \left(x^2 + 5\right)\left(x^2 + 5\right) = \left(x^2 + 5\right)^2$

195. $y^6 + 18y^3 + 81 = \left(y^3 + 9\right)\left(y^3 + 9\right) = \left(y^3 + 9\right)^2$

197. $u^4 - 2u^2 + 1 = \left(u^2 - 1\right)\left(u^2 - 1\right) = \underbrace{\left(u + 1\right)\left(u - 1\right)}_{u^2 - 1}\underbrace{\left(u + 1\right)\left(u - 1\right)}_{u^2 - 1} = \left(u + 1\right)^2\left(u - 1\right)^2$

199. $16x^4 - 81 = \left(4x^2\right)^2 - \left(9\right)^2 = \underbrace{\left(4x^2 + 9\right)}_{\text{prime}}\left(4x^2 - 9\right) = \left(x^2 + 9\right)\underbrace{\left(2x + 3\right)\left(2x - 3\right)}_{4x^2 - 9}$

201. $x^6 + 2x^3 + 1 = \left(x^3 + 1\right)\left(x^3 + 1\right) = \underbrace{\left(x + 1\right)\left(x^2 - x + 1\right)}_{x^3 + 1}\underbrace{\left(x + 1\right)\left(x^2 - x + 1\right)}_{x^3 + 1} = \left(x + 1\right)^2\left(x^2 - x + 1\right)^2$

203. $m^4 - 13m^2 - 48 = \left(m^2 + 3\right)\left(m^2 - 16\right) = \left(m^2 + 3\right)\underbrace{\left(m + 4\right)\left(m - 4\right)}_{m^2 - 16}$

205. $a^6 - 10a^3 + 16 = \left(a^3 - 8\right)\left(a^3 - 2\right) = \underbrace{\left(a - 2\right)\left(a^2 + 2a + 4\right)}_{a^3 - 8}\left(a^3 - 2\right)$

207. $1 - p^6 = \left(1\right)^2 - \left(p^3\right)^2 = \left(1 + p^3\right)\left(1 - p^3\right) = \underbrace{\left(1 + p\right)\left(1 - p + p^2\right)}_{1 + p^3}\underbrace{\left(1 - p\right)\left(1 + p + p^2\right)}_{1 - p^3}$

209. $1 - 64x^6 = \left(1\right)^2 - \left(8x^3\right)^2 = \left(1 + 8x^3\right)\left(1 - 8x^3\right) = \underbrace{\left(1 + 2x\right)\left(1 - 2x + 4x^2\right)}_{1 + 8x^3}\underbrace{\left(1 - 2x\right)\left(1 + 2x + 4x^2\right)}_{1 - 8x^3}$

211. $28a^2 + 25ab + 3b^2 = \left(4a + 3b\right)\left(7a + b\right)$

213. $9m^2 - 42mn + 49n^2 = \left(3m - 7n\right)\left(3m - 7n\right) = \left(3m - 7n\right)^2$

215. $8x^4y + 42x^3y^2 + 54x^2y^3 = 2x^2y\left(4x^2 + 21xy + 27y^2\right) = 2x^2y\left(4x + 9y\right)\left(x + 3y\right)$

Chapter 4 Exercise 4.1

1. $\dfrac{4x^2}{7x} = \dfrac{4x}{7}$

3. $\dfrac{\overset{1}{\cancel{5}x^2}}{\underset{2}{\cancel{10}x^6}} = \dfrac{1}{2x^4}$

5. $\dfrac{\overset{8}{\cancel{32}}}{\underset{3}{\cancel{12}x^7}} = \dfrac{8}{3x^7}$

7. $\dfrac{8x^3}{x^{10}} = \dfrac{8}{x^7}$

9. $\dfrac{x^{11}y^2}{x^6y^5} = \dfrac{x^5}{y^3}$

11. $\dfrac{\overset{5}{\cancel{-10}a^5b^6}}{\underset{8}{\cancel{16}ab^4}} = -\dfrac{5a^4b^2}{8}$

13. $\dfrac{\overset{2}{\cancel{6}a^2b^3}}{\underset{7}{\cancel{21}a^7b^{10}}} = \dfrac{2}{7a^5b^7}$

15. $\dfrac{\overset{2}{\cancel{8}r^2s^8t^6}}{\underset{5}{\cancel{20}r^4st^9}} = \dfrac{2s^7}{5r^2t^3}$

17. $\dfrac{\overset{9}{\cancel{-18}m^{16}n^8p^7}}{\underset{4}{\cancel{-8}m^4p^7}} = \dfrac{9m^{12}n^8}{4}$

19. $\dfrac{\overset{8}{\cancel{-56}ac^7}}{\underset{1}{\cancel{7}a^8b^6}} = -\dfrac{8c^7}{a^7b^6}$

21. $\dfrac{3x + 6}{7x + 14} = \dfrac{3\underset{1}{\cancel{(x + 2)}}}{7\underset{1}{\cancel{(x + 2)}}} = \dfrac{3}{7}$

23. $\dfrac{9y - 36}{3y - 12} = \dfrac{9(\cancel{y - 4})}{3(\cancel{y - 4})} = \dfrac{9}{3} = 3$

25. $\dfrac{8t - 20}{8t + 20} = \dfrac{\cancel{4}(2t - 5)}{\cancel{4}(2t + 5)} = \dfrac{2t - 5}{2t + 5}$

27. $\dfrac{3x - 1}{3 - 9x} = \dfrac{1(\cancel{3x - 1})}{-3(\cancel{-1 + 3x})} = \dfrac{1}{-3} = -\dfrac{1}{3}$

29. $\dfrac{12 - 6x^2}{3x^2 - 6} = \dfrac{-\cancel{6}(\cancel{-2 + x^2})}{\cancel{3}(\cancel{x^2 - 2})} = \dfrac{-2}{1} = -2$

31. $\dfrac{8x^2 + 16}{-30 - 15x^2} = \dfrac{8(\cancel{x^2 + 2})}{-15(\cancel{2 + x^2})} = \dfrac{8}{-15} = -\dfrac{8}{15}$

33. $\dfrac{7p^2 + p}{8p^2 - 3p} = \dfrac{\cancel{p}(7p + 1)}{\cancel{p}(8p - 3)} = \dfrac{7p + 1}{8p - 3}$

35. $\dfrac{10x^2 + 10x}{10x^2 + 15x} = \dfrac{\cancel{10x}\,(x + 1)}{\cancel{5x}\,(2x + 3)} = \dfrac{2(x + 1)}{2x + 3}$

37. $\dfrac{2x^3y^3 - 2x^2y^4}{12x^5y + 12x^4y^2} = \dfrac{\cancel{2x^2y^3}\,(x - y)}{\cancel{12x^4y}\,(x + y)} = \dfrac{y^2\,(x - y)}{6x^2\,(x + y)}$

39. $\dfrac{4x^2 - 8x}{6x - 3x^2} = \dfrac{4x(\cancel{x - 2})}{-3x(\cancel{-2 + x})} = \dfrac{4}{-3} = -\dfrac{4}{3}$

41. $\dfrac{x^2 + 4x + 4}{6x + 12} = \dfrac{(x + 2)\,(\cancel{x + 2})}{6(\cancel{x + 2})} = \dfrac{x + 2}{6}$

43. $\dfrac{7x^2 - 63}{2x^2 - 6x} = \dfrac{7\left(x^2 - 9\right)}{2x\,(x - 3)} = \dfrac{7\,(x + 3)\,(\cancel{x - 3})}{2x(\cancel{x - 3})} = \dfrac{7\,(x + 3)}{2x}$

45. $\dfrac{x^3 - 1}{x^2 - 1} = \dfrac{(\cancel{x - 1})\left(x^2 + x + 1\right)}{(x + 1)\,(\cancel{x - 1})} = \dfrac{x^2 + x + 1}{x + 1}$

47. $\dfrac{9t^2 - 30t + 25}{6t^2 - 7t - 5} = \dfrac{(\cancel{3t - 5})(3t - 5)}{(\cancel{3t - 5})(2t + 1)} = \dfrac{3t - 5}{2t + 1}$

49. $\dfrac{16x^3 - 8x^2}{4x^2 - 1} = \dfrac{8x^2(\cancel{2x - 1})}{(2x + 1)\,(\cancel{2x - 1})} = \dfrac{8x^2}{2x + 1}$

51. $\dfrac{5x^2 + 22x + 21}{x^4 - 9x^2} = \dfrac{(5x + 7)\,(x + 3)}{x^2\left(x^2 - 9\right)} = \dfrac{(5x + 7)\,(\cancel{x + 3})}{x^2(\cancel{x + 3})\,(x - 3)} = \dfrac{5x + 7}{x^2\,(x - 3)}$

Chapter 4 Exercise 4.2

1. $\dfrac{8x^7y}{3x^2y^6} \cdot \dfrac{9x^4y^4}{7xy^{12}} = \dfrac{\left(8x^7y\right)\left(\cancel{9}x^4y^4\right)}{\left(\cancel{3}x^2y^6\right)\left(7xy^{12}\right)} = \dfrac{24x^{11}y^5}{7x^3y^{18}} = \dfrac{24x^8}{7y^{13}}$

3. $\left(-\dfrac{10a^2}{b^6c^4}\right) \cdot \dfrac{2ab^3c^4}{5} = -\dfrac{\left(\cancel{10}a^2\right)\left(2ab^3c^4\right)}{\left(b^6c^4\right)(\cancel{5})} = -\dfrac{4a^3b^3c^4}{b^6c^4} = -\dfrac{4a^3}{b^3}$

5. $\dfrac{4x + 12}{8x - 16} \cdot \dfrac{9x - 18}{5x + 15} = \dfrac{\cancel{4}(\cancel{x + 3})}{\cancel{8}(\cancel{x - 2})} \cdot \dfrac{9(\cancel{x - 2})}{5(\cancel{x + 3})} = \dfrac{9}{10}$

7. $\dfrac{12y^2 + 6y}{4y + 4} \cdot \dfrac{5y - 10}{3y^3 - 6y^2} = \dfrac{\cancel{6}y\,(2y + 1)}{\cancel{4}\,(y + 1)} \cdot \dfrac{5(\cancel{y - 2})}{\cancel{3}y^2(\cancel{y - 2})} = \dfrac{5\,(2y + 1)}{2y\,(y + 1)}$

196

9. $\dfrac{2a^2 - 2a - 12}{2a^2 + 10a + 12} \cdot \dfrac{3a - 9}{a + 1} = \dfrac{2\left(a^2 - a - 6\right)}{2\left(a^2 + 5a + 6\right)} \cdot \dfrac{3\left(a - 3\right)}{a + 1} = \dfrac{\overset{1}{\cancel{2}}\overset{1}{\left(\cancel{a + 2}\right)}\left(a - 3\right)}{\underset{1}{\cancel{2}}\underset{1}{\left(\cancel{a + 2}\right)}\left(a + 3\right)} \cdot \dfrac{3\left(a - 3\right)}{a + 1}$

$$= \dfrac{a - 3}{a + 3} \cdot \dfrac{3\left(a - 3\right)}{a + 1} = \dfrac{3\left(a - 3\right)^2}{\left(a + 3\right)\left(a + 1\right)}$$

11. $\dfrac{8y^3 - 64}{4y + 2} \cdot \dfrac{12y^2 + 12y + 3}{y^2 + 2y + 4} = \dfrac{8\left(y^3 - 8\right)}{2\left(2y + 1\right)} \cdot \dfrac{3\left(4y^2 + 4y + 1\right)}{y^2 + 2y + 4} = \dfrac{\overset{4}{\cancel{8}}\left(y - 2\right)\overset{1}{\left(\cancel{y^2 + 2y + 4}\right)}}{\underset{1}{\cancel{2}}\underset{1}{\left(\cancel{2y + 1}\right)}} \cdot \dfrac{3\overset{1}{\left(\cancel{2y + 1}\right)}\left(2y + 1\right)}{\underset{1}{\cancel{y^2 + 2y + 4}}}$

$$= \dfrac{12\left(2y + 1\right)\left(y - 2\right)}{1} = 12\left(2y + 1\right)\left(y - 2\right)$$

13. $\dfrac{x^2 - 25}{x^2 - 64} \cdot \dfrac{x^2 - 10x + 16}{x^2 + 9x + 20} = \dfrac{\overset{1}{\left(\cancel{x + 5}\right)}\left(x - 5\right)}{\left(x + 8\right)\underset{1}{\left(\cancel{x - 8}\right)}} \cdot \dfrac{\overset{1}{\left(\cancel{x - 8}\right)}\left(x - 2\right)}{\left(x + 4\right)\underset{1}{\left(\cancel{x + 5}\right)}} = \dfrac{\left(x - 5\right)\left(x - 2\right)}{\left(x + 8\right)\left(x + 4\right)}$

15. $\dfrac{-4u^2 - 5u + 6}{8u - 6} \cdot \dfrac{8u}{u + 2} = \dfrac{-1\left(4u^2 + 5u - 6\right)}{2\left(4u - 3\right)} \cdot \dfrac{8u}{u + 2} = \dfrac{-1\overset{1}{\left(\cancel{4u - 3}\right)}\overset{1}{\left(\cancel{u + 2}\right)}}{\underset{1}{\cancel{2}}\underset{1}{\left(\cancel{4u - 3}\right)}} \cdot \dfrac{\overset{4}{\cancel{8}}u}{\underset{1}{\cancel{u + 2}}} = \dfrac{-4u}{1} = -4u$

17. $\dfrac{x}{4} \div \dfrac{x^3}{20} = \dfrac{x}{4} \cdot \dfrac{20}{x^3} = \dfrac{\overset{5}{\cancel{20}}x}{\underset{1}{\cancel{4}}x^3} = \dfrac{5}{x^2}$

19. $\left(\dfrac{-25}{6y^8}\right) \div \left(\dfrac{10}{-9y^4}\right) = \left(\dfrac{-25}{6y^8}\right) \cdot \left(\dfrac{-9y^4}{10}\right) = \dfrac{\left(\overset{5}{\cancel{-25}}\right)\left(\overset{3}{-\cancel{9}y^4}\right)}{\left(\underset{1}{\cancel{6}}y^8\right)\left(\underset{2}{\cancel{10}}\right)} = \dfrac{15y^4}{2y^8} = \dfrac{15}{2y^4}$

21. $\left(\dfrac{a}{-15}\right) \div \dfrac{b^2}{12} = \left(\dfrac{a}{-15}\right) \cdot \dfrac{12}{b^2} = \dfrac{\overset{4}{\cancel{12}}a}{\underset{5}{\cancel{-15}}b^2} = -\dfrac{4a}{5b^2}$

23. $\dfrac{3x^9y^3}{5x^4y} \div \dfrac{10xy}{15x^4y^3} = \dfrac{3x^9y^3}{5x^4y} \cdot \dfrac{15x^4y^3}{10xy} = \dfrac{\left(3x^9y^3\right)\left(\overset{3}{\cancel{15}}x^4y^3\right)}{\left(\underset{1}{\cancel{5}}x^4y\right)\left(10xy\right)} = \dfrac{9x^{13}y^6}{10x^5y^2} = \dfrac{9x^8y^4}{10}$

25. $\left(\dfrac{-10u^5v}{8uv^5}\right) \div \left(\dfrac{15u^3v}{-16u^4v}\right) = \left(\dfrac{-10u^5v}{8uv^5}\right) \cdot \left(\dfrac{-16u^4v}{15u^3v}\right) = \dfrac{\left(\overset{2}{-\cancel{10}}u^5v\right)\left(\overset{2}{-\cancel{16}}u^4v\right)}{\left(\underset{1}{\cancel{8}}uv^5\right)\left(\underset{3}{\cancel{15}}u^3v\right)} = \dfrac{4u^9v^2}{3u^4v^6} = \dfrac{4u^5}{3v^4}$

27. $\dfrac{7x}{6} \div \dfrac{x^2 + x}{4x + 4} = \dfrac{7x}{6} \cdot \dfrac{4x + 4}{x^2 + x} = \dfrac{7x}{6} \cdot \dfrac{4\overset{1}{\left(\cancel{x + 1}\right)}}{x\underset{1}{\left(\cancel{x + 1}\right)}} = \dfrac{\overset{14}{\cancel{28}}}{\underset{3}{\cancel{6}}} = \dfrac{14}{3}$

29. $\dfrac{2t - 14}{3t + 18} \div \dfrac{2t + 14}{6t + 36} = \dfrac{2t - 14}{3t + 18} \cdot \dfrac{6t + 36}{2t + 14} = \dfrac{\overset{1}{\cancel{2}}\left(t - 7\right)}{\underset{1}{\cancel{3}}\underset{1}{\left(\cancel{t + 6}\right)}} \cdot \dfrac{\overset{2}{\cancel{6}}\overset{1}{\left(\cancel{t + 6}\right)}}{\underset{1}{\cancel{2}}\left(t + 7\right)} = \dfrac{2\left(t - 7\right)}{t + 7}$

31. $\dfrac{x^2 + 3x - 4}{6x - 6} \div \dfrac{x^2 - 6x + 8}{x - 2} = \dfrac{x^2 + 3x - 4}{6x - 6} \cdot \dfrac{x - 2}{x^2 - 6x + 8} = \dfrac{\overset{1}{\left(\cancel{x - 1}\right)}\left(x + 4\right)}{6\underset{1}{\left(\cancel{x - 1}\right)}} \cdot \dfrac{\overset{1}{\left(\cancel{x - 2}\right)}}{\underset{1}{\left(\cancel{x - 2}\right)}\left(x - 4\right)} = \dfrac{x + 4}{6\left(x - 4\right)}$

33. $\dfrac{2y^3 - 16}{4y^2 - 5y - 6} \div \dfrac{3y^2 + 6y + 12}{8y^2 - 22y - 21} = \dfrac{2y^3 - 16}{4y^2 - 5y - 6} \cdot \dfrac{8y^2 - 22y - 21}{3y^2 + 6y + 12}$

$$= \dfrac{2(\overset{1}{\cancel{y-2}})\left(y^2 + 2y + 4\right)}{(\cancel{4y+3})(\underset{1}{\cancel{y-2}})} \cdot \dfrac{(\overset{1}{\cancel{4y+3}})(2y-7)}{3(\underset{1}{y^2+2y+4})} = \dfrac{2(2y-7)}{3}$$

35. $\dfrac{7t^3 + 2t^2 - 21t - 6}{35t + 10} \div \dfrac{14t^3 + 4t^2 + 7t + 2}{6t^3 + 3t} = \dfrac{7t^3 + 2t^2 - 21t - 6}{35t + 10} \cdot \dfrac{6t^3 + 3t}{14t^3 + 4t^2 + 7t + 2}$

$$= \dfrac{\left(t^2 - 3\right)(\overset{1}{\cancel{7t+2}})}{5(\underset{1}{\cancel{7t+2}})} \cdot \dfrac{3t(\overset{1}{\cancel{2t^2+1}})}{(\underset{1}{\cancel{2t^2+1}})(7t+2)} = \dfrac{3t\left(t^2 - 3\right)}{5\left(7t+2\right)}$$

37. $\dfrac{9x^2 + 38xy + 8y^2}{3x^2y^3 + 12xy^4} \div \dfrac{x^2 - 2xy + y^2}{27x^3y + 6x^2y^2} = \dfrac{9x^2 + 38xy + 8y^2}{3x^2y^3 + 12xy^4} \cdot \dfrac{27x^3y + 6x^2y^2}{x^2 - 2xy + y^2}$

$$= \dfrac{(9x + 2y)(\overset{1}{\cancel{x + 4y}})}{\cancel{3}xy^3(\underset{1}{\cancel{x+4y}})} \cdot \dfrac{\overset{1}{\cancel{3}}x^2y(9x + 2y)}{(x - y)(x - y)}$$

$$= \dfrac{x(9x + 2y)(9x + 2y)}{y^2(x - y)(x - y)} = \dfrac{x(9x + 2y)^2}{y^2(x - y)^2}$$

Chapter 4 Exercise 4.3

1. $\dfrac{5}{x} + \dfrac{1}{x} = \dfrac{5 + 1}{x} = \dfrac{6}{x}$ 3. $\dfrac{10}{7b} + \dfrac{2}{7b} = \dfrac{10 + 2}{7b} = \dfrac{12}{7b}$ 5. $\dfrac{10}{3y} - \dfrac{4}{3y} = \dfrac{10 - 4}{3y} = \dfrac{\overset{2}{\cancel{6}}}{\underset{1}{\cancel{3}}y} = \dfrac{2}{y}$

7. $\dfrac{3}{x + 5} + \dfrac{x + 3}{x + 5} = \dfrac{3 + (x + 3)}{x + 5} = \dfrac{x + 6}{x + 5}$ 9. $\dfrac{2t - 8}{7t - 1} + \dfrac{5t}{7t - 1} = \dfrac{(2t - 8) + 5t}{7t - 1} = \dfrac{7t - 8}{7t - 1}$

11. $\dfrac{m - 7}{8m + 5} + \dfrac{3m - 9}{8m + 5} = \dfrac{(m - 7) + (3m - 9)}{8m + 5} = \dfrac{4m - 16}{8m + 5} = \dfrac{4(m - 4)}{8m + 5}$

13. $\dfrac{4x + 1}{x^2 - 25} - \dfrac{3x - 4}{x^2 - 25} = \dfrac{(4x + 1) - (3x - 4)}{x^2 - 25} = \dfrac{4x + 1 - 3x + 4}{x^2 - 25} = \dfrac{x + 5}{x^2 - 25} = \dfrac{\overset{1}{\cancel{x + 5}}}{(\underset{1}{\cancel{x + 5}})(x - 5)} = \dfrac{1}{x - 5}$

15. $\dfrac{5t - 7}{7t - 8} - \dfrac{3t + 7}{7t - 8} = \dfrac{(5t - 7) - (3t + 7)}{7t - 8} = \dfrac{5t - 7 - 3t - 7}{7t - 8} = \dfrac{2t - 14}{7t - 8} = \dfrac{2(t - 7)}{7t - 8}$

17. $\dfrac{9u^2 - 10}{5u + 2} - \dfrac{4u^2 + 13u - 4}{5u + 2} = \dfrac{\left(9u^2 - 10\right) - \left(4u^2 + 13u - 4\right)}{5u + 2} = \dfrac{9u^2 - 10 - 4u^2 - 13u + 4}{5u + 2}$

$$= \dfrac{5u^2 - 13u - 6}{5u + 2} = \dfrac{(\overset{1}{\cancel{5u + 2}})(u - 3)}{\underset{1}{\cancel{5u + 2}}} = \dfrac{u - 3}{1} = u - 3$$

19. $\dfrac{-2y^2 + 8y - 7}{3y^2 + y + 10} + \dfrac{4y^2 - 11y - 2}{3y^2 + y + 10} = \dfrac{\left(-2y^2 + 8y - 7\right) + \left(4y^2 - 11y - 2\right)}{3y^2 + y + 10} = \dfrac{2y^2 - 3y - 9}{3y^2 + y + 10} = \dfrac{(2y + 3)(y - 3)}{3y^2 + y + 10}$

21. $$\underbrace{\frac{3x}{x-3} + \frac{5}{3-x} = \frac{3x}{x-3} - \frac{5}{x-3}}_{} = \frac{3x-5}{x-3}$$

$x-3$ and $3-x$ are additive inverses of each other.

23. $$\underbrace{\frac{2u+3}{2u-9} - \frac{7u}{9-2u} = \frac{2u+3}{2u-9} + \frac{7u}{2u-9}}_{} = \frac{(2u+3)+7u}{2u-9} = \frac{9u+3}{2u-9} = \frac{3(3u+1)}{2u-9}$$

$2u-9$ and $9-2u$ are additive inverses of each other.

25. $$\underbrace{\frac{5x-4}{6-8x} + \frac{4x-9}{8x-6} = \frac{5x-4}{6-8x} - \frac{4x-9}{6-8x}}_{} = \frac{(5x-4)-(4x-9)}{6-8x} = \frac{5x-4-4x+9}{6-8x}$$

$6-8x$ and $8x-6$ are additive inverses of each other.

$$= \frac{x+5}{6-8x} = \frac{x+5}{2(3-4x)}$$

27. $$\underbrace{\frac{7a+12}{3a-13} - \frac{7-5a}{13-3a} = \frac{7a+12}{3a-13} + \frac{7-5a}{3a-13}}_{} = \frac{(7a+12)+(7-5a)}{3a-13} = \frac{2a+19}{3a-13}$$

$3a-13$ and $13-3a$ are additive inverses of each other.

29. The LCM of 5 and 3 is $5 \times 3 = 15$.

31. The LCM of $40 = 2^3 \times 5^1$ and $6 = 3^1 \times 2^1$ is $2^3 \times 5^1 \times 3^1 = 120$.

33. The LCM of $16 = 2^4$ and $10 = 5^1 \times 2^1$ is $2^4 \times 5^1 = 80$.

35. The LCM of $90 = 3^2 \times 2^1 \times 5^1$ and $75 = 3^1 \times 5^2$ is $3^2 \times 2^1 \times 5^2 = 450$.

37. The LCM of $2x^5$ and $7x^2$ is $14x^5$ (the LCM of 2 and 7 is 14).

39. The LCM of $12a^3b^5$ and $20ab^7$ is $60a^3b^7$ (the LCM of 12 and 20 is 60).

41. The LCM of $9x^2y^6$ and $9x^5y^6$ is $9x^5y^6$ (the LCM of 9 and 9 is just 9).

43. The LCM of $2a$ and $19b$ is $38ab$ (the LCM of 2 and 19 is 38).

45. The LCM of $4x^2$ and $18y$ is $36x^2y$ (the LCM of 4 and 18 is 36).

47. The LCM of 14 and mn^2 is $14mn^2$. 49. The LCM of x and $x-7$ is $x(x-7)$.

51. The LCM of x and $x+h$ is $x(x+h)$. 53. The LCM of $3x$ and $5x+1$ is $3x(5x+1)$.

55. The LCM of $x+4$ and $x-4$ is $(x+4)(x-4)$. 57. The LCM of $3y-5$ and $y+2$ is $(3y-5)(y+2)$.

59. The LCM of $3t-9 = 3(t-3)^1$ and $4t-12 = 4(t-3)^1$ is $\underbrace{12(t-3)}_{}$.

Only put one $(t-3)$.

61. The LCM of $x^2-8x = x^1(x-8)^1$ and $x^2+2x = x^1(x+2)^1$ is $\underbrace{x(x-8)(x+2)}_{}$.

Only put one x.

63. The LCM of $y^3+7y^2 = y^2(y+7)^1$ and $y^2-49 = (y+7)^1(y-7)^1$ is $\underbrace{y^2(y+7)(y-7)}_{}$.

Only put one $(y+7)$.

65. The LCM of $x^2-5x+4 = (x-4)^1(x-1)^1$ and $x^2+3x-28 = (x-4)^1(x+7)^1$ is $\underbrace{(x-4)(x-1)(x+7)}_{}$.

Only put one $(x-4)$.

67. The LCM of $\underbrace{3x^4-3x^3-18x^2 = 3x^2(x+2)^1(x-3)^1}_{\text{Factor completely.}}$ and $\underbrace{6x^3+30x^2+36x = 6x(x+2)^1(x+3)^1}_{\text{Factor completely.}}$

is $6x^2(x+2)(x-3)(x+3)$.

69. The LCM of $\underbrace{10x^3\,(x-2)^2\,(x+1)\text{ and }25x^3\,(x-2)\,(x+1)^3}_{\text{Both are already factored for us.}}$ is $50x^3\,(x-2)^2\,(x+1)^3$.

71. The LCM of $\underbrace{18a^4\,(3a+4)\,(a-6)^2\text{ and }a^5\,(3a-4)^2\,(a-6)^2}_{\text{Both are already factored for us.}}$ is $18a^5\,(3a+4)\,(a-6)^2\,(3a-4)^2$.

73. The LCM of $\underbrace{2\,(x-3)^2\,(x^2+4)^2\text{ and }2\,(x-3)^2\,(x^2-3)}_{\text{Both are already factored for us.}}$ is $2\,(x-3)^2\,(x^2+4)^2\,(x^2-3)$.

75. $\underbrace{\dfrac{3x}{5}+\dfrac{4}{3}=\left(\dfrac{3}{3}\right)\dfrac{3x}{5}+\left(\dfrac{5}{5}\right)\dfrac{4}{3}}_{\text{The LCM of 5 and 3 is 15.}}=\dfrac{3\,(3x)+5\,(4)}{15}=\dfrac{9x+20}{15}$

77. $\underbrace{\dfrac{5y}{9}-\dfrac{7}{12}=\left(\dfrac{4}{4}\right)\dfrac{5y}{9}-\left(\dfrac{3}{3}\right)\dfrac{7}{12}}_{\text{The LCM of 9 and 12 is 36.}}=\dfrac{4\,(5y)-3\,(7)}{36}=\dfrac{20y-21}{36}$

79. $\underbrace{\dfrac{11}{4x}+\dfrac{1}{6}=\left(\dfrac{3}{3}\right)\dfrac{11}{4x}+\left(\dfrac{2x}{2x}\right)\dfrac{1}{6}}_{\text{The LCM of 4x and 6 is 12x.}}=\dfrac{3\,(11)+2x\,(1)}{12x}=\dfrac{33+2x}{12x}$

81. $\underbrace{\dfrac{2}{x+8}+\dfrac{5}{x-1}=\left(\dfrac{x-1}{x-1}\right)\dfrac{2}{x+8}+\left(\dfrac{x+8}{x+8}\right)\dfrac{5}{x-1}}_{\text{The LCM of }x+8\text{ and }x-1\text{ is }(x+8)(x-1).}=\dfrac{2\,(x-1)+5\,(x+8)}{(x-1)\,(x+8)}=\dfrac{2x-2+5x+40}{(x-1)\,(x+8)}$

$$=\dfrac{7x+38}{(x-1)\,(x+8)}$$

83. $\underbrace{\dfrac{3a}{3a+1}-\dfrac{2}{5a-2}=\left(\dfrac{5a-2}{5a-2}\right)\dfrac{3a}{3a+1}-\left(\dfrac{3a+1}{3a+1}\right)\dfrac{2}{5a-2}}_{\text{The LCM of }3a+1\text{ and }5a-2\text{ is }(3a+1)(5a-2).}=\dfrac{3a\,(5a-2)-2\,(3a+1)}{(5a-2)\,(3a+1)}$

$$=\dfrac{15a^2-6a-6a-2}{(5a-2)\,(3a+1)}=\dfrac{15a^2-12a-2}{(5a-2)\,(3a+1)}$$

85. $\underbrace{\dfrac{t+4}{t-2}+\dfrac{t+2}{t-4}=\left(\dfrac{t-4}{t-4}\right)\dfrac{t+4}{t-2}+\left(\dfrac{t-2}{t-2}\right)\dfrac{t+2}{t-4}}_{\text{The LCM of }t-2\text{ and }t-4\text{ is }(t-2)(t-4).}=\dfrac{(t-4)\,(t+4)+(t-2)\,(t+2)}{(t-4)\,(t-2)}$

$$=\dfrac{\overbrace{t^2-16}^{(t-4)(t+4)}+\overbrace{t^2-4}^{(t-2)(t+2)}}{(t-4)\,(t-2)}=\dfrac{2t^2-20}{(t-4)\,(t-2)}=\dfrac{2\,(t^2-10)}{(t-4)\,(t-2)}$$

87. $\underbrace{\dfrac{1}{5+h}-\dfrac{1}{5}=\left(\dfrac{5}{5}\right)\dfrac{1}{5+h}-\left(\dfrac{5+h}{5+h}\right)\dfrac{1}{5}}_{\text{The LCM of 5 and }5+h\text{ is }5(5+h).}=\dfrac{5-1\,(5+h)}{5\,(5+h)}=\dfrac{5-5-h}{5\,(5+h)}=\dfrac{-h}{5\,(5+h)}$

200

89. $\underbrace{\dfrac{1}{(4+h)^2} - \dfrac{1}{16} = \left(\dfrac{16}{16}\right)\dfrac{1}{(4+h)^2} - \left(\dfrac{(4+h)^2}{(4+h)^2}\right)\dfrac{1}{16}}_{\text{The LCM of 16 and }(4+h)^2\text{ is }16(4+h)^2.} = \dfrac{16 - 1\,(4+h)^2}{16\,(4+h)^2} = \dfrac{16 - \left(16 + 8h + h^2\right)}{16\,(4+h)^2}$

$$= \dfrac{16 - 16 - 8h - h^2}{16\,(4+h)^2} = \dfrac{-8h - h^2}{16\,(4+h)^2} = \dfrac{h\,(-8-h)}{16\,(4+h)^2} \text{ or } \dfrac{-h\,(8+h)}{16\,(4+h)^2}$$

91. $\underbrace{\dfrac{2m-1}{3m+2} - \dfrac{m+2}{m-4} = \left(\dfrac{m-4}{m-4}\right)\dfrac{2m-1}{3m+2} - \left(\dfrac{3m+2}{3m+2}\right)\dfrac{m+2}{m-4}}_{\text{The LCM of }3m+2\text{ and }m-4\text{ is }(3m+2)(m-4).} = \dfrac{(m-4)\,(2m-1) - (3m+2)\,(m+2)}{(m-4)\,(3m+2)}$

$$= \dfrac{\overset{(m-4)(2m-1)}{2m^2 - m - 8m + 4} - \overset{(3m+2)(m+2)}{\left(3m^2 + 6m + 2m + 4\right)}}{(m-4)\,(3m+2)} = \dfrac{2m^2 - m - 8m + 4 - 3m^2 - 6m - 2m - 4}{(m-4)\,(3m+2)}$$

$$= \dfrac{-m^2 - 17m}{(m-4)\,(3m+2)} = \dfrac{-m\,(m+17)}{(m-4)\,(3m+2)}$$

93. $\underbrace{\dfrac{5}{12xy} + \dfrac{1}{9x^2} = \dfrac{3x}{3x}\left(\dfrac{5}{12xy}\right) + \dfrac{4y}{4y}\left(\dfrac{1}{9x^2}\right)}_{\text{The LCM of }12xy\text{ and }9x^2\text{ is }36x^2y.} = \dfrac{3x\,(5) + 4y\,(1)}{36x^2y} = \dfrac{15x + 4y}{36x^2y}$

95. $\underbrace{\dfrac{6}{11a^2b} - \dfrac{10}{3ab^2} = \left(\dfrac{3b}{3b}\right)\dfrac{6}{11a^2b} - \left(\dfrac{11a}{11a}\right)\dfrac{10}{3ab^2}}_{\text{The LCM of }11a^2b\text{ and }3ab^2\text{ is }33a^2b^2.} = \dfrac{3b\,(6) - 11a\,(10)}{33a^2b^2} = \dfrac{18b - 110a}{33a^2b^2}$

97. $\underbrace{\dfrac{11x}{18y^2} - \dfrac{7y}{6x^3} = \left(\dfrac{x^3}{x^3}\right)\dfrac{11x}{18y^2} - \left(\dfrac{3y^2}{3y^2}\right)\dfrac{7y}{6x^3}}_{\text{The LCM of }18y^2\text{ and }6x^3\text{ is }18x^3y^2.} = \dfrac{x^3\,(11x) - 3y^2\,(7y)}{18x^3y^2} = \dfrac{11x^4 - 21y^3}{18x^3y^2}$

99. $\underbrace{\dfrac{1}{x+6} + \dfrac{12}{x^2-36} = \left(\dfrac{x-6}{x-6}\right)\dfrac{1}{x+6} + \dfrac{12}{(x+6)\,(x-6)}}_{\text{The LCM of }x+6\text{ and }x^2-36=(x+6)(x-6)\text{ is }(x+6)(x-6).} = \dfrac{(x-6) + 12}{(x+6)\,(x-6)} = \dfrac{\overset{1}{\cancel{x+6}}}{\underset{1}{\cancel{(x+6)}}\,(x-6)} = \dfrac{1}{x-6}$

101. $\underbrace{\dfrac{6}{a^2-a} - \dfrac{9}{a^2-1} = \left(\dfrac{a+1}{a+1}\right)\dfrac{6}{a\,(a-1)} - \left(\dfrac{a}{a}\right)\dfrac{9}{(a+1)\,(a-1)}}_{\text{The LCM of }a^2-a=a(a-1)\text{ and }a^2-1=(a+1)(a-1)\text{ is }a(a+1)(a-1).} = \dfrac{6\,(a+1) - 9a}{a\,(a+1)\,(a-1)} = \dfrac{6a + 6 - 9a}{a\,(a+1)\,(a-1)}$

$$= \dfrac{-3a + 6}{a\,(a+1)\,(a-1)} = \dfrac{-3\,(a-2)}{a\,(a+1)\,(a-1)}$$

103. $\underbrace{\dfrac{a+3}{a^2-4a-5} - \dfrac{a}{a^2-8a+15} = \left(\dfrac{a-3}{a-3}\right)\dfrac{a+3}{(a+1)\,(a-5)} - \left(\dfrac{a+1}{a+1}\right)\dfrac{a}{(a-3)\,(a-5)}}_{\text{The LCM of }a^2-4a-5=(a+1)(a-5)\text{ and }a^2-8a+15=(a-3)(a-5)\text{ is }(a-3)(a+1)(a-5).}$

$$= \dfrac{(a-3)\,(a+3) - a\,(a+1)}{(a-3)\,(a+1)\,(a-5)}$$

$$= \dfrac{a^2 - 9 - a^2 - a}{(a-3)\,(a+1)\,(a-5)} = \dfrac{-9 - a}{(a-3)\,(a+1)\,(a-5)}$$

105. $\underbrace{\dfrac{3x-10}{2x^2-11x+5} - \dfrac{7x+8}{2x^2-7x-15} = \left(\dfrac{2x+3}{2x+3}\right)\dfrac{3x-10}{(2x-1)(x-5)} - \left(\dfrac{2x-1}{2x-1}\right)\dfrac{7x+8}{(2x+3)(x-5)}}$

The LCM of $2x^2-11x+5=(2x-1)(x-5)$ and $2x^2-7x-15=(2x+3)(x-5)$ is $(2x+3)(2x-1)(x-5)$.

$$= \dfrac{(2x+3)(3x-10) - (2x-1)(7x+8)}{(2x+3)(2x-1)(x-5)} = \dfrac{6x^2-20x+9x-30 - \left(14x^2+16x-7x-8\right)}{(2x+3)(2x-1)(x-5)}$$

$$= \dfrac{6x^2-20x+9x-30-14x^2-16x+7x+8}{(2x+3)(2x-1)(x-5)} = \dfrac{-8x^2-20x-22}{(2x+3)(2x-1)(x-5)} = \dfrac{-2\left(4x^2+10x+11\right)}{(2x+3)(2x-1)(x-5)}$$

107. $\underbrace{\dfrac{4m-1}{m^2+2m+1} + \dfrac{2}{m-3} = \left(\dfrac{m-3}{m-3}\right)\dfrac{4m-1}{(m+1)^2} + \left(\dfrac{(m+1)^2}{(m+1)^2}\right)\dfrac{2}{m-3}} = \dfrac{(m-3)(4m-1)+2(m+1)^2}{(m-3)(m+1)^2}$

the LCM of $m^2+2m+1=(m+1)^2$ and $m-3$ is $(m-3)(m+1)^2$

$$= \dfrac{\overbrace{4m^2-m-12m+3}^{(m-3)(4m-1)} + \overbrace{2m^2+2m+2m+2}^{2(m+1)^2=2(m+1)(m+1)}}{(m-3)(m+1)^2} = \dfrac{6m^2-9m+5}{(m-3)(m+1)^2}$$

109. $\underbrace{\dfrac{1}{x} - \dfrac{3x+2}{x+1} + \dfrac{2}{x-2} = \left(\dfrac{(x+1)(x-2)}{(x+1)(x-2)}\right)\dfrac{1}{x} - \left(\dfrac{x(x-2)}{x(x-2)}\right)\dfrac{3x+2}{x+1} + \left(\dfrac{x(x+1)}{x(x+1)}\right)\dfrac{2}{x-2}}$

The LCM of x, $x+1$ and $x-2$ is $x(x+1)(x-2)$.

$$= \dfrac{(x+1)(x-2) - x(x-2)(3x+2) + 2x(x+1)}{x(x+1)(x-2)}$$

$$= \dfrac{\overbrace{x^2-2x+x-2}^{(x+1)(x-2)} - x\overbrace{\left(3x^2+2x-6x-4\right)}^{(x-2)(3x+2)} + 2x^2+2x}{x(x+1)(x-2)}$$

$$= \dfrac{x^2-2x+x-2-3x^3-2x^2+6x^2+4x+2x^2+2x}{x(x+1)(x-2)} = \dfrac{-3x^3+7x^2+5x-2}{x(x+1)(x-2)}$$

111. The LCM of $a^2-6a=a(a-6)$, $a^2+5a=a(a+5)$, and $a+1$ is $a(a-6)(a+5)(a+1)$. Therefore,

$$\dfrac{7}{a^2-6a} + \dfrac{4}{a^2+5a} + \dfrac{3}{a+1} = \left(\dfrac{(a+5)(a+1)}{(a+5)(a+1)}\right)\dfrac{7}{a(a-6)}$$

$$+ \left(\dfrac{(a-6)(a+1)}{(a-6)(a+1)}\right)\dfrac{4}{a(a+5)} + \left(\dfrac{a(a-6)(a+5)}{a(a-6)(a+5)}\right)\dfrac{3}{a+1}$$

$$= \dfrac{7(a+5)(a+1) + 4(a-6)(a+1) + 3a(a-6)(a+5)}{a(a-6)(a+5)(a+1)}$$

$$= \dfrac{7\overbrace{\left(a^2+a+5a+5\right)}^{(a+5)(a+1)} + 4\overbrace{\left(a^2+a-6a-6\right)}^{(a-6)(a+1)} + 3a\overbrace{\left(a^2+5a-6a-30\right)}^{(a-6)(a+5)}}{a(a-6)(a+5)(a+1)}$$

$$= \dfrac{7a^2+7a+35a+35 + 4a^2+4a-24a-24 + 3a^3+15a^2-18a^2-90a}{a(a-6)(a+5)(a+1)}$$

$$= \dfrac{3a^3+8a^2-68a+11}{a(a-6)(a+5)(a+1)}$$

113. $3 + \dfrac{x-7}{4x+3} = \left(\dfrac{4x+3}{4x+3}\right)\dfrac{3}{1} + \dfrac{x-7}{4x+3} = \dfrac{3(4x+3)+(x-7)}{4x+3} = \dfrac{12x+9+x-7}{4x+3} = \dfrac{13x+2}{4x+3}$

115. $4b - \dfrac{1}{2b+1} = \left(\dfrac{2b+1}{2b+1}\right)\dfrac{4b}{1} - \dfrac{1}{2b+1} = \dfrac{4b(2b+1)-1}{2b+1} = \dfrac{8b^2+4b-1}{2b+1}$

117. $x^2 + 4x + \dfrac{10}{x} = \left(\dfrac{x}{x}\right)\dfrac{x^2+4x}{1} + \dfrac{10}{x} = \dfrac{x(x^2+4x)+10}{x} = \dfrac{x^3+4x^2+10}{x}$

119. $3u - 4 - \dfrac{14}{u-1} = \left(\dfrac{u-1}{u-1}\right)\dfrac{3u-4}{1} - \dfrac{14}{u-1} = \dfrac{(u-1)(3u-4)-14}{u-1}$

$$= \dfrac{\overbrace{3u^2-4u-3u+4}^{(u-1)(3u-4)}-14}{u-1} = \dfrac{3u^2-7u-10}{u-1} = \dfrac{(3u-10)(u+1)}{u-1}$$

Chapter 4 Exercise 4.4

1. The LCM of the 'little denominators' 8, 4, and 16 is 16. Following the steps, we have

$$\dfrac{\frac{1}{8}-\frac{3}{4}}{\frac{1}{16}} = \left(\dfrac{\frac{1}{8}-\frac{3}{4}}{\frac{1}{16}}\right)\left(\dfrac{\frac{16}{1}}{\frac{16}{1}}\right) = \dfrac{\frac{1}{8}\left(\frac{\cancel{16}^{2}}{1}\right) - \frac{3}{4}\left(\frac{\cancel{16}^{4}}{1}\right)}{\frac{1}{\cancel{16}}\left(\frac{\cancel{16}}{1}\right)} = \dfrac{2-3(4)}{1} = \dfrac{2-12}{1} = \dfrac{-10}{1} = -10.$$

3. The LCM of the 'little denominators' 5 and 10 is 10. Following the steps, we have

$$\dfrac{1+\frac{2}{5}}{3-\frac{1}{10}} = \left(\dfrac{1+\frac{2}{5}}{3-\frac{1}{10}}\right)\left(\dfrac{\frac{10}{1}}{\frac{10}{1}}\right) = \dfrac{1\left(\frac{10}{1}\right) + \frac{2}{\cancel{5}}\left(\frac{\cancel{10}^{2}}{1}\right)}{3\left(\frac{10}{1}\right) - \frac{1}{\cancel{10}}\left(\frac{\cancel{10}}{1}\right)} = \dfrac{1(10)+2(2)}{3(10)-1} = \dfrac{10+4}{30-1} = \dfrac{14}{29}.$$

5. The LCM of the 'little denominators' is 7.

$$\dfrac{4-\frac{5}{7}}{4} = \left(\dfrac{4-\frac{5}{7}}{4}\right)\left(\dfrac{\frac{7}{1}}{\frac{7}{1}}\right) = \dfrac{4\left(\frac{7}{1}\right) - \frac{5}{\cancel{7}}\left(\frac{\cancel{7}}{1}\right)}{4\left(\frac{7}{1}\right)} = \dfrac{4(7)-5}{4(7)} = \dfrac{28-5}{28} = \dfrac{23}{28}$$

7. The LCM of the 'little denominators' is 3.

$$\dfrac{5}{2+\frac{2}{3}} = \left(\dfrac{5}{2+\frac{2}{3}}\right)\left(\dfrac{\frac{3}{1}}{\frac{3}{1}}\right) = \dfrac{5\left(\frac{3}{1}\right)}{2\left(\frac{3}{1}\right) + \frac{2}{\cancel{3}}\left(\frac{\cancel{3}}{1}\right)} = \dfrac{5(3)}{2(3)+2} = \dfrac{15}{6+2} = \dfrac{15}{8}$$

9. The LCM of the 'little denominators' 18, 6, 12, and 36 is 36. Therefore,

$$\dfrac{\frac{1}{18}+\frac{5}{6}}{\frac{7}{12}-\frac{1}{36}} = \left(\dfrac{\frac{1}{18}+\frac{5}{6}}{\frac{7}{12}-\frac{1}{36}}\right)\left(\dfrac{\frac{36}{1}}{\frac{36}{1}}\right) = \dfrac{\frac{1}{\cancel{18}}\left(\frac{\cancel{36}^{2}}{1}\right) + \frac{5}{\cancel{6}}\left(\frac{\cancel{36}^{6}}{1}\right)}{\frac{7}{\cancel{12}}\left(\frac{\cancel{36}^{3}}{1}\right) - \frac{1}{\cancel{36}}\left(\frac{\cancel{36}}{1}\right)} = \dfrac{2+5(6)}{7(3)-1} = \dfrac{2+30}{21-1} = \dfrac{\cancel{32}^{8}}{\cancel{20}_{5}} = \dfrac{8}{5}.$$

11. The LCM of the 'little denominators' $3x$ and $9x$ is $9x$. Therefore,

$$\dfrac{\frac{1}{3x}-4}{\frac{2}{9x}+3} = \left(\dfrac{\frac{1}{3x}-4}{\frac{2}{9x}+3}\right)\left(\dfrac{\frac{9x}{1}}{\frac{9x}{1}}\right) = \dfrac{\frac{1}{\cancel{3x}}\left(\frac{\cancel{9x}^{3}}{1}\right) - 4\left(\frac{9x}{1}\right)}{\frac{2}{\cancel{9x}}\left(\frac{\cancel{9x}}{1}\right) + 3\left(\frac{9x}{1}\right)} = \dfrac{3-4(9x)}{2+3(9x)} = \dfrac{3-36x}{2+27x} = \dfrac{3(1-12x)}{2+27x}.$$

13. The LCM of the 'little denominators' $y-2$, $y+5$, and $y^2+3y-10 = (y-2)(y+5)$ is $(y-2)(y+5)$.

$$\frac{\frac{1}{y-2} - \frac{4}{y+5}}{\frac{3}{y^2+3y-10}} = \left(\frac{\frac{1}{y-2} - \frac{4}{y+5}}{\frac{3}{(y-2)(y+5)}}\right)\left(\frac{\frac{(y-2)(y+5)}{1}}{\frac{(y-2)(y+5)}{1}}\right) = \frac{\frac{1}{y-2}\left(\frac{(y-2)(y+5)}{1}\right) - \frac{4}{y+5}\left(\frac{(y-2)(y+5)}{1}\right)}{\frac{3}{(y-2)(y+5)}\left(\frac{(y-2)(y+5)}{1}\right)}$$

$$= \frac{y+5 - 4(y-2)}{3} = \frac{y+5-4y+8}{3} = \frac{-3y+13}{3}$$

15. The LCM of the 'little denominators' $12x^2$, $4x$, and $3x^2$ is $12x^2$.

$$\frac{\frac{1}{12x^2} - \frac{5}{4x}}{\frac{2}{3x^2}} = \left(\frac{\frac{1}{12x^2} - \frac{5}{4x}}{\frac{2}{3x^2}}\right)\left(\frac{\frac{12x^2}{1}}{\frac{12x^2}{1}}\right) = \frac{\frac{1}{12x^2}\left(\frac{12x^2}{1}\right) - \frac{5}{4x}\left(\frac{12x^2}{1}\right)^{3x}}{\frac{2}{3x^2}\left(\frac{12x^2}{1}\right)^{4}} = \frac{1-5(3x)}{2(4)} = \frac{1-15x}{8}$$

17. The LCM of the 'little denominators' $a^2-6a = a(a-6)$, $a^2-36 = (a+6)(a-6)$, and $a^2+6a = a(a+6)$ is $a(a+6)(a-6)$.

$$\frac{\frac{2a}{a^2-6a} + \frac{3}{a^2-36}}{\frac{4}{a^2+6a}} = \left(\frac{\frac{2a}{a(a-6)} + \frac{3}{(a+6)(a-6)}}{\frac{4}{a(a+6)}}\right)\left(\frac{\frac{a(a+6)(a-6)}{1}}{\frac{a(a+6)(a-6)}{1}}\right)$$

$$= \frac{\frac{2a}{a(a-6)}\left(\frac{a(a+6)(a-6)}{1}\right) + \frac{3}{(a+6)(a-6)}\left(\frac{a(a+6)(a-6)}{1}\right)}{\frac{4}{a(a+6)}\left(\frac{a(a+6)(a-6)}{1}\right)}$$

$$= \frac{2a(a+6)+3(a)}{4(a-6)} = \frac{2a^2+12a+3a}{4(a-6)} = \frac{2a^2+15a}{4(a-6)} = \frac{a(2a+15)}{4(a-6)}$$

19. The LCM of the 'little denominators' is $x-5$.

$$\frac{-x+2+\frac{1}{x-5}}{x+3} = \left(\frac{-x+2+\frac{1}{x-5}}{x+3}\right)\left(\frac{\frac{x-5}{1}}{\frac{x-5}{1}}\right) = \frac{-x\left(\frac{x-5}{1}\right) + 2\left(\frac{x-5}{1}\right) + \frac{1}{x-5}\left(\frac{x-5}{1}\right)}{x\left(\frac{x-5}{1}\right) + 3\left(\frac{x-5}{1}\right)}$$

$$= \frac{-x(x-5)+2(x-5)+1}{x(x-5)+3(x-5)}$$

$$= \frac{-x^2+5x+2x-10+1}{x^2-5x+3x-15} = \frac{-x^2+7x-9}{x^2-2x-15} = \frac{-\left(x^2-7x+9\right)}{(x-5)(x+3)} = -\frac{x^2-7x+9}{(x-5)(x+3)}$$

21. The LCM of the 'little denominators' is $2(x-2)$.

$$\frac{\frac{5}{2}+\frac{3}{x-2}}{4x-9} = \left(\frac{\frac{5}{2}+\frac{3}{x-2}}{4x-9}\right)\left(\frac{\frac{2(x-2)}{1}}{\frac{2(x-2)}{1}}\right) = \frac{\frac{5}{2}\left(\frac{2(x-2)}{1}\right) + \frac{3}{x-2}\left(\frac{2(x-2)}{1}\right)}{(4x-9)\left(\frac{2(x-2)}{1}\right)} = \frac{5(x-2)+3(2)}{(4x-9)(2(x-2))}$$

$$= \frac{5x-10+6}{2(4x-9)(x-2)} = \frac{5x-4}{2(4x-9)(x-2)}$$

23. The LCM of the 'little denominators' is $3(3+h)$.

$$\frac{\frac{1}{3+h}-\frac{1}{3}}{h} = \left(\frac{\frac{1}{3+h}-\frac{1}{3}}{h}\right)\left(\frac{\frac{3(3+h)}{1}}{\frac{3(3+h)}{1}}\right) = \frac{\frac{1}{3+h}\left(\frac{3(3+h)}{1}\right) - \frac{1}{3}\left(\frac{3(3+h)}{1}\right)}{h\left(\frac{3(3+h)}{1}\right)} = \frac{3-(3+h)}{3h(3+h)}$$

$$= \frac{3-3-h}{3h(3+h)} = \frac{-h}{3h(3+h)} = \frac{-1}{3(3+h)}$$

204

25. The LCM of the 'little denominators' 8 and $(8+h)^2$ is $64(8+h)^2$.

$$\frac{\frac{1}{(8+h)^2} - \frac{1}{64}}{h} = \left(\frac{\frac{1}{(8+h)^2} - \frac{1}{64}}{h}\right)\left(\frac{\frac{64(8+h)^2}{1}}{\frac{64(8+h)^2}{1}}\right) = \frac{\frac{1}{(8+h)^2}\left(\frac{64(8+h)^2}{1}\right) - \frac{1}{64}\left(\frac{64(8+h)^2}{1}\right)}{h\left(\frac{64(8+h)^2}{1}\right)}$$

$$= \frac{64 - (8+h)^2}{64h(8+h)^2} = \frac{64 - (64+16h+h^2)}{64h(8+h)^2} = \frac{64 - 64 - 16h - h^2}{64h(8+h)^2} = \frac{-16h - h^2}{64h(8+h)^2}$$

$$= \frac{-\overset{1}{\cancel{h}}(16+h)}{64\underset{1}{\cancel{h}}(8+h)^2} = \frac{-(16+h)}{64(8+h)^2} = -\frac{16+h}{64(8+h)^2}$$

27. First, simplify $\dfrac{1}{1+\frac{1}{2}}$ as follows:

$$\frac{1}{1+\frac{1}{2}} = \left(\frac{1}{1+\frac{1}{2}}\right)\left(\frac{\frac{2}{1}}{\frac{2}{1}}\right) = \frac{1\left(\frac{2}{1}\right)}{1\left(\frac{2}{1}\right) + \frac{1}{2}\left(\frac{2}{1}\right)} = \frac{2}{2+1} = \frac{2}{3}$$

Now, $1 + \dfrac{1}{1+\frac{1}{2}} = 1 + \dfrac{2}{3} = \dfrac{3}{3} + \dfrac{2}{3} = \dfrac{5}{3}$.

29. First, simplify $\dfrac{x}{1+\frac{x+1}{2}}$ as follows:

$$\frac{x}{1+\frac{x+1}{2}} = \left(\frac{x}{1+\frac{x+1}{2}}\right)\left(\frac{\frac{2}{1}}{\frac{2}{1}}\right) = \frac{x\left(\frac{2}{1}\right)}{1\left(\frac{2}{1}\right) + \frac{x+1}{2}\left(\frac{2}{1}\right)} = \frac{2x}{2+x+1} = \frac{2x}{x+3}$$

Now, $x - \dfrac{x}{1+\frac{x+1}{2}} = x - \dfrac{2x}{x+3} = \left(\dfrac{x+3}{x+3}\right)\dfrac{x}{1} - \dfrac{2x}{x+3} = \dfrac{x(x+3) - 2x}{x+3}$

$$= \frac{x^2 + 3x - 2x}{x+3} = \frac{x^2 + x}{x+3} = \frac{x(x+1)}{x+3}.$$

31. First, simplify $\dfrac{1}{1+\frac{a}{4}}$ as follows:

$$\frac{1}{1+\frac{a}{4}} = \left(\frac{1}{1+\frac{a}{4}}\right)\left(\frac{\frac{4}{1}}{\frac{4}{1}}\right) = \frac{1\left(\frac{4}{1}\right)}{1\left(\frac{4}{1}\right) + \frac{a}{4}\left(\frac{4}{1}\right)} = \frac{4}{4+a}$$

Now, $\dfrac{a}{2+\frac{1}{1+\frac{a}{4}}} = \dfrac{a}{2+\frac{4}{4+a}} = \left(\dfrac{a}{2+\frac{4}{4+a}}\right)\left(\dfrac{\frac{4+a}{1}}{\frac{4+a}{1}}\right) = \dfrac{a\left(\frac{4+a}{1}\right)}{2\left(\frac{4+a}{1}\right) + \frac{4}{4+a}\left(\frac{4+a}{1}\right)} = \dfrac{a(4+a)}{2(4+a)+4}$

$$= \frac{a(4+a)}{8+2a+4} = \frac{a(4+a)}{12+2a} = \frac{a(4+a)}{2(6+a)}.$$

33. First, simplify $\dfrac{1}{1-\frac{1}{x+3}}$ as follows:

$$\frac{1}{1-\frac{1}{x+3}} = \left(\frac{1}{1-\frac{1}{x+3}}\right)\left(\frac{\frac{x+3}{1}}{\frac{x+3}{1}}\right) = \frac{1\left(\frac{x+3}{1}\right)}{1\left(\frac{x+3}{1}\right) - \frac{1}{x+3}\left(\frac{x+3}{1}\right)} = \frac{x+3}{(x+3)-1} = \frac{x+3}{x+2}$$

Now, $1 - \dfrac{1}{1-\frac{1}{x+3}} = 1 - \dfrac{x+3}{x+2} = \left(\dfrac{x+2}{x+2}\right)\dfrac{1}{1} - \dfrac{x+3}{x+2} = \dfrac{1(x+2) - (x+3)}{x+2} = \dfrac{x+2-x-3}{x+2} = \dfrac{-1}{x+2}.$

35. $\dfrac{6^{-1}+12^{-1}}{6^{-1}}=\dfrac{\frac{1}{6}+\frac{1}{12}}{\frac{1}{6}}=\left(\dfrac{\frac{1}{6}+\frac{1}{12}}{\frac{1}{6}}\right)\left(\dfrac{\frac{12}{1}}{\frac{12}{1}}\right)=\dfrac{\frac{1}{6}\left(\frac{\overset{2}{\cancel{12}}}{1}\right)+\frac{1}{12}\left(\frac{\cancel{12}}{1}\right)}{\frac{1}{\cancel{6}}\left(\frac{\overset{2}{\cancel{12}}}{1}\right)}=\dfrac{2+1}{2}=\dfrac{3}{2}$

37. $\dfrac{2+4^{-2}}{1+8^{-1}}=\dfrac{2+\frac{1}{16}}{1+\frac{1}{8}}=\left(\dfrac{2+\frac{1}{16}}{1+\frac{1}{8}}\right)\left(\dfrac{\frac{16}{1}}{\frac{16}{1}}\right)=\dfrac{2\left(\frac{16}{1}\right)+\frac{1}{16}\left(\frac{\cancel{16}}{1}\right)}{1\left(\frac{16}{1}\right)+\frac{1}{\cancel{8}}\left(\frac{\overset{2}{\cancel{16}}}{1}\right)}=\dfrac{32+1}{16+2}=\dfrac{\overset{11}{\cancel{33}}}{\underset{6}{\cancel{18}}}=\dfrac{11}{6}$

39. $\dfrac{x^{-2}+x^{-3}}{x^3}=\dfrac{\frac{1}{x^2}+\frac{1}{x^3}}{x^3}=\left(\dfrac{\frac{1}{x^2}+\frac{1}{x^3}}{x^3}\right)\left(\dfrac{\frac{x^3}{1}}{\frac{x^3}{1}}\right)=\dfrac{\frac{1}{x^2}\left(\frac{\overset{x}{\cancel{x^3}}}{1}\right)+\frac{1}{x^3}\left(\frac{\cancel{x^3}}{1}\right)}{x^3\left(\frac{x^3}{1}\right)}=\dfrac{x+1}{x^3\left(x^3\right)}=\dfrac{x+1}{x^6}$

41. $\dfrac{1-3a^{-1}+a^{-2}}{1+3a^{-1}+a^{-2}}=\dfrac{1-\frac{3}{a}+\frac{1}{a^2}}{1+\frac{3}{a}+\frac{1}{a^2}}=\left(\dfrac{1-\frac{3}{a}+\frac{1}{a^2}}{1+\frac{3}{a}+\frac{1}{a^2}}\right)\left(\dfrac{\frac{a^2}{1}}{\frac{a^2}{1}}\right)=\dfrac{1\left(\frac{a^2}{1}\right)-\frac{3}{\cancel{a}}\left(\frac{\overset{a}{\cancel{a^2}}}{1}\right)+\frac{1}{\cancel{a^2}}\left(\frac{\cancel{a^2}}{1}\right)}{1\left(\frac{a^2}{1}\right)+\frac{3}{\cancel{a}}\left(\frac{\overset{a}{\cancel{a^2}}}{1}\right)+\frac{1}{\cancel{a^2}}\left(\frac{\cancel{a^2}}{1}\right)}=\dfrac{a^2-3a+1}{a^2+3a+1}$

Chapter 5 Exercise 5.1.1

1. $\sqrt{1}=1$ 3. $\sqrt{0}=0$ 5. $-\sqrt{4}=-2$ 7. $\sqrt{5^2}=\sqrt{25}=5$ 9. $\sqrt{(-12)^2}=\sqrt{144}=12$

11. $-\sqrt{13^2}=-\sqrt{169}=-13$ 13. $-\sqrt{-13^2}=-\sqrt{-169}$ is not a real number.

15. $\sqrt{(81)(81)}=\sqrt{81}\cdot\sqrt{81}=9\cdot 9=81$ 17. $\sqrt{(144)(4)}=\sqrt{144}\cdot\sqrt{4}=12\cdot 2=24$

19. $\sqrt{-100}\sqrt{9}$ is not a real number since $\sqrt{-100}$ is not a real number.   21. $\sqrt{\dfrac{1}{16}}=\dfrac{\sqrt{1}}{\sqrt{16}}=\dfrac{1}{4}$

23. $\sqrt{\dfrac{25}{36}}=\dfrac{\sqrt{25}}{\sqrt{36}}=\dfrac{5}{6}$ 25. $\sqrt{\dfrac{169}{4}}=\dfrac{\sqrt{169}}{\sqrt{4}}=\dfrac{13}{2}$ 27. $-\sqrt{\dfrac{144}{49}}=-\dfrac{\sqrt{144}}{\sqrt{49}}=-\dfrac{12}{7}$

29. $-\sqrt{\left(\dfrac{36}{25}\right)\left(\dfrac{144}{121}\right)}=-\sqrt{\dfrac{36}{25}}\sqrt{\dfrac{144}{121}}=-\dfrac{6}{5}\cdot\dfrac{12}{11}=-\dfrac{72}{55}$

31. $\sqrt{x^2}=|x|=x$ since x represents a positive number.

33. $\sqrt{64a^2}=\sqrt{64}\sqrt{a^2}=8|a|=8a$ since a represents a positive number.

35. $\sqrt{(-5x)^2}=|-5x|=|-5|\cdot|x|=5x$ since x represents a positive number.

37. $-\sqrt{(2y)^2}=-|2y|=-|2|\cdot|y|=-2y$ since y represents a positive number.

39. $\sqrt{(15ab^2)^2}=|15ab^2|=|15|\cdot|ab^2|=15ab^2$ since a and b represent positive numbers.

41. $\sqrt{\dfrac{y^2}{16}}=\dfrac{\sqrt{y^2}}{\sqrt{16}}=\dfrac{|y|}{4}=\dfrac{y}{4}$ since y represents a positive number.

43. $\sqrt{\dfrac{121}{t^2}}=\dfrac{\sqrt{121}}{\sqrt{t^2}}=\dfrac{11}{|t|}=\dfrac{11}{t}$ since t represents a positive number.

45. $\sqrt{\dfrac{(7x)^2}{100}} = \dfrac{\sqrt{(7x)^2}}{\sqrt{100}} = \dfrac{|7x|}{10} = \dfrac{|7| \cdot |x|}{10} = \dfrac{7x}{10}$ since x represents a positive number.

47. $\sqrt{\left(\dfrac{17}{10x^4}\right)^2} = \left|\dfrac{17}{10x^4}\right| = \dfrac{|17|}{|10x^4|} = \dfrac{17}{10x^4}$ since x represents a positive number.

49. $\sqrt{1}$ is rational.   51. $\sqrt{17}$ is irrational.   53. $\sqrt{\dfrac{9}{100}}$ is rational.   55. $-\sqrt{\dfrac{5}{6}}$ is irrational.

57. $\sqrt{0.16}$ is rational (note that $0.16 = \frac{16}{100}$).   59. $\sqrt{0.2}$ is irrational (note that $0.2 = \frac{2}{10} = \frac{1}{5}$).

61. $\sqrt{1.69}$ is rational (note that $1.69 = \frac{169}{100}$).

Chapter 5 Exercise 5.1.2

1. $\sqrt{12} = \sqrt{4 \cdot 3} = \sqrt{4} \cdot \sqrt{3} = 2\sqrt{3}$ 3. $\sqrt{27} = \sqrt{9 \cdot 3} = \sqrt{9} \cdot \sqrt{3} = 3\sqrt{3}$

5. $\sqrt{44} = \sqrt{4 \cdot 11} = \sqrt{4} \cdot \sqrt{11} = 2\sqrt{11}$ 7. $-\sqrt{125} = -\sqrt{25 \cdot 5} = -\sqrt{25} \cdot \sqrt{5} = -5\sqrt{5}$

9. $\sqrt{32} = \sqrt{16 \cdot 2} = \sqrt{16} \cdot \sqrt{2} = 4\sqrt{2}$ 11. $\sqrt{60} = \sqrt{4 \cdot 15} = \sqrt{4} \cdot \sqrt{15} = 2\sqrt{15}$

13. $-\sqrt{48} = -\sqrt{16 \cdot 3} = -\sqrt{16} \cdot \sqrt{3} = -4\sqrt{3}$ 15. $-\sqrt{54} = -\sqrt{9 \cdot 6} = -\sqrt{9} \cdot \sqrt{6} = -3\sqrt{6}$

17. $\underbrace{\sqrt{y^2} = y}_{2 \div 2 = 1 \text{ R } 0}$ 19. $\underbrace{\sqrt{y^4} = y^2}_{4 \div 2 = 2 \text{ R } 0}$ 21. $\underbrace{\sqrt{b^{19}} = b^9\sqrt{b}}_{19 \div 2 = 9 \text{ R } 1}$ 23. $\sqrt{64y} = 8\sqrt{y}$

25. $\sqrt{81b^4} = 9b^2$ since $\sqrt{81} = 9$ and $\underbrace{\sqrt{b^4} = b^2}_{4 \div 2 = 2 \text{ R } 0}$.

27. $\sqrt{32a^7b^4} = 4a^3b^2\sqrt{2a}$ since $\sqrt{32} = \sqrt{16}\sqrt{2} = 4\sqrt{2}$, $\sqrt{a^7} = \underbrace{a^3\sqrt{a}}_{7 \div 2 = 3 \text{ R } 1}$, and $\sqrt{b^4} = b^2$.

29. $\sqrt{33mn^3} = n\sqrt{33mn}$ since $\sqrt{33}$ is simplified, $\sqrt{m}$ is simplified, and $\underbrace{\sqrt{n^3} = n\sqrt{n}}_{3 \div 2 = 1 \text{ R } 1}$.

31. $-\sqrt{80xy^5} = -4y^2\sqrt{5xy}$ since $\sqrt{80} = \sqrt{16}\sqrt{5} = 4\sqrt{5}$, $\sqrt{x}$ is simplified, and $\underbrace{\sqrt{y^5} = y^2\sqrt{y}}_{5 \div 2 = 2 \text{ R } 1}$.

33. $\sqrt{56a^6b^{15}c} = 2a^3b^7\sqrt{14bc}$ since $\sqrt{56} = \sqrt{4}\sqrt{14} = 2\sqrt{14}$, $\underbrace{\sqrt{a^6} = a^3}_{6 \div 2 = 3 \text{ R } 0}$, $\underbrace{\sqrt{b^{15}} = b^7\sqrt{b}}_{15 \div 2 = 7 \text{ R } 1}$, and $\sqrt{c}$ is simplified.

Chapter 5 Exercise 5.1.3

1. $\sqrt{7} \cdot \sqrt{2} = \sqrt{7 \cdot 2} = \sqrt{14}$ 3. $\sqrt{10} \cdot \sqrt{3} = \sqrt{10 \cdot 3} = \sqrt{30}$

5. $\sqrt{5} \cdot \sqrt{10} = \sqrt{5 \cdot 10} = \sqrt{50} = \sqrt{25} \cdot \sqrt{2} = 5\sqrt{2}$

7. $\sqrt{6} \cdot \sqrt{6} = \sqrt{6 \cdot 6} = \sqrt{36} = 6$ 9. $\sqrt{14} \cdot \sqrt{6} = \sqrt{14 \cdot 6} = \sqrt{84} = \sqrt{4} \cdot \sqrt{21} = 2\sqrt{21}$

11. $\sqrt{12} \cdot \sqrt{3} = \sqrt{12 \cdot 3} = \sqrt{36} = 6$ 13. $\sqrt{y^4} \cdot \sqrt{y^7} = \sqrt{y^4 \cdot y^7} = \underbrace{\sqrt{y^{11}} = y^5\sqrt{y}}_{11 \div 2 = 5 \text{ R } 1}$

15. $\sqrt{xy^3} \cdot \sqrt{x^4y} = \sqrt{xy^3 \cdot x^4y} = \underbrace{\sqrt{x^5y^4} = x^2y^2\sqrt{x}}_{5\div2=2 \text{ R } 1 \text{ and } 4\div2=2 \text{ R } 0.}$

17. $\sqrt{5a^5b} \cdot \sqrt{a^4b^3} = \sqrt{5a^5b \cdot a^4b^3} = \underbrace{\sqrt{5a^9b^4} = a^4b^2\sqrt{5a}}_{9\div2=4 \text{ R } 1 \text{ and } 4\div2=2 \text{ R } 0.}$

19. $\sqrt{8x^5y^4} \cdot \sqrt{5x^2y^2} = \sqrt{8x^5y^4 \cdot 5x^2y^2} = \underbrace{\sqrt{40x^7y^6} = 2x^3y^3\sqrt{10x}}_{7\div2=3 \text{ R } 1 \text{ and } 6\div2=3 \text{ R } 0.}$ (Notice that $\sqrt{40} = \sqrt{4}\sqrt{10} = 2\sqrt{10}$.)

21. $\sqrt{10a^4b^3} \cdot \sqrt{10a^4b} = \sqrt{10a^4b^3 \cdot 10a^4b} = \underbrace{\sqrt{100a^8b^4} = 10a^4b^2}_{8\div2=4 \text{ R } 0 \text{ and } 4\div2=2 \text{ R } 0.}$

23. $\sqrt{12m^3n} \cdot \sqrt{12m^2n} = \sqrt{12m^3n \cdot 12m^2n} = \underbrace{\sqrt{144m^5n^2} = 12m^2n\sqrt{m}}_{5\div2=2 \text{ R } 1 \text{ and } 2\div2=1 \text{ R } 0.}$ 25. $\dfrac{\sqrt{32}}{\sqrt{2}} = \sqrt{\dfrac{32}{2}} = \sqrt{16} = 4$

27. $\dfrac{\sqrt{56}}{\sqrt{7}} = \sqrt{\dfrac{56}{7}} = \sqrt{8} = \sqrt{4}\sqrt{2} = 2\sqrt{2}$ 29. $\dfrac{\sqrt{24x^5}}{\sqrt{2x^4}} = \sqrt{\dfrac{24x^5}{2x^4}} = \underbrace{\sqrt{12x} = 2\sqrt{3x}}_{\sqrt{12}=\sqrt{4}\sqrt{3}=2\sqrt{3}}$

31. $\dfrac{\sqrt{48y^{11}}}{\sqrt{8y^4}} = \sqrt{\dfrac{48y^{11}}{8y^4}} = \underbrace{\sqrt{6y^7} = y^3\sqrt{6y}}_{7\div2=3 \text{ R } 1}$

33. $\dfrac{\sqrt{200x^{15}y^4}}{\sqrt{4x^8y^4}} = \sqrt{\dfrac{200x^{15}y^4}{4x^8y^4}} = \underbrace{\sqrt{50x^7} = 5x^3\sqrt{2x}}_{\sqrt{50}=\sqrt{25}\sqrt{2}=5\sqrt{2} \text{ and } 7\div2=3 \text{ R } 1.}$

35. $\dfrac{\sqrt{5a^4b}}{\sqrt{45a^3b^5}} = \sqrt{\dfrac{5a^4b}{45a^3b^5}} = \underbrace{\sqrt{\dfrac{a}{9b^4}} = \dfrac{\sqrt{a}}{3b^2}}_{4\div2=2 \text{ R } 0}$

37. $\dfrac{\sqrt{23xy^5z^7}}{\sqrt{14x^2y^3}} = \sqrt{\dfrac{23xy^5z^7}{14x^2y^3}} = \underbrace{\sqrt{\dfrac{23y^2z^7}{14x}} = \dfrac{yz^3\sqrt{23z}}{\sqrt{14x}}}_{2\div2=1 \text{ R } 0 \text{ and } 7\div2=3 \text{ R } 1.} = yz^3\sqrt{\dfrac{23z}{14x}}$

Chapter 5 Exercise 5.1.4

1. $\sqrt{3} + 4\sqrt{3} = 5\sqrt{3}$ 3. $9\sqrt{10} - 13\sqrt{10} = -4\sqrt{10}$ 5. $9\sqrt{5} + 8\sqrt{5} - 16\sqrt{5} = 1\sqrt{5} = \sqrt{5}$

7. $-9\sqrt{7} + 4\sqrt{7} - \sqrt{7} = -6\sqrt{7}$ 9. $\underbrace{\sqrt{5} + \sqrt{20} = \sqrt{5} + 2\sqrt{5}}_{\sqrt{20}=\sqrt{4}\sqrt{5}=2\sqrt{5}} = 3\sqrt{5}$

11. $\underbrace{4\sqrt{6} - 5\sqrt{72} = 4\sqrt{6} - 5\left(6\sqrt{2}\right)}_{\sqrt{72}=\sqrt{36}\sqrt{2}=6\sqrt{2}} = 4\sqrt{6} - 30\sqrt{2}$ do not combine into a single square root.

13. $\underbrace{-7\sqrt{8} - 2\sqrt{18} = -7\left(2\sqrt{2}\right) - 2\left(3\sqrt{2}\right)}_{\sqrt{18}=\sqrt{9}\sqrt{2}=3\sqrt{2} \text{ and } \sqrt{8}=\sqrt{4}\sqrt{2}=2\sqrt{2}.} = -14\sqrt{2} - 6\sqrt{2} = -20\sqrt{2}$

15. $\underbrace{8\sqrt{6} - 3\sqrt{24} + \sqrt{54} = 8\sqrt{6} - 3\left(2\sqrt{6}\right) + \left(3\sqrt{6}\right)}_{\sqrt{24}=\sqrt{4}\sqrt{6}=2\sqrt{6} \text{ and } \sqrt{54}=\sqrt{9}\sqrt{6}=3\sqrt{6}.} = 8\sqrt{6} - 6\sqrt{6} + 3\sqrt{6} = 5\sqrt{6}$

17. $3\sqrt{7} + \sqrt{3}$ do not combine into a single square root.

19. $\underbrace{-4\sqrt{3} + 2\sqrt{40} + 9\sqrt{243} = -4\sqrt{3} + 2\left(2\sqrt{10}\right) + 9\left(9\sqrt{3}\right)}_{\sqrt{40}=\sqrt{4}\sqrt{10}=2\sqrt{10}\ \text{and}\ \sqrt{243}=\sqrt{81}\sqrt{3}=9\sqrt{3}.} = -4\sqrt{3} + 4\sqrt{10} + 81\sqrt{3} = 77\sqrt{3} + 4\sqrt{10}$

21. $\underbrace{5\sqrt{16} - 8\sqrt{7} - \sqrt{63} + \sqrt{144} = 5\left(4\right) - 8\sqrt{7} - 3\sqrt{7} + 12}_{\sqrt{16}=4,\ \sqrt{63}=\sqrt{9}\sqrt{7}=3\sqrt{7},\ \text{and}\ \sqrt{144}=12.} = 20 - 8\sqrt{7} - 3\sqrt{7} + 12 = 32 - 11\sqrt{7}$

23. $\dfrac{3\sqrt{7} + 9\sqrt{28}}{9} = \dfrac{3\sqrt{7} + 9\left(2\sqrt{7}\right)}{9} = \dfrac{3\sqrt{7} + 18\sqrt{7}}{9} = \dfrac{\overset{7}{\cancel{21}}\sqrt{7}}{\underset{3}{\cancel{9}}} = \dfrac{7\sqrt{7}}{3}$

25. $\dfrac{-\sqrt{9} + 4\sqrt{81}}{11} = \dfrac{-3 + 4\left(9\right)}{11} = \dfrac{-3 + 36}{11} = \dfrac{33}{11} = 3$

27. $\dfrac{10 + \sqrt{32}}{2} = \dfrac{10 + 4\sqrt{2}}{2} = \dfrac{\overset{1}{\cancel{2}}\left(5 + 2\sqrt{2}\right)}{\underset{1}{\cancel{2}}} = \dfrac{5 + 2\sqrt{2}}{1} = 5 + 2\sqrt{2}$

29. $\dfrac{9\sqrt{5} + 12\sqrt{7}}{3} = \dfrac{\overset{1}{\cancel{3}}\left(3\sqrt{5} + 4\sqrt{7}\right)}{\underset{1}{\cancel{3}}} = \dfrac{3\sqrt{5} + 4\sqrt{7}}{1} = 3\sqrt{5} + 4\sqrt{7}$

31. $\dfrac{2 + \sqrt{24}}{2} = \dfrac{2 + 2\sqrt{6}}{2} = \dfrac{\overset{1}{\cancel{2}}\left(1 + \sqrt{6}\right)}{\underset{1}{\cancel{2}}} = \dfrac{1 + \sqrt{6}}{1} = 1 + \sqrt{6}$

33. $\dfrac{-18 - \sqrt{18}}{-9} = \dfrac{-18 - 3\sqrt{2}}{-9} = \dfrac{\overset{1}{-\cancel{3}}\left(6 + \sqrt{2}\right)}{\underset{3}{-\cancel{9}}} = \dfrac{6 + \sqrt{2}}{3}$

Chapter 5 Exercise 5.1.5

1. $\sqrt{2}\left(5\sqrt{2}\right) = 5\sqrt{4} = 5\left(2\right) = 10$

3. $\left(4\sqrt{6}\right)\left(3\sqrt{6}\right) = 12\sqrt{36} = 12\left(6\right) = 72$

5. $\left(-6\sqrt{5}\right)\left(3\sqrt{5}\right) = -18\sqrt{25} = -18\left(5\right) = -90$

7. $\left(8\sqrt{6}\right)\left(2\sqrt{2}\right) = 16\sqrt{12} = 16\left(2\sqrt{3}\right) = 32\sqrt{3}$

9. $\left(6\sqrt{2}\right)\left(2\sqrt{12}\right) = \underbrace{12\sqrt{24} = 12\left(2\sqrt{6}\right)}_{\sqrt{24}=\sqrt{4}\sqrt{6}=2\sqrt{6}} = 24\sqrt{6}$

11. $\left(-2\sqrt{49}\right)\left(3\sqrt{2}\right) = \underbrace{-6\sqrt{98} = -6\left(7\sqrt{2}\right)}_{\sqrt{98}=\sqrt{49}\sqrt{2}=7\sqrt{2}} = -42\sqrt{2}$

13. $\left(\sqrt{7}\right)\left(4\sqrt{20}\right) = \underbrace{4\sqrt{140} = 4\left(2\sqrt{35}\right)}_{\sqrt{140}=\sqrt{4}\sqrt{35}=2\sqrt{35}} = 8\sqrt{35}$

15. $\left(-9\sqrt{7}\right)\left(-4\sqrt{8}\right) = \underbrace{36\sqrt{56} = 36\left(2\sqrt{14}\right)}_{\sqrt{56}=\sqrt{4}\sqrt{14}=2\sqrt{14}} = 72\sqrt{14}$

17. $\left(6\sqrt{3}\right)^2 = \left(6\sqrt{3}\right)\left(6\sqrt{3}\right) = 36\sqrt{9} = 36\left(3\right) = 108$

19. $\left(-5\sqrt{5}\right)^2 = \left(-5\sqrt{5}\right)\left(-5\sqrt{5}\right) = 25\sqrt{25} = 25\left(5\right) = 125$

21. $\sqrt{2}\left(3\sqrt{2} + 4\right) = \sqrt{2}\left(3\sqrt{2}\right) + \sqrt{2}\left(4\right) = 3\sqrt{4} + 4\sqrt{2} = 3\left(2\right) + 4\sqrt{2} = 6 + 4\sqrt{2}$

23. $2\sqrt{3}\left(4\sqrt{27} + 6\sqrt{3}\right) = 2\sqrt{3}\left(4\sqrt{27}\right) + 2\sqrt{3}\left(6\sqrt{3}\right) = 8\sqrt{81} + 12\sqrt{9} = 8\left(9\right) + 12\left(3\right) = 72 + 36 = 108$

25. $-10\sqrt{6}\left(4\sqrt{3}+\sqrt{2}\right) = -10\sqrt{6}\left(4\sqrt{3}\right)+\left(-10\sqrt{6}\right)\left(\sqrt{2}\right)$

$\qquad = \underbrace{-40\sqrt{18}-10\sqrt{12} = -40\left(3\sqrt{2}\right)-10\left(2\sqrt{3}\right)}_{\sqrt{18}=\sqrt{9}\sqrt{2}=3\sqrt{2}\text{ and }\sqrt{12}=\sqrt{4}\sqrt{3}=2\sqrt{3}.} = -120\sqrt{2}-20\sqrt{3}$

27. $6\sqrt{3}\left(3\sqrt{3}+\sqrt{6}-5\sqrt{10}\right) = 6\sqrt{3}\left(3\sqrt{3}\right)+6\sqrt{3}\left(\sqrt{6}\right)+6\sqrt{3}\left(-5\sqrt{10}\right)$

$\qquad = \underbrace{18\sqrt{9}+6\sqrt{18}-30\sqrt{30} = 18\left(3\right)+6\left(3\sqrt{2}\right)-30\sqrt{30}}_{\sqrt{9}=3\text{ and }\sqrt{18}=\sqrt{9}\sqrt{2}=3\sqrt{2}.}$

$\qquad = 54+18\sqrt{2}-30\sqrt{30}$

29. $\left(\sqrt{3}-2\sqrt{7}\right)\left(\sqrt{3}-\sqrt{7}\right) = \left(\sqrt{3}\right)\left(\sqrt{3}\right)+\left(\sqrt{3}\right)\left(-\sqrt{7}\right)+\left(-2\sqrt{7}\right)\left(\sqrt{3}\right)+\left(-2\sqrt{7}\right)\left(-\sqrt{7}\right)$

$\qquad = \left(\sqrt{3}\right)^2-\sqrt{21}-2\sqrt{21}+2\left(\sqrt{7}\right)^2 = 3-3\sqrt{21}+2\left(7\right)$

$\qquad = 3-3\sqrt{21}+14 = 17-3\sqrt{21}$

31. $\left(5\sqrt{2}+2\sqrt{10}\right)\left(2\sqrt{2}-2\sqrt{10}\right) = \left(5\sqrt{2}\right)\left(2\sqrt{2}\right)+\left(5\sqrt{2}\right)\left(-2\sqrt{10}\right)+\left(2\sqrt{10}\right)\left(2\sqrt{2}\right)+\left(2\sqrt{10}\right)\left(-2\sqrt{10}\right)$

$\qquad = 10\left(\sqrt{2}\right)^2-10\sqrt{20}+4\sqrt{20}-4\left(\sqrt{10}\right)^2 = 10\left(2\right)-6\underbrace{\sqrt{20}}_{2\sqrt{5}}-4\left(10\right)$

$\qquad = 20-6\left(2\sqrt{5}\right)-40 = -20-12\sqrt{5}$

33. $\underbrace{\left(\sqrt{5}+\sqrt{7}\right)^2 = \left(\sqrt{5}\right)^2+2\left(\sqrt{5}\right)\left(\sqrt{7}\right)+\left(\sqrt{7}\right)^2}_{\text{Using the formula }(A+B)^2=A^2+2AB+B^2,\text{ with }A=\sqrt{5}\text{ and }B=\sqrt{7}.} = 5+2\sqrt{35}+7 = 12+2\sqrt{35}$

35. $\underbrace{\left(\sqrt{11}-5\sqrt{2}\right)^2 = \left(\sqrt{11}\right)^2-2\left(\sqrt{11}\right)\left(5\sqrt{2}\right)+\left(5\sqrt{2}\right)^2}_{\text{Using the formula }(A-B)^2=A^2-2AB+B^2,\text{ with }A=\sqrt{11}\text{ and }B=5\sqrt{2}.} = 11-10\sqrt{22}+5^2\left(\sqrt{2}\right)^2 = 11-10\sqrt{22}+25\left(2\right)$

$\qquad = 11-10\sqrt{22}+50 = 61-10\sqrt{22}$

37. $\underbrace{\left(\sqrt{y}-6\right)^2 = \left(\sqrt{y}\right)^2-2\left(\sqrt{y}\right)\left(6\right)+\left(6\right)^2}_{\text{Using the formula }(A-B)^2=A^2-2AB+B^2,\text{ with }A=\sqrt{y}\text{ and }B=6.} = y-12\sqrt{y}+36$

39. $\left(12+\sqrt{y}\right)\left(5-\sqrt{y}\right) = \left(12\right)\left(5\right)+\left(12\right)\left(-\sqrt{y}\right)+\left(\sqrt{y}\right)\left(5\right)+\left(\sqrt{y}\right)\left(-\sqrt{y}\right)$

$\qquad = 60-12\sqrt{y}+5\sqrt{y}-\left(\sqrt{y}\right)^2 = 60-7\sqrt{y}-y$

41. $\underbrace{\left(\sqrt{3}-\sqrt{13}\right)\left(\sqrt{3}+\sqrt{13}\right) = \left(\sqrt{3}\right)^2-\left(\sqrt{13}\right)^2}_{\text{Using the formula }(A+B)(A-B)=A^2-B^2,\text{ with }A=\sqrt{3}\text{ and }B=\sqrt{13}.} = 3-13 = -10$

43. $\underbrace{\left(2\sqrt{3}+5\right)\left(2\sqrt{3}-5\right) = \left(2\sqrt{3}\right)^2-\left(5\right)^2}_{\text{Using the formula }(A+B)(A-B)=A^2-B^2,\text{ with }A=2\sqrt{3}\text{ and }B=5.} = 2^2\left(\sqrt{3}\right)^2-25 = 4\left(3\right)-25 = 12-25 = -13$

45. $\underbrace{\left(-6\sqrt{2}+9\right)\left(-6\sqrt{2}-9\right) = \left(-6\sqrt{2}\right)^2-\left(9\right)^2}_{\text{Using the formula }(A+B)(A-B)=A^2-B^2,\text{ with }A=-6\sqrt{2}\text{ and }B=9.} = \left(-6\right)^2\left(\sqrt{2}\right)^2-81 = \underbrace{36\left(2\right)}_{72}-81 = -9$

47. $\underbrace{\left(\sqrt{b}-14\right)\left(\sqrt{b}+14\right) = \left(\sqrt{b}\right)^2-\left(14\right)^2}_{\text{Using the formula }(A+B)(A-B)=A^2-B^2,\text{ with }A=\sqrt{b}\text{ and }B=14.} = b-196$

Chapter 5 Exercise 5.1.6

1. $\dfrac{1}{\sqrt{5}} = \dfrac{1}{\sqrt{5}}\left(\dfrac{\sqrt{5}}{\sqrt{5}}\right) = \dfrac{\sqrt{5}}{\left(\sqrt{5}\right)^2} = \dfrac{\sqrt{5}}{5}$ 3. $\dfrac{5}{\sqrt{3}} = \dfrac{5}{\sqrt{3}}\left(\dfrac{\sqrt{3}}{\sqrt{3}}\right) = \dfrac{5\sqrt{3}}{\left(\sqrt{3}\right)^2} = \dfrac{5\sqrt{3}}{3}$

5. $\dfrac{11}{\sqrt{22}} = \dfrac{11}{\sqrt{22}}\left(\dfrac{\sqrt{22}}{\sqrt{22}}\right) = \dfrac{11\sqrt{22}}{\left(\sqrt{22}\right)^2} = \dfrac{\overset{1}{\cancel{11}}\sqrt{22}}{\underset{2}{\cancel{22}}} = \dfrac{\sqrt{22}}{2}$

7. $\dfrac{16}{\sqrt{10}} = \dfrac{16}{\sqrt{10}}\left(\dfrac{\sqrt{10}}{\sqrt{10}}\right) = \dfrac{16\sqrt{10}}{\left(\sqrt{10}\right)^2} = \dfrac{\overset{8}{\cancel{16}}\sqrt{10}}{\underset{5}{\cancel{10}}} = \dfrac{8\sqrt{10}}{5}$

9. $\underbrace{\dfrac{10}{\sqrt{8}} = \dfrac{\overset{5}{\cancel{10}}}{\underset{1}{\cancel{2}}\sqrt{2}}}_{\sqrt{8}=\sqrt{4}\sqrt{2}=2\sqrt{2}} = \dfrac{5}{\sqrt{2}} = \dfrac{5}{\sqrt{2}}\left(\dfrac{\sqrt{2}}{\sqrt{2}}\right) = \dfrac{5\sqrt{2}}{\left(\sqrt{2}\right)^2} = \dfrac{5\sqrt{2}}{2}$

11. $\underbrace{\dfrac{21}{4\sqrt{18}} = \dfrac{21}{4\left(3\sqrt{2}\right)}}_{\sqrt{18}=\sqrt{9}\sqrt{2}=3\sqrt{2}} = \dfrac{\overset{7}{\cancel{21}}}{\underset{4}{\cancel{12}}\sqrt{2}} = \dfrac{7}{4\sqrt{2}}\left(\dfrac{\sqrt{2}}{\sqrt{2}}\right) = \dfrac{7\sqrt{2}}{4\left(\sqrt{2}\right)^2} = \dfrac{7\sqrt{2}}{4\left(2\right)} = \dfrac{7\sqrt{2}}{8}$

13. $\underbrace{\dfrac{-6}{7\sqrt{52}} = \dfrac{-6}{7\left(2\sqrt{13}\right)}}_{\sqrt{52}=\sqrt{4}\sqrt{13}=2\sqrt{13}} = \dfrac{\overset{3}{\cancel{-6}}}{\underset{7}{\cancel{14}}\sqrt{13}} = \dfrac{-3}{7\sqrt{13}}\left(\dfrac{\sqrt{13}}{\sqrt{13}}\right) = \dfrac{-3\sqrt{13}}{7\left(\sqrt{13}\right)^2} = \dfrac{-3\sqrt{13}}{7\left(13\right)} = \dfrac{-3\sqrt{13}}{91}$

15. $\sqrt{\dfrac{1}{6}} = \dfrac{\sqrt{1}}{\sqrt{6}} = \dfrac{1}{\sqrt{6}} = \dfrac{1}{\sqrt{6}}\left(\dfrac{\sqrt{6}}{\sqrt{6}}\right) = \dfrac{\sqrt{6}}{\left(\sqrt{6}\right)^2} = \dfrac{\sqrt{6}}{6}$

17. $\sqrt{\dfrac{13}{7}} = \dfrac{\sqrt{13}}{\sqrt{7}} = \dfrac{\sqrt{13}}{\sqrt{7}}\left(\dfrac{\sqrt{7}}{\sqrt{7}}\right) = \dfrac{\sqrt{91}}{\left(\sqrt{7}\right)^2} = \dfrac{\sqrt{91}}{7}$

19. $\sqrt{\dfrac{7}{12}} = \underbrace{\dfrac{\sqrt{7}}{\sqrt{12}} = \dfrac{\sqrt{7}}{2\sqrt{3}}}_{\sqrt{12}=\sqrt{4}\sqrt{3}=2\sqrt{3}} = \dfrac{\sqrt{7}}{2\sqrt{3}}\left(\dfrac{\sqrt{3}}{\sqrt{3}}\right) = \dfrac{\sqrt{21}}{2\left(\sqrt{3}\right)^2} = \dfrac{\sqrt{21}}{2\left(3\right)} = \dfrac{\sqrt{21}}{6}$

21. $\dfrac{5}{\sqrt{y}} = \dfrac{5}{\sqrt{y}}\left(\dfrac{\sqrt{y}}{\sqrt{y}}\right) = \dfrac{5\sqrt{y}}{\left(\sqrt{y}\right)^2} = \dfrac{5\sqrt{y}}{y}$

23. $\dfrac{4}{9\sqrt{2x}} = \dfrac{4}{9\sqrt{2x}}\left(\dfrac{\sqrt{2x}}{\sqrt{2x}}\right) = \dfrac{4\sqrt{2x}}{9\left(\sqrt{2x}\right)^2} = \dfrac{4\sqrt{2x}}{9\left(2x\right)} = \dfrac{\overset{2}{\cancel{4}}\sqrt{2x}}{\underset{9}{\cancel{18}}x} = \dfrac{2\sqrt{2x}}{9x}$

25. $\dfrac{1}{\sqrt{2}-1} = \underbrace{\dfrac{1}{\sqrt{2}-1}\left(\dfrac{\sqrt{2}+1}{\sqrt{2}+1}\right) = \dfrac{\sqrt{2}+1}{\left(\sqrt{2}\right)^2-\left(1\right)^2}}_{\text{Using the formula } (A+B)(A-B)=A^2-B^2,\text{ with } A=\sqrt{2}\text{ and }B=1.} = \dfrac{\sqrt{2}+1}{2-1} = \dfrac{\sqrt{2}+1}{1} = \sqrt{2}+1$

27. $\dfrac{1}{\sqrt{5}+2} = \underbrace{\dfrac{1}{\sqrt{5}+2}\left(\dfrac{\sqrt{5}-2}{\sqrt{5}-2}\right) = \dfrac{\sqrt{5}-2}{\left(\sqrt{5}\right)^2-(2)^2}}_{} = \dfrac{\sqrt{5}-2}{5-4} = \dfrac{\sqrt{5}-2}{1} = \sqrt{5}-2$

Using the formula $(A+B)(A-B)=A^2-B^2$, with $A=\sqrt{5}$ and $B=2$.

29. $\dfrac{2}{\sqrt{5}+3} = \underbrace{\dfrac{2}{\sqrt{5}+3}\left(\dfrac{\sqrt{5}-3}{\sqrt{5}-3}\right) = \dfrac{2\left(\sqrt{5}-3\right)}{\left(\sqrt{5}\right)^2-(3)^2}}_{} = \dfrac{2\left(\sqrt{5}-3\right)}{5-9} = \dfrac{\overset{1}{\cancel{2}}\left(\sqrt{5}-3\right)}{\underset{2}{\cancel{-4}}} = \dfrac{\sqrt{5}-3}{-2}$

Using the formula $(A+B)(A-B)=A^2-B^2$, with $A=\sqrt{5}$ and $B=3$.

31. $\dfrac{2-\sqrt{3}}{1+\sqrt{3}} = \underbrace{\dfrac{2-\sqrt{3}}{1+\sqrt{3}}\left(\dfrac{1-\sqrt{3}}{1-\sqrt{3}}\right) = \dfrac{(2-\sqrt{3})(1-\sqrt{3})}{(1)^2-\left(\sqrt{3}\right)^2}}_{} = \dfrac{2-2\sqrt{3}-\sqrt{3}+\overset{3}{\overbrace{\left(\sqrt{3}\right)^2}}}{1-3} = \dfrac{5-3\sqrt{3}}{-2}$

Using the formula $(A+B)(A-B)=A^2-B^2$, with $A=1$ and $B=\sqrt{3}$.

33. $\dfrac{\sqrt{10}-\sqrt{2}}{\sqrt{10}+\sqrt{2}} = \underbrace{\dfrac{\sqrt{10}-\sqrt{2}}{\sqrt{10}+\sqrt{2}}\left(\dfrac{\sqrt{10}-\sqrt{2}}{\sqrt{10}-\sqrt{2}}\right) = \dfrac{(\sqrt{10}-\sqrt{2})(\sqrt{10}-\sqrt{2})}{\left(\sqrt{10}\right)^2-\left(\sqrt{2}\right)^2}}_{} = \dfrac{\overset{10}{\overbrace{\left(\sqrt{10}\right)^2}}-\sqrt{20}-\sqrt{20}+\overset{2}{\overbrace{\left(\sqrt{2}\right)^2}}}{10-2}$

Using the formula $(A+B)(A-B)=A^2-B^2$, with $A=\sqrt{10}$ and $B=\sqrt{2}$.

$= \dfrac{12-2\overset{2\sqrt{5}}{\overbrace{\sqrt{20}}}}{8} = \dfrac{12-4\sqrt{5}}{8} = \dfrac{\overset{1}{\cancel{4}}\left(3-\sqrt{5}\right)}{\underset{2}{\cancel{8}}} = \dfrac{3-\sqrt{5}}{2}$

35. $\dfrac{-2\sqrt{6}+3}{3\sqrt{2}+\sqrt{6}} = \underbrace{\dfrac{-2\sqrt{6}+3}{3\sqrt{2}+\sqrt{6}}\left(\dfrac{3\sqrt{2}-\sqrt{6}}{3\sqrt{2}-\sqrt{6}}\right) = \dfrac{(-2\sqrt{6}+3)(3\sqrt{2}-\sqrt{6})}{\left(3\sqrt{2}\right)^2-\left(\sqrt{6}\right)^2}}_{} = \dfrac{-6\sqrt{12}+2\left(\sqrt{6}\right)^2+9\sqrt{2}-3\sqrt{6}}{3^2\left(\sqrt{2}\right)^2-6}$

Using the formula $(A+B)(A-B)=A^2-B^2$, with $A=3\sqrt{2}$ and $B=\sqrt{6}$.

$= \dfrac{-6\left(2\sqrt{3}\right)+2(6)+9\sqrt{2}-3\sqrt{6}}{9(2)-6} = \dfrac{-12\sqrt{3}+12+9\sqrt{2}-3\sqrt{6}}{18-6}$

$= \dfrac{-12\sqrt{3}+12+9\sqrt{2}-3\sqrt{6}}{12} = \dfrac{\overset{1}{\cancel{3}}\left(-4\sqrt{3}+4+3\sqrt{2}-\sqrt{6}\right)}{\underset{4}{\cancel{12}}} = \dfrac{-4\sqrt{3}+4+3\sqrt{2}-\sqrt{6}}{4}$

37. $\dfrac{3+\sqrt{x}}{8-\sqrt{x}} = \underbrace{\dfrac{3+\sqrt{x}}{8-\sqrt{x}}\left(\dfrac{8+\sqrt{x}}{8+\sqrt{x}}\right) = \dfrac{(3+\sqrt{x})(8+\sqrt{x})}{(8)^2-\left(\sqrt{x}\right)^2}}_{} = \dfrac{24+3\sqrt{x}+8\sqrt{x}+\left(\sqrt{x}\right)^2}{64-x}$

Using the formula $(A+B)(A-B)=A^2-B^2$, with $A=2$ and $B=\sqrt{x}$.

$= \dfrac{24+11\sqrt{x}+x}{64-x}$

39. $\dfrac{\sqrt{3}}{2} = \dfrac{\sqrt{3}}{2}\left(\dfrac{\sqrt{3}}{\sqrt{3}}\right) = \dfrac{\left(\sqrt{3}\right)^2}{2\sqrt{3}} = \dfrac{3}{2\sqrt{3}}$

41. $\dfrac{\sqrt{12}}{4} = \underbrace{\dfrac{\overset{1}{\cancel{2}}\sqrt{3}}{\underset{2}{\cancel{4}}}}_{\sqrt{12}=\sqrt{4}\sqrt{3}=2\sqrt{3}} = \dfrac{\sqrt{3}}{2}\left(\dfrac{\sqrt{3}}{\sqrt{3}}\right) = \dfrac{\left(\sqrt{3}\right)^2}{2\sqrt{3}} = \dfrac{3}{2\sqrt{3}}$

43. $\dfrac{\sqrt{7}}{2\sqrt{5}} = \dfrac{\sqrt{7}}{2\sqrt{5}}\left(\dfrac{\sqrt{7}}{\sqrt{7}}\right) = \dfrac{\left(\sqrt{7}\right)^2}{2\sqrt{35}} = \dfrac{7}{2\sqrt{35}}$

212

45. $\underbrace{\dfrac{\sqrt{24}}{\sqrt{5}}}_{\sqrt{24}=\sqrt{4}\sqrt{6}=2\sqrt{6}} = \dfrac{2\sqrt{6}}{\sqrt{5}} = \dfrac{2\sqrt{6}}{\sqrt{5}}\left(\dfrac{\sqrt{6}}{\sqrt{6}}\right) = \dfrac{2\left(\sqrt{6}\right)^2}{\sqrt{30}} = \dfrac{2\left(6\right)}{\sqrt{30}} = \dfrac{12}{\sqrt{30}}$

47. $\sqrt{\dfrac{11}{9}} = \dfrac{\sqrt{11}}{\sqrt{9}} = \dfrac{\sqrt{11}}{3} = \dfrac{\sqrt{11}}{3}\left(\dfrac{\sqrt{11}}{\sqrt{11}}\right) = \dfrac{\left(\sqrt{11}\right)^2}{3\sqrt{11}} = \dfrac{11}{3\sqrt{11}}$

49. $\dfrac{\sqrt{x}}{6} = \dfrac{\sqrt{x}}{6}\left(\dfrac{\sqrt{x}}{\sqrt{x}}\right) = \dfrac{\left(\sqrt{x}\right)^2}{6\sqrt{x}} = \dfrac{x}{6\sqrt{x}}$

51. $\dfrac{2-\sqrt{6}}{4} = \underbrace{\dfrac{2-\sqrt{6}}{4}\left(\dfrac{2+\sqrt{6}}{2+\sqrt{6}}\right) = \dfrac{(2)^2-\left(\sqrt{6}\right)^2}{4\left(2+\sqrt{6}\right)}}_{\text{Using the formula } (A+B)(A-B)=A^2-B^2,\text{ with } A=2\text{ and } B=\sqrt{6}.} = \dfrac{4-6}{4\left(2+\sqrt{6}\right)} = \dfrac{\overset{1}{\cancel{-2}}}{\underset{2}{\cancel{4}}\left(2+\sqrt{6}\right)} = \dfrac{-1}{2\left(2+\sqrt{6}\right)}$

53. $\dfrac{\sqrt{2}+\sqrt{5}}{\sqrt{3}} = \underbrace{\dfrac{\sqrt{2}+\sqrt{5}}{\sqrt{3}}\left(\dfrac{\sqrt{2}-\sqrt{5}}{\sqrt{2}-\sqrt{5}}\right) = \dfrac{\left(\sqrt{2}\right)^2-\left(\sqrt{5}\right)^2}{\sqrt{3}\left(\sqrt{2}-\sqrt{5}\right)}}_{\text{Using the formula } (A+B)(A-B)=A^2-B^2,\text{ with } A=\sqrt{2}\text{ and } B=\sqrt{5}.} = \dfrac{2-5}{\sqrt{6}-\sqrt{15}} = \dfrac{-3}{\sqrt{6}-\sqrt{15}}$

55. $\dfrac{\sqrt{6}+4}{\sqrt{6}-4} = \underbrace{\dfrac{\sqrt{6}+4}{\sqrt{6}-4}\left(\dfrac{\sqrt{6}-4}{\sqrt{6}-4}\right) = \dfrac{\left(\sqrt{6}\right)^2-(4)^2}{\left(\sqrt{6}-4\right)\left(\sqrt{6}-4\right)}}_{\text{Using the formula } (A+B)(A-B)=A^2-B^2,\text{ with } A=\sqrt{6}\text{ and } B=4.} = \dfrac{6-16}{\underbrace{\left(\sqrt{6}\right)^2}_{6}-4\sqrt{6}-4\sqrt{6}+16}$

$= \dfrac{-10}{22-8\sqrt{6}} = \dfrac{\overset{5}{\cancel{-10}}}{\underset{1}{\cancel{2}}\left(11-4\sqrt{6}\right)} = \dfrac{-5}{11-4\sqrt{6}}$

57. $\dfrac{\sqrt{x}+3}{\sqrt{x}-9} = \underbrace{\dfrac{\sqrt{x}+3}{\sqrt{x}-9}\left(\dfrac{\sqrt{x}-3}{\sqrt{x}-3}\right) = \dfrac{\left(\sqrt{x}\right)^2-(3)^2}{\left(\sqrt{x}-9\right)\left(\sqrt{x}-3\right)}}_{\text{Using the formula } (A+B)(A-B)=A^2-B^2,\text{ with } A=\sqrt{x}\text{ and } B=3.} = \dfrac{x-9}{\left(\sqrt{x}\right)^2-3\sqrt{x}-9\sqrt{x}+27}$

$= \dfrac{x-9}{x-12\sqrt{x}+27}$

59. $\dfrac{\sqrt{6+h}-\sqrt{6}}{h} = \underbrace{\dfrac{\sqrt{6+h}-\sqrt{6}}{h}\left(\dfrac{\sqrt{6+h}+\sqrt{6}}{\sqrt{6+h}+\sqrt{6}}\right) = \dfrac{\left(\sqrt{6+h}\right)^2-\left(\sqrt{6}\right)^2}{h\left(\sqrt{6+h}+\sqrt{6}\right)}}_{\text{Using the formula } (A+B)(A-B)=A^2-B^2,\text{ with } A=\sqrt{6+h}\text{ and } B=\sqrt{6}.}$

$= \dfrac{6+h-6}{h\left(\sqrt{6+h}+\sqrt{6}\right)} = \dfrac{\overset{1}{\cancel{h}}}{\underset{1}{\cancel{h}}\left(\sqrt{6+h}+\sqrt{6}\right)} = \dfrac{1}{\sqrt{6+h}+\sqrt{6}}$

Chapter 5 Exercise 5.2

1. $\sqrt[3]{8} = 2$ 3. $-\sqrt[3]{-8} = -(-2) = 2$ 5. $\sqrt[3]{-27} = -3$ 7. $\sqrt[3]{\dfrac{1}{64}} = \dfrac{1}{4}$

9. $\sqrt[3]{-\dfrac{1}{64}} = -\dfrac{1}{4}$ 11. $\sqrt[3]{-\dfrac{125}{8}} = -\dfrac{5}{2}$ 13. $\sqrt[3]{(27)(0)} = \underbrace{\sqrt[3]{27}}_{3} \cdot \underbrace{\sqrt[3]{0}}_{0} = 3 \cdot 0 = 0$

15. $\left(\sqrt[3]{12}\right)^3 = 12$ 17. $\left(\sqrt[3]{-21}\right)^3 = -21$ 19. $\sqrt[3]{15^3\,(8)} = \underbrace{\sqrt[3]{15^3}}_{15} \cdot \underbrace{\sqrt[3]{8}}_{2} = 15 \cdot 2 = 30$

21. $\sqrt[3]{32} = \sqrt[3]{8 \cdot 4} = \sqrt[3]{8} \cdot \sqrt[3]{4} = 2\sqrt[3]{4}$ 23. $\sqrt[3]{-24} = \sqrt[3]{-8 \cdot 3} = \sqrt[3]{-8} \cdot \sqrt[3]{3} = -2\sqrt[3]{3}$

25. $\sqrt[3]{54} = \sqrt[3]{27 \cdot 2} = \sqrt[3]{27} \cdot \sqrt[3]{2} = 3\sqrt[3]{2}$ 27. $\sqrt[3]{-54} = \sqrt[3]{-27 \cdot 2} = \sqrt[3]{-27} \cdot \sqrt[3]{2} = -3\sqrt[3]{2}$

29. $\sqrt[3]{2,000} = \sqrt[3]{1,000 \cdot 2} = \sqrt[3]{1,000} \cdot \sqrt[3]{2} = 10\sqrt[3]{2}$ 31. $\sqrt[3]{y^3} = y$ 33. $\underbrace{\sqrt[3]{x^{13}} = x^4\sqrt[3]{x}}_{13\div 3=4\text{ R }1}$

35. $\underbrace{\sqrt[3]{y^{23}} = y^7\sqrt[3]{y^2}}_{23\div 3=7\text{ R }2}$ 37. $\underbrace{\sqrt[3]{14x^6y^{11}} = x^2y^3\sqrt[3]{14y^2}}_{6\div 3=2\text{ R }0\text{ and }11\div 3=3\text{ R }2.}$ 39. $\underbrace{\sqrt[3]{-40x^{10}y^2} = -2x^3\sqrt[3]{5xy^2}}_{\sqrt[3]{-40}=\sqrt[3]{-8}\sqrt[3]{5}=-2\sqrt[3]{5},\ 10\div 3=3\text{ R }1,\text{ and }2\div 3=0\text{ R }2.}$

41. $2\sqrt[3]{2} + 9\sqrt[3]{2} = 11\sqrt[3]{2}$ 43. $12\sqrt[3]{9} - 7\sqrt[3]{9} = 5\sqrt[3]{9}$

45. $3\underbrace{\sqrt[3]{16} + \sqrt[3]{24} = 3\left(2\sqrt[3]{2}\right) + 2\sqrt[3]{3}}\ = 6\sqrt[3]{2} + 2\sqrt[3]{3}$ do not combine.

       $\sqrt[3]{16}=\sqrt[3]{8}\sqrt[3]{2}=2\sqrt[3]{2}$ and $\sqrt[3]{24}=\sqrt[3]{8}\sqrt[3]{3}=2\sqrt[3]{3}.$

47. $12\underbrace{\sqrt[3]{2} + 5\sqrt[3]{16} - 7\sqrt[3]{54} = 12\sqrt[3]{2} + 5\left(2\sqrt[3]{2}\right) - 7\left(3\sqrt[3]{2}\right)}\ = 12\sqrt[3]{2} + 10\sqrt[3]{2} - 21\sqrt[3]{2} = 1\sqrt[3]{2} = \sqrt[3]{2}$

       $\sqrt[3]{16}=\sqrt[3]{8}\sqrt[3]{2}=2\sqrt[3]{2}$ and $\sqrt[3]{54}=\sqrt[3]{27}\sqrt[3]{2}=3\sqrt[3]{2}.$

49. $\underbrace{-3x\sqrt[3]{2x} - \sqrt[3]{250x^4} = -3x\sqrt[3]{2x} - 5x\sqrt[3]{2x}}\ = -8x\sqrt[3]{2x}$ 51. $\left(\sqrt[3]{4}\right)\left(\sqrt[3]{2}\right) = \sqrt[3]{8} = 2$

     $\sqrt[3]{250x^4}=5x\sqrt[3]{2x}$ since $\sqrt[3]{250}=\sqrt[3]{125}\sqrt[3]{2}=5\sqrt[3]{2}$ and $4\div 3=1$ R $1.$

53. $\left(\sqrt[3]{3}\right)\left(-\sqrt[3]{9}\right) = -\sqrt[3]{27} = -3$ 55. $\left(\sqrt[3]{-4}\right)\underbrace{\left(\sqrt[3]{-10}\right)}_{-\sqrt[3]{10}=\sqrt[3]{-10}}\ = \sqrt[3]{40} = \sqrt[3]{8}\sqrt[3]{5} = 2\sqrt[3]{5}$

57. $\left(\sqrt[3]{27}\right)^2 = (3)^2 = 9$ 59. $\left(\sqrt[3]{100}\right)^2 = \left(\sqrt[3]{100}\right)\left(\sqrt[3]{100}\right) = \sqrt[3]{10,000} = \sqrt[3]{1,000}\sqrt[3]{10} = 10\sqrt[3]{10}$

61. $\sqrt[3]{3}\left(\sqrt[3]{9} + 12\right) = \sqrt[3]{3}\left(\sqrt[3]{9}\right) + \sqrt[3]{3}\,(12) = \sqrt[3]{27} + 12\sqrt[3]{3} = 3 + 12\sqrt[3]{3}$

63. $\sqrt[3]{16}\left(\sqrt[3]{2} + 5\sqrt[3]{3}\right) = \sqrt[3]{16}\left(\sqrt[3]{2}\right) + \sqrt[3]{16}\left(5\sqrt[3]{3}\right) = \underbrace{\sqrt[3]{32} + 5\sqrt[3]{48} = 2\sqrt[3]{4} + 5\left(2\sqrt[3]{6}\right)}\ = 2\sqrt[3]{4} + 10\sqrt[3]{6}$

       $\sqrt[3]{32}=\sqrt[3]{8}\sqrt[3]{4}=2\sqrt[3]{4}$ and $\sqrt[3]{48}=\sqrt[3]{8}\sqrt[3]{6}=2\sqrt[3]{6}.$

65. $\left(\sqrt[3]{2} - 3\right)\left(\sqrt[3]{2} + 1\right) = \left(\sqrt[3]{2}\right)\left(\sqrt[3]{2}\right) + \left(\sqrt[3]{2}\right)(1) + (-3)\left(\sqrt[3]{2}\right) + (-3)(1)$

                     $= \sqrt[3]{4} + \sqrt[3]{2} - 3\sqrt[3]{2} - 3 = \sqrt[3]{4} - 2\sqrt[3]{2} - 3$

67. $\underbrace{\left(\sqrt[3]{4} + 2\right)^2 = \left(\sqrt[3]{4}\right)^2 + 2\left(\sqrt[3]{4}\right)(2) + (2)^2}\ = \underbrace{\sqrt[3]{16} + 4\sqrt[3]{4} + 4 = 2\sqrt[3]{2} + 4\sqrt[3]{4} + 4}_{\sqrt[3]{16}=\sqrt[3]{8}\sqrt[3]{2}=2\sqrt[3]{2}}$

     Using the formula $(A+B)^2=A^2+2AB+B^2$, with $A=\sqrt[3]{4}$ and $B=2.$

69. $\left(\sqrt[3]{x} + 8\right)\left(\sqrt[3]{x} + 5\right) = \left(\sqrt[3]{x}\right)\left(\sqrt[3]{x}\right) + \left(\sqrt[3]{x}\right)(5) + (8)\left(\sqrt[3]{x}\right) + (8)(5)$

                     $= \sqrt[3]{x^2} + 5\sqrt[3]{x} + 8\sqrt[3]{x} + 40 = \sqrt[3]{x^2} + 13\sqrt[3]{x} + 40$

71. $\left(\sqrt[3]{x^2} - 12\right)\left(\sqrt[3]{x^5} - 7\right) = \left(\sqrt[3]{x^2}\right)\left(\sqrt[3]{x^5}\right) + \left(\sqrt[3]{x^2}\right)(-7) + (-12)\left(\sqrt[3]{x^5}\right) + (-12)(-7)$

                     $= \sqrt[3]{x^7} - 7\sqrt[3]{x^2} - 12\sqrt[3]{x^5} + 84$

                     $= x^2\sqrt[3]{x} - 7\sqrt[3]{x^2} - 12x\sqrt[3]{x^2} + 84$

Chapter 5 Exercise 5.3

1. $\sqrt[4]{81} = 3$ 3. $\sqrt[5]{243} = 3$ 5. $\sqrt[5]{-32} = -2$ 7. $\sqrt[6]{64} = 2$

9. $\sqrt[4]{\dfrac{81}{256}} = \dfrac{\sqrt[4]{81}}{\sqrt[4]{256}} = \dfrac{3}{4}$ 11. $\sqrt[4]{48} = \sqrt[4]{16 \cdot 3} = \sqrt[4]{16} \cdot \sqrt[4]{3} = 2\sqrt[4]{3}$

13. $-\sqrt[4]{162} = -\sqrt[4]{81 \cdot 2} = -\sqrt[4]{81} \cdot \sqrt[4]{2} = -3\sqrt[4]{2}$ 15. $\sqrt[5]{7^5} = 7$ 17. $\sqrt[7]{(-25)^7} = -25$

19. $\sqrt[5]{64} = \sqrt[5]{32 \cdot 2} = \sqrt[5]{32} \cdot \sqrt[5]{2} = 2\sqrt[5]{2}$ 21. $\underbrace{\sqrt[6]{x^{29}} = x^4 \sqrt[6]{x^5}}_{29 \div 6 = 4 \text{ R } 5}$

23. $\underbrace{\sqrt[5]{x^{14}y^8} = x^2 y \sqrt[5]{x^4 y^3}}_{14 \div 5 = 2 \text{ R } 4 \text{ and } 8 \div 5 = 1 \text{ R } 3.}$ 25. $\underbrace{\sqrt[7]{x^{24}y^2} = x^3 \sqrt[7]{x^3 y^2}}_{24 \div 7 = 3 \text{ R } 3 \text{ and } 2 \div 7 = 0 \text{ R } 2.}$ 27. $\underbrace{\sqrt[4]{48x^{12}y^3} = 2x^3 \sqrt[4]{3y^3}}_{\sqrt[4]{48} = \sqrt[4]{16}\sqrt[4]{3} = 2\sqrt[4]{3},\ 12 \div 4 = 3 \text{ R } 0,\text{ and } 3 \div 4 = 0 \text{ R } 3.}$

29. $\sqrt[5]{3}\left(4\sqrt[5]{3} + 7\right) = \sqrt[5]{3}\left(4\sqrt[5]{3}\right) + \sqrt[5]{3}\,(7) = 4\sqrt[5]{9} + 7\sqrt[5]{3}$

31. $\sqrt[7]{11}\left(2\sqrt[7]{11} - 9\sqrt[7]{5}\right) = \sqrt[7]{11}\left(2\sqrt[7]{11}\right) + \sqrt[7]{11}\left(-9\sqrt[7]{5}\right) = 2\sqrt[7]{121} - 9\sqrt[7]{55}$

33. $\left(\sqrt[5]{3} + 4\right)\left(\sqrt[5]{3} - 1\right) = \left(\sqrt[5]{3}\right)\left(\sqrt[5]{3}\right) + \left(\sqrt[5]{3}\right)(-1) + (4)\left(\sqrt[5]{3}\right) + (4)(-1)$

$$= \sqrt[5]{9} - \sqrt[5]{3} + 4\sqrt[5]{3} - 4 = \sqrt[5]{9} + 3\sqrt[5]{3} - 4$$

35. $\underbrace{\left(\sqrt[7]{6} + 7\right)^2 = \left(\sqrt[7]{6}\right)^2 + 2\left(\sqrt[7]{6}\right)(7) + (7)^2}\quad = \sqrt[7]{6} + 14\sqrt[7]{36} + 49$

Using the formula $(A+B)^2 = A^2 + 2AB + B^2$, with $A = \sqrt[7]{6}$ and $B = 7$.

37. $\underbrace{\left(\sqrt[5]{3} + 2\right)\left(\sqrt[5]{3} - 2\right) = \left(\sqrt[5]{3}\right)^2 - (2)^2}\quad = \sqrt[5]{9} - 4$

Using the formula $(A+B)(A-B) = A^2 - B^2$, with $A = \sqrt[5]{3}$ and $B = 2$.

39. $\left(\sqrt[3]{x} + 4\right)\left(\sqrt[3]{x} + 5\right) = \left(\sqrt[3]{x}\right)\left(\sqrt[3]{x}\right) + \left(\sqrt[3]{x}\right)(5) + (4)\left(\sqrt[3]{x}\right) + (4)(5)$

$$= \sqrt[3]{x^2} + 5\sqrt[3]{x} + 4\sqrt[3]{x} + 20 = \sqrt[3]{x^2} + 9\sqrt[3]{x} + 20$$

41. $\underbrace{\left(\sqrt[5]{m} + n\right)^2 = \left(\sqrt[5]{m}\right)^2 + 2\left(\sqrt[5]{m}\right)(n) + (n)^2}\quad = \sqrt[5]{m^2} + 2n\sqrt[5]{m} + n^2$

Using the formula $(A+B)^2 = A^2 + 2AB + B^2$, with $A = \sqrt[5]{m}$ and $B = n$.

43. $\underbrace{\left(\sqrt[9]{x} - \sqrt[9]{y}\right)\left(\sqrt[9]{x} + \sqrt[9]{y}\right) = \left(\sqrt[9]{x}\right)^2 - \left(\sqrt[9]{y}\right)^2}\quad = \sqrt[9]{x^2} - \sqrt[9]{y^2}$

Using the formula $(A+B)(A-B) = A^2 - B^2$, with $A = \sqrt[9]{x}$ and $B = \sqrt[9]{y}$.

45. $\sqrt[5]{x^2}\left(\sqrt[5]{x^3} + 5x\right) = \sqrt[5]{x^2}\left(\sqrt[5]{x^3}\right) + \sqrt[5]{x^2}\,(5x) = \sqrt[5]{x^5} + 5x\sqrt[5]{x^2} = x + 5x\sqrt[5]{x^2}$

47. $12\sqrt[5]{x^3}\left(x - 3\sqrt[5]{x^2}\right) = 12\sqrt[5]{x^3}\,(x) + 12\sqrt[5]{x^3}\left(-3\sqrt[5]{x^2}\right) = 12x\sqrt[5]{x^3} - 36\sqrt[5]{x^5} = 12x\sqrt[5]{x^3} - 36x$

Chapter 6 Exercises

1. $4^{\frac{1}{2}} = \sqrt{4} = 2$ 3. $36^{\frac{1}{2}} = \sqrt{36} = 6$ 5. $49^{\frac{3}{2}} = \left(\sqrt{49}\right)^3 = 7^3 = 343$

7. $100^{\frac{3}{2}} = \left(\sqrt{100}\right)^3 = 10^3 = 1,000$ 9. $27^{\frac{1}{3}} = \sqrt[3]{27} = 3$ 11. $8^{\frac{2}{3}} = \left(\sqrt[3]{8}\right)^2 = 2^2 = 4$

13. $1,000^{\frac{2}{3}} = \left(\sqrt[3]{1,000}\right)^2 = 10^2 = 100$ 15. $81^{\frac{3}{4}} = \left(\sqrt[4]{81}\right)^3 = 3^3 = 27$ 17. $-16^{\frac{1}{2}} = -\sqrt{16} = -4$

19. $(-125)^{\frac{1}{3}} = \sqrt[3]{-125} = -5$ 21. $-64^{\frac{2}{3}} = -\left(\sqrt[3]{64}\right)^2 = -(4)^2 = -16$

23. $(-25)^{\frac{3}{2}} = \left(\sqrt{-25}\right)^3$ is undefined.   25. $36^{-\frac{1}{2}} = \frac{1}{\sqrt{36}} = \frac{1}{6}$ 27. $216^{-\frac{1}{3}} = \frac{1}{\sqrt[3]{216}} = \frac{1}{6}$

29. $125^{-\frac{2}{3}} = \frac{1}{\left(\sqrt[3]{125}\right)^2} = \frac{1}{5^2} = \frac{1}{25}$ 31. $16^{-\frac{3}{4}} = \frac{1}{\left(\sqrt[4]{16}\right)^3} = \frac{1}{2^3} = \frac{1}{8}$

33. $\left(\frac{16}{9}\right)^{\frac{1}{2}} = \sqrt{\frac{16}{9}} = \frac{4}{3}$ 35. $\left(\frac{216}{125}\right)^{\frac{2}{3}} = \left(\sqrt[3]{\frac{216}{125}}\right)^2 = \left(\frac{6}{5}\right)^2 = \frac{36}{25}$

37. $\left(\frac{1}{27}\right)^{-\frac{1}{3}} = \left(\frac{27}{1}\right)^{\frac{1}{3}} = \sqrt[3]{27} = 3$ 39. $\left(\frac{343}{1,000}\right)^{-\frac{2}{3}} = \left(\frac{1,000}{343}\right)^{\frac{2}{3}} = \left(\sqrt[3]{\frac{1,000}{343}}\right)^2 = \left(\frac{10}{7}\right)^2 = \frac{100}{49}$

41. $-81^{-\frac{1}{2}} = -\frac{1}{\sqrt{81}} = -\frac{1}{9}$ 43. $(-8)^{-\frac{1}{3}} = \frac{1}{\sqrt[3]{-8}} = -\frac{1}{2}$ 45. $-64^{-\frac{2}{3}} = -\frac{1}{\left(\sqrt[3]{64}\right)^2} = -\frac{1}{(4)^2} = -\frac{1}{16}$

47. $9^{\frac{3}{2}} \cdot 4^{\frac{1}{2}} = \left(\sqrt{9}\right)^3 \cdot \sqrt{4} = (3)^3 \cdot 2 = 27 \cdot 2 = 54$

49. $81^{\frac{1}{4}} \cdot 144^{-\frac{1}{2}} = \frac{81^{\frac{1}{4}} \cdot 144^{-\frac{1}{2}}}{1} = \frac{81^{\frac{1}{4}}}{144^{\frac{1}{2}}} = \frac{\sqrt[4]{81}}{\sqrt{144}} = \frac{3}{12} = \frac{1}{4}$

51. $\frac{16^{-\frac{1}{2}}}{27^{\frac{1}{3}}} = \frac{1}{27^{\frac{1}{3}} \cdot 16^{\frac{1}{2}}} = \frac{1}{\sqrt[3]{27} \cdot \sqrt{16}} = \frac{1}{3 \cdot 4} = \frac{1}{12}$

53. $\frac{169^{\frac{1}{2}}}{8^{-\frac{1}{3}}} = \frac{169^{\frac{1}{2}} \cdot 8^{\frac{1}{3}}}{1} = \sqrt{169} \cdot \sqrt[3]{8} = 13 \cdot 2 = 26$

55. $\frac{81^{-\frac{1}{2}}}{8^{-\frac{2}{3}}} = \frac{8^{\frac{2}{3}}}{81^{\frac{1}{2}}} = \frac{\left(\sqrt[3]{8}\right)^2}{\sqrt{81}} = \frac{(2)^2}{9} = \frac{4}{9}$

57. $\frac{1^{\frac{1}{2}} + 8^{-\frac{1}{3}}}{4^{-\frac{1}{2}} + 27^{\frac{1}{3}}} = \frac{\sqrt{1} + \frac{1}{\sqrt[3]{8}}}{\frac{1}{\sqrt{4}} + \sqrt[3]{27}} = \frac{1 + \frac{1}{2}}{\frac{1}{2} + 3} = \left(\frac{1 + \frac{1}{2}}{\frac{1}{2} + 3}\right)\left(\frac{\frac{2}{1}}{\frac{2}{1}}\right) = \frac{1\left(\frac{2}{1}\right) + \frac{1}{2}\left(\frac{2}{1}\right)}{\frac{1}{2}\left(\frac{2}{1}\right) + 3\left(\frac{2}{1}\right)} = \frac{2 + 1}{1 + 6} = \frac{3}{7}$

59. $x^{\frac{1}{4}} = \sqrt[4]{x}$ 61. $y^{\frac{1}{2}} = \sqrt{y}$ 63. $a^{\frac{2}{5}} = \sqrt[5]{a^2}$ 65. $b^{\frac{4}{5}} = \sqrt[5]{b^4}$

67. $t^{\frac{5}{9}} = \sqrt[9]{t^5}$ 69. $x^{-\frac{1}{2}} = \frac{1}{\sqrt{x}}$ 71. $m^{-\frac{1}{3}} = \frac{1}{\sqrt[3]{m}}$ 73. $y^{-\frac{3}{10}} = \frac{1}{\sqrt[10]{y^3}}$

75. $a^{\frac{1}{2}} b^{\frac{1}{2}} = \sqrt{a}\sqrt{b} = \sqrt{ab}$ 77. $25^{\frac{1}{2}} p^{\frac{1}{2}} = \sqrt{25}\sqrt{p} = 5\sqrt{p}$ 79. $a^{\frac{1}{2}} b^{\frac{3}{4}} = \sqrt{a}\sqrt[4]{b^3}$

81. $m^{\frac{2}{5}} n^{\frac{3}{4}} = \sqrt[5]{m^2}\sqrt[4]{n^3}$ 83. $x(x-3)^{\frac{1}{2}} = x\sqrt{x-3}$ 85. $x^2(2x+3)^{-\frac{1}{2}} = \frac{x^2(2x+3)^{-\frac{1}{2}}}{1} = \frac{x^2}{\sqrt{2x+3}}$

87. $\frac{1}{2}x^{-\frac{1}{2}} = \frac{1}{2}\left(\frac{1}{\sqrt{x}}\right) = \frac{1}{2\sqrt{x}}$ 89. $\frac{1}{4}(x^2 - 7x + 3)^{-\frac{3}{4}} = \frac{1}{4}\left(\frac{1}{\sqrt[4]{(x^2 - 7x + 3)^3}}\right) = \frac{1}{4\sqrt[4]{(x^2 - 7x + 3)^3}}$

91. $\left(\dfrac{x}{36}\right)^{\frac{1}{2}} = \sqrt{\dfrac{x}{36}} = \dfrac{\sqrt{x}}{\sqrt{36}} = \dfrac{\sqrt{x}}{6}$ 93. $x^{\frac{1}{2}}_{144} = \dfrac{\sqrt{x}}{144}$ 95. $\left(\dfrac{t}{16}\right)^{-\frac{1}{2}} = \left(\dfrac{16}{t}\right)^{\frac{1}{2}} = \sqrt{\dfrac{16}{t}} = \dfrac{\sqrt{16}}{\sqrt{t}} = \dfrac{4}{\sqrt{t}}$

97. $\left(\dfrac{x}{125}\right)^{-\frac{2}{3}} = \left(\dfrac{125}{x}\right)^{\frac{2}{3}} = \left(\sqrt[3]{\dfrac{125}{x}}\right)^2 = \left(\dfrac{\sqrt[3]{125}}{\sqrt[3]{x}}\right)^2 = \left(\dfrac{5}{\sqrt[3]{x}}\right)^2 = \dfrac{25}{\sqrt[3]{x^2}}$

99. $\dfrac{x^{-\frac{2}{3}}}{125} = \dfrac{1}{125x^{\frac{2}{3}}} = \dfrac{1}{125\sqrt[3]{x^2}}$ 101. $\sqrt{x} = x^{\frac{1}{2}}$ 103. $\sqrt[3]{a^2} = a^{\frac{2}{3}}$

105. $\sqrt[6]{m} = m^{\frac{1}{6}}$ 107. $\sqrt[3]{n^7} = n^{\frac{7}{3}}$ 109. $\sqrt[3]{a}\sqrt{b} = a^{\frac{1}{3}}b^{\frac{1}{2}}$ 111. $\sqrt{\dfrac{x}{6}} = \left(\dfrac{x}{6}\right)^{\frac{1}{2}}$

113. $\dfrac{\sqrt{x}}{6} = \dfrac{x^{\frac{1}{2}}}{6}$ 115. $\left(\sqrt[7]{u^2v}\right)^4 = (u^2v)^{\frac{4}{7}}$ 117. $m^4\sqrt[4]{n} = m^4 n^{\frac{1}{4}}$ 119. $\dfrac{(\sqrt[3]{m})^2}{9} = \dfrac{m^{\frac{2}{3}}}{9}$

121. $x^{\frac{1}{6}} \cdot x^{\frac{1}{8}} = x^{\frac{1}{6}+\frac{1}{8}} = x^{\frac{4}{24}+\frac{3}{24}} = x^{\frac{7}{24}}$ 123. $b^{-\frac{4}{5}} \cdot b^{\frac{2}{5}} = b^{-\frac{4}{5}+\frac{2}{5}} = b^{-\frac{2}{5}} = \dfrac{1}{b^{\frac{2}{5}}}$

125. $y^{-\frac{5}{6}} \cdot y^{-\frac{1}{9}} = y^{-\frac{5}{6}+\left(-\frac{1}{9}\right)} = y^{-\frac{15}{18}-\frac{2}{18}} = y^{-\frac{17}{18}} = \dfrac{1}{y^{\frac{17}{18}}}$

127. $\left(x^{-\frac{2}{3}}\right)\left(x^{\frac{5}{6}}\right)\left(x^{\frac{1}{3}}\right) = x^{-\frac{2}{3}+\frac{5}{6}+\frac{1}{3}} = x^{-\frac{4}{6}+\frac{5}{6}+\frac{2}{6}} = x^{\frac{3}{6}} = x^{\frac{1}{2}}$

129. $\dfrac{u^{\frac{9}{10}}}{u^{\frac{1}{10}}} = u^{\frac{9}{10}-\frac{1}{10}} = u^{\frac{8}{10}} = u^{\frac{4}{5}}$ 131. $\dfrac{n^{\frac{1}{2}}}{n^{-\frac{3}{4}}} = n^{\frac{1}{2}-\left(-\frac{3}{4}\right)} = n^{\frac{2}{4}+\frac{3}{4}} = n^{\frac{5}{4}}$

133. $\dfrac{x^{-\frac{3}{2}}}{x^{-\frac{7}{6}}} = x^{-\frac{3}{2}-\left(-\frac{7}{6}\right)} = x^{-\frac{18}{12}+\frac{14}{12}} = x^{-\frac{4}{12}} = x^{-\frac{1}{3}} = \dfrac{1}{x^{\frac{1}{3}}}$

135. $\left(a^{\frac{1}{2}}\right)^2 = a^{\left(\frac{1}{2}\right)\left(\frac{2}{1}\right)} = a^1 = a$ 137. $\left(s^{\frac{4}{13}}\right)^{26} = s^{\left(\frac{4}{13}\right)\left(\frac{26}{1}\right)} = s^8$

139. $(a^8b^2)^{\frac{3}{2}} - (a^8)^{\frac{3}{2}}(b^2)^{\frac{3}{2}} = a^{\left(\frac{8}{1}\right)\left(\frac{3}{2}\right)}b^{\left(\frac{2}{1}\right)\left(\frac{3}{2}\right)} = u^{12}b^3$

141. $\left(x^{\frac{8}{11}}y^{\frac{2}{7}}\right)^{\frac{22}{3}} = \left(x^{\frac{8}{11}}\right)^{\frac{22}{3}}\left(y^{\frac{2}{7}}\right)^{\frac{22}{3}} = x^{\left(\frac{8}{11}\right)\left(\frac{22}{3}\right)}y^{\left(\frac{2}{7}\right)\left(\frac{22}{3}\right)} = x^{\frac{16}{3}}y^{\frac{44}{21}}$

143. $(s^8t^{-2})^{-\frac{3}{4}} = (s^8)^{-\frac{3}{4}}(t^{-2})^{-\frac{3}{4}} = s^{\left(\frac{8}{1}\right)\left(-\frac{3}{4}\right)}t^{\left(\frac{-2}{1}\right)\left(-\frac{3}{4}\right)} = s^{-6}t^{\frac{3}{2}} = \dfrac{s^{-6}t^{\frac{3}{2}}}{1} = \dfrac{t^{\frac{3}{2}}}{s^6}$

145. $\left(\dfrac{p^{\frac{2}{5}}}{q^{-\frac{3}{5}}}\right)^{\frac{1}{4}} = \dfrac{\left(p^{\frac{2}{5}}\right)^{\frac{1}{4}}}{\left(q^{-\frac{3}{5}}\right)^{\frac{1}{4}}} = \dfrac{p^{\left(\frac{2}{5}\right)\left(\frac{1}{4}\right)}}{q^{\left(-\frac{3}{5}\right)\left(\frac{1}{4}\right)}} = \dfrac{p^{\frac{1}{10}}}{q^{-\frac{3}{20}}} = \dfrac{p^{\frac{1}{10}}q^{\frac{3}{20}}}{1} = p^{\frac{1}{10}}q^{\frac{3}{20}}$

147. $\left(\dfrac{a^5b}{c^{-\frac{1}{6}}}\right)^{\frac{1}{5}} = \dfrac{(a^5)^{\frac{1}{5}}b^{\frac{1}{5}}}{\left(c^{-\frac{1}{6}}\right)^{\frac{1}{5}}} = \dfrac{a^{\left(\frac{5}{1}\right)\left(\frac{1}{5}\right)}b^{\frac{1}{5}}}{c^{\left(-\frac{1}{6}\right)\left(\frac{1}{5}\right)}} = \dfrac{ab^{\frac{1}{5}}}{c^{-\frac{1}{30}}} = \dfrac{ab^{\frac{1}{5}}c^{\frac{1}{30}}}{1} = ab^{\frac{1}{5}}c^{\frac{1}{30}}$

149. $\left(\sqrt[4]{x}\right)(\sqrt{x}) = \left(x^{\frac{1}{4}}\right)\left(x^{\frac{1}{2}}\right) = x^{\frac{1}{4}+\frac{1}{2}} = x^{\frac{1}{4}+\frac{2}{4}} = x^{\frac{3}{4}} = \sqrt[4]{x^3}$

151. $\left(\sqrt[9]{a^2}\right)\left(\sqrt[3]{a^2}\right) = \left(a^{\frac{2}{9}}\right)\left(a^{\frac{2}{3}}\right) = a^{\frac{2}{9}+\frac{2}{3}} = a^{\frac{2}{9}+\frac{6}{9}} = a^{\frac{8}{9}} = \sqrt[9]{a^8}$

153. $\left(\sqrt[8]{x}\right)\left(\sqrt[8]{x}\right) = \left(x^{\frac{1}{8}}\right)\left(x^{\frac{1}{8}}\right) = x^{\frac{1}{8}+\frac{1}{8}} = x^{\frac{2}{8}} = x^{\frac{1}{4}} = \sqrt[4]{x}$

155. $\dfrac{\sqrt[5]{m}}{\sqrt[10]{m^3}} = \dfrac{m^{\frac{1}{5}}}{m^{\frac{3}{10}}} = m^{\frac{1}{5}-\frac{3}{10}} = m^{\frac{2}{10}-\frac{3}{10}} = m^{-\frac{1}{10}} = \dfrac{1}{\sqrt[10]{m}}$

157. $\left(\sqrt[9]{x^2}\right)^{18} = \left(x^{\frac{2}{9}}\right)^{18} = x^{\left(\frac{2}{9}\right)\left(\frac{18}{1}\right)} = x^4$

159. $\sqrt[21]{a^7} = a^{\frac{7}{21}} = a^{\frac{1}{3}} = \sqrt[3]{a}$

161. $\sqrt[4]{t^2} = t^{\frac{2}{4}} = t^{\frac{1}{2}} = \sqrt{t}$

163. $\sqrt[3]{\sqrt{t}} = \left(t^{\frac{1}{2}}\right)^{\frac{1}{3}} = t^{\left(\frac{1}{2}\right)\left(\frac{1}{3}\right)} = t^{\frac{1}{6}} = \sqrt[6]{t}$

165. $\sqrt[5]{\sqrt[5]{b}} = \left(b^{\frac{1}{5}}\right)^{\frac{1}{5}} = b^{\left(\frac{1}{5}\right)\left(\frac{1}{5}\right)} = b^{\frac{1}{25}} = \sqrt[25]{b}$

167. $\sqrt[3]{\sqrt[8]{x^{12}}} = \left(x^{\frac{12}{8}}\right)^{\frac{1}{3}} = x^{\left(\frac{12}{8}\right)\left(\frac{1}{3}\right)} = x^{\frac{1}{2}} = \sqrt{x}$

169. $\left(\sqrt[10]{x^3} \cdot \sqrt[5]{x^2}\right)^5 = \left(x^{\frac{3}{10}} \cdot x^{\frac{2}{5}}\right)^5 = \left(x^{\frac{3}{10}+\frac{2}{5}}\right)^5 = \left(x^{\frac{3}{10}+\frac{4}{10}}\right)^5 = \left(x^{\frac{7}{10}}\right)^5$

$= x^{\left(\frac{7}{10}\right)\left(\frac{5}{1}\right)} = x^{\frac{7}{2}} = \sqrt{x^7} = x^3\sqrt{x}$

171. $\left(\dfrac{\sqrt[14]{a}}{\sqrt[7]{a}}\right)^{21} = \left(\dfrac{a^{\frac{1}{14}}}{a^{\frac{1}{7}}}\right)^{21} = \left(a^{\frac{1}{14}-\frac{1}{7}}\right)^{21} = \left(a^{\frac{1}{14}-\frac{2}{14}}\right)^{21} = \left(a^{-\frac{1}{14}}\right)^{21} = a^{\left(-\frac{1}{14}\right)\left(\frac{21}{1}\right)} = a^{-\frac{3}{2}} = \dfrac{1}{a\sqrt{a}}$

173. $\left(\dfrac{\sqrt{m}\cdot\sqrt[3]{m}}{\sqrt[6]{m^5}}\right)^9 = \left(\dfrac{m^{\frac{1}{2}}\cdot m^{\frac{1}{3}}}{m^{\frac{5}{6}}}\right)^9 = \left(m^{\frac{1}{2}+\frac{1}{3}-\frac{5}{6}}\right)^9 = \left(m^{\frac{3}{6}+\frac{2}{6}-\frac{5}{6}}\right)^9 = \left(m^0\right)^9 = (1)^9 = 1$

175. $\sqrt[3]{\sqrt{a}\cdot\sqrt[5]{a^2}} = \left(a^{\frac{1}{2}}\cdot a^{\frac{2}{5}}\right)^{\frac{1}{3}} = \left(a^{\frac{1}{2}+\frac{2}{5}}\right)^{\frac{1}{3}} = \left(x^{\frac{5}{10}+\frac{4}{10}}\right)^{\frac{1}{3}} = \left(a^{\frac{9}{10}}\right)^{\frac{1}{3}} = a^{\left(\frac{9}{10}\right)\left(\frac{1}{3}\right)} = a^{\frac{3}{10}} = \sqrt[10]{a^3}$

Index

A

Absolute value, 21–24
Addition
  horizontal, 66
  of polynomials, 63–67
  of rational expressions, 106–113
  of radicals, 129–130
  of square roots, 129–130
  vertical, 66
Additive identity, 17
Additive inverse, 18, 65, 107
Addition sign, 8
Algebra, 24–26
Area
  of a trapezoid, 32
  of a triangle, 32
Associative property, 16, 35, 66, 107

B

Base, 6, 35, 43
Binomial, 68, 70
  definition of, 60
  square of, 87

C

Coefficient(s)
  definition, 57
  leading, 60, 89
  of a monomial, 57, 84, 87
  of a term of a polynomial, 60
Commutative property, 16, 59, 64–65, 70, 89, 108
Complex fractions, 12, 115–117
Constant
  monomial, 57–58, 100
  term of a polynomial, 81
Coordinate(s), 19, 22
Counting numbers, 1
Cube(s)
  definition, 35
  difference of two, 74, 87–89
  perfect, 87, 138–139
  sum of two, 74, 87
  volume of, 32
Cube root, 137–143

D

Decimals
  non-repeating, 4, 19, 123
  non-terminating, 3–4, 14, 19–20, 123
  repeating, 3–4, 19–20
  rounding off, 14, 123
  terminating, 3–4, 19, 50–52
  truncating, 14
Degree
  of a monomial, 58–59
  of a polynomial, 60–62

Denominator

  of a fraction, 148
  rationalizing, 133–136
Difference
  of polynomials, 57
  of radicals, 129–130
  of rational expressions, 106–113
  of square roots, 129–130
  of two cubes, 74, 87–89
  of two squares, 71, 85–87, 89
Distance formula
  for real numbers on the real line, 22, 24
Distributive property, 17, 40, 63, 69, 72, 122, 131
Division
  of polynomials, 75–81
  of radicals, 127–128
  of rational expressions, 100, 104–105
Division sign, 12, 78
Domain
  of a variable, 25, 100, 104, 107

E

Elements of a set, 1
Equal sign, 7
Exponents
  negative integer, 42, 45–46, 57
  positive integer, 150
  properties of, 36, 51, 53, 147, 148, 151
  rational, 143, 147–152
  scientific notation, 51, 53
  zero, 35, 39, 45, 48

F

Factoring
  natural numbers, 83
  polynomials, 83–95
    difference of cubes, 87–89
    difference of squares, 85–87, 89
    greatest common factor, 84–85
    grouping method, 91–94
    quadratic equations, 89
    reverse FOIL, 89, 91, 95
    sum of cubes, 74, 87
    sum of squares, 87
    trial and error, 91–93
Factors
  natural number, 83, 85, 87
  polynomial, 83
FOIL method, 70–71, 73, 79, 89, 91, 122
Formula(s)
  distance, 22, 24
  geometry, 32
  temperature, 32